M. R. Lunt

Oxford 1963

Mary Lunt

1963

Sexuality and the Genetics of Bacteria

Sexuality and the Genetics of Bacteria

François Jacob and Elie L. Wollman
Institut Pasteur, Paris

1961

ACADEMIC PRESS • New York & London

ACADEMIC PRESS INC.
111 FIFTH AVENUE
NEW YORK 3, N. Y.

United Kingdom Edition
Published by
ACADEMIC PRESS INC. (LONDON) LTD.
17 OLD QUEEN STREET, LONDON S.W. 1

Library of Congress Catalog Card Number 61-16625

PRINTED IN THE UNITED STATES OF AMERICA

Preface

"La seule différence entre les microbes et les espèces supérieures consisterait dans la rapidité des variations chez les virus, opposée à leur lenteur chez les grands êtres. Chaque culture d'un virus, n'eût-elle qu'une durée de vingt-quatre heures, représente des nombres immenses de générations successives tandis que, chez les êtres élevés, il faut, à l'accomplissement de tels nombres de générations, des milliers et des milliers d'années."

LOUIS PASTEUR (1883)

Preface

Although the world of microorganisms was discovered three centuries ago, following the invention of the microscope, it was not until the work of Pasteur, however, that microbiology became an experimental science. In the space of a few years, man was amazed to discover the manifold roles of microorganisms, in the maintenance of life on earth and in the determination of his own destiny. The role played by the microbes in human affairs for a long time overshadowed their importance for the study of fundamental biological problems; during this period, microbiology remained isolated from the other biological sciences. Only a few decades ago was the emphasis on microorganisms as biological agents supplemented by the study of their own properties. The ensuing discoveries in microbial physiology largely contributed to establishing the fundamental unity of structure and function of all biological systems. When it was at last realized that microorganisms, and more especially bacteria, provide convenient material for the study of many problems in cellular biology, microbiology found itself established in a central and hitherto unanticipated position in the domain of biological sciences.

Among the basic disciplines of biology, it is with genetics that microbiology had the greatest difficulties in finding a common ground. For many years both geneticists and microbiologists tacitly agreed that the concepts and the methods of genetics did not apply to organisms devoid of sexual reproduction. It was only after genetics had been extended to microscopic fungi, and particularly after the fundamental work of Beadle and Tatum on the biochemical genetics of *Neurospora,* that an experimental approach to bacterial genetics was initiated. Within a few years, the study of mutations in bacteria and in bacterial viruses by Delbrück and Luria, together with the discovery of phenomena of genetic recombination in bacteria by Lederberg and Tatum and in bacterial viruses by Delbrück and by Hershey, demonstrated the fundamental unity of hereditary mechanisms throughout the living world. At the same time, the striking discovery by Avery, MacLeod, and McCarty that a bacterial character can be transformed by means of DNA extracted from a mutant provided the first information concerning the chemical basis of heredity.

Although these basic observations are all less than twenty years old, bacterial genetics has developed rapidly. This rapid development can be ascribed to several different causes. First of all is the simplicity, the extreme precision and the high resolving power of the methods available for the study of bacterial genetics. This has placed the fundamental problems of genetics within the competence of non-geneticists; some of the most remarkable contributions to microbial genetics have in fact been made by investigators trained in other branches of science, such as theoretical physics and physical chemistry. In the second place, with microorganisms it has proved relatively easy to relate genetic phenomena to the problems of structure and function of biologically important macromolecules. Finally, among microorganisms a variety of genetic systems and of genetic mechanisms are found which greatly facilitate genetic analysis. These factors have not only contributed to the very rapid progress of microbial genetics, but in addition, they have greatly extended knowledge about the nature and properties of the genetic material. As a result, bacterial and viral genetics have played a large part in the establishment of a new discipline, molecular biology, which occupies in the biological sciences the position that atomic physics has long occupied in the physical sciences.

* * *

One of the most remarkable discoveries of microbial genetics is the revelation that the transfer of genetic information and genetic recombination do not occur uniquely through the classical mechanisms of sexual reproduction, but may also take place in a variety of other ways. In bacteria, for instance, there exist a number of types of genetic transfer which can cause a permanent modification of the hereditary properties of an organism. *Transformation,* discovered in *Pneumococcus* by Griffith and analyzed by Avery, McLeod, and McCarthy, involves the absorption by a recipient cell of DNA chemically extracted from a donor. *Transduction,* discovered in *Salmonella* by Zinder and Lederberg, is the transfer of genetic material from a donor to a recipient, by a bacteriophage acting as vector. *Bacterial conjugation,* which was discovered in *Escherichia coli* by Lederberg and Tatum, consists of the transfer of genetic material as a consequence of cellular contact between sexually differentiated bacteria. Of all phenomena of genetic transfer in bacteria, conjugation is the one which most closely resembles the sexual processes that exist in higher forms. It exhibits, however, certain peculiarities which relate it clearly to the other processes of genetic transfer in bacteria. *Lysogeny,* although differing somewhat from the other processes mentioned, is also a case of permanent modification of bacterial heredity. As shown by the work of

Lwoff and his group, it comprises an association, at the genetic level, between the genetic material of a bacterial virus and the bacterial host. Each of these genetic phenomena has its own characteristics and each of them presents its own particular advantages for the study of specific genetic problems.

* * *

This monograph is an attempt to summarize our present knowledge concerning the process of sexual conjugation in bacteria and its use as a genetic system for the investigation of problems of cellular genetics. It also considers in detail the genetic aspects of lysogeny. The connection between these two subjects perhaps requires some explanation. Our work was initiated by an interest in the genetic determination of lysogeny; i.e., of the stable association which may become established between the genetic material of a virus and that of the host cell. The elucidation of this problem depended on a convenient method of genetic analysis; but, at the beginning of our investigation, knowledge of the mechanism operating in the process of bacterial conjugation was still very scanty. It fairly soon became apparent that, if progress in the genetic analysis of lysogeny was dependent upon a better understanding of the mechanism of bacterial conjugation, the information obtained in the study of lysogeny in turn helped considerably to unravel the mechanism of bacterial conjugation. The interdependence of progress in the two fields explains why the two subjects are treated together.

The way in which this book came to be written also needs to be explained. Originally, one of us had to publish a thesis which gave an account of some of the work done in our laboratory on bacterial conjugation. The need for a comprehensive source of information in French on bacterial genetics led us to prepare an enlarged and revised version of the original report.[1] When Academic Press kindly offered to publish an English translation of this monograph, we accepted with some reluctance, since we felt substantial changes would be necessary. Indeed, it soon became evident that the evolution of certain aspects of the subject necessitated extensive modification and development of the French version. Instead of rewriting the whole book, we chose to enlarge some of the existing chapters and to add new ones. The sporadic growth of the present book accordingly explains a certain lack of balance between the different parts, some discontinuity in the exposition, and some unavoidable repetitions. We ask the reader's indulgence for such unevenness. Had it not been written in so many stages, this monograph might have taken a

[1] E. L. Wollman and F. Jacob. La sexualité des bactéries. Masson ed. Paris, 1959.

rather different form. It is more likely, however, that it would have not been written at all!

* * *

This monograph is composed of three parts. In the first part, the origin and early development of bacterial genetics are briefly outlined. The discovery of genetic recombination in bacteria and the characteristics of bacterial crosses with a low frequency of recombination, as originally described by Lederberg and Tatum, are then examined in more detail.

The second part is devoted to a detailed analysis of the process of sexual conjugation in bacteria. After describing the techniques and the characteristic features of crosses with a high frequency of recombination, we consider in turn the genetic analysis of lysogeny, the successive steps that can be defined in the processes of mating and genetic recombination, and the mechanism of genetic transfer during sexual conjugation. This analysis is followed by a comprehensive account of the different aspects of sexual conjugation in bacteria and of the genetic determination of sexual types. This section is more detailed than the other two. The different problems are analyzed in terms of the experimental results, and the theoretical conclusions are deduced step by step. This analytical approach will perhaps appear too technical and somewhat tedious to many readers. We have nonetheless adopted it, because we felt that it might prove useful for readers who are more directly interested in these problems, and particularly those who may be faced with the analysis of similar phenomena in groups of bacteria other than the Enterobacteriaceae.

In the third part, emphasis is placed on bacterial conjugation as a genetic system for the experimental attack on various problems of cellular genetics: specifically the structure of the genetic material, genetic recombination, and functional analysis. Certain problems raised by genetic studies with bacteria are also discussed: the genetic implications of incomplete fertilization, cellular regulation and gene action, the function of viruses as cellular genetic elements and, finally, the existence of other related cellular elements, or episomes, which are distinct from the normal constituents of the chromosomes.

Much of the experimental work described in this monograph has resulted from a close collaboration between the two authors in the Service de Physiologie microbienne at the Institut Pasteur. We are happy to have this opportunity of expressing our gratitude and our affection to Dr. André Lwoff and Dr. Jacques Monod, who have succeeded in creating around themselves a unique climate for research, characterized alike by friendliness, by scientific enthusiasm, and by acute and pertinent criticism. We are particularly glad to express our sincere appreciation to Dr. J. Tréfouël, Director of the Institut Pasteur. We also wish to thank Mrs. Alberte Ungar for having undertaken the translation of a large part of the French monograph. Finally, we are greatly indebted to Dr. Robert Austrian and Dr. Roger Stanier for having helped with the revision of the final English version, and to Mrs. Gisèle Houzet, who has been indefatigable in preparing the successive drafts of this work.

Institut Pasteur
June, 1961

F. Jacob
E. L. Wollman

Contents

PART I

Bacterial Genetics and the Discovery of Genetic Recombination in Bacteria

"Ce que nous devons viser, c'est moins de constater les ressemblances et les différences, que de retrouver les similitudes cachées sous les divergences apparentes."

HENRI POINCARÉ
(Science et Méthode)

CHAPTER 1

The Variability of Bacteria

Genetics originated from the study, in organisms which reproduce sexually, of hybridization between races or varieties of the same species, which differ in certain hereditary characters. The initial definition of the gene as the unit of recombination and segregation was only later extended to include also the unit of mutation and the unit of function. Finally, the integration of genetic data with cytological and cytochemical data led to the establishment and expansion of modern genetics.

For a long time, the methods of genetics seemed inapplicable to microorganisms in general, and to bacteria in particular. Bacteria reproduce vegetatively. Their small size made them unsuitable for cytological studies. Because of their low degree of organization, no distinction between soma and germen or between genotype and phenotype could be established. Consequently, it was long widely believed that the differences, both genetic and physiological, between higher organisms and microorganisms were of a fundamental nature, and that the laws valid for the former could not be applied to the latter. Bacteriologists and geneticists alike believed that bacteria did not have a differentiated genetic apparatus and that the mechanism of transmission of their hereditary characters was different from that revealed by genetic analysis in sexually reproducing organisms.

Because of their small size and rapid growth, bacteria can quickly produce an enormous population in a very small volume of culture medium. These conditions are highly favorable for the appearance of variant forms and for their study. The very characters that originally seemed to exclude genetic analysis of bacteria, in fact make them objects of choice for the study of variation, and it was from such studies that bacterial genetics was born.

Three phases in the evolution of ideas concerning the genetic constitution of bacteria can be broadly distinguished. The first one, covering the second half of the 19th century, was principally devoted to the description and isolation of bacterial species. During the second period, which extends from about 1900 to 1940, a large number of variations, affecting the most diverse properties of bacteria, were identified and described. Lastly, in the third period, starting about 1940, the facts concerning bacterial heredity were coordinated and analyzed in the light of classical genetic theory; and the simultaneous discovery of new phenomena, not explicable in terms of classical genetics, gave a further stimulus to bacterial genetics. It is not our intention to describe in detail this historical development; we shall content ourselves with outlining its main steps. Accounts of early work can be found in the following articles and reviews: Löhnis, 1921; Hadley, 1927; Brierley, 1929; Arkwright, 1930; Marchal, 1932; Bulloch, 1938. More recent work has likewise been frequently summarized (Dubos, 1945; Luria, 1947; Braun, 1947, 1953; Lederberg, 1948, 1949a; Tatum and Perkins, 1950; Catcheside, 1951; Kaplan, 1952; Wyss and Haas, 1953; Spiegelman and Landman, 1954; Zelle, 1955; Cavalli-Sforza, 1957; Ravin, 1958; Pontecorvo, 1958; Hartman and Goodgal, 1959; Beadle, 1960).

I. BACTERIAL SPECIES

Pasteur's investigations, starting with fermentations and continuing with infectious diseases, established both the microbial causation of these phenomena and the specificity of the causative agents. During the same period, a number of microscopists, the most eminent being F. Cohn (1872), observed and described a great many morphological varieties of microorganisms. The initial concern of bacteriologists was, accordingly, to grow and describe the microorganisms which they isolated and to establish the relation between their biological activity and their microscopic appearance. Because of the limited number of properties which could be used at this period to characterize bacteria, the proposed classifications were based mainly on morphological data. Some workers, such as Naegeli (1877), Büchner (1882), Zopf (1885), questioned the validity of a classification based on morphological criteria, and defended the theory of *pleomorphism.* According to this theory, bacteria may exhibit structures and even functions that are highly variable, with the result that the definition of bacterial *species* is illusory. The major contribution of F. Cohn (1879), and later of R. Koch (1881) and his school, was their defense of the opposing theory of *monomorphism,* which postulates the existence of bacterial categories that can be distinguished and classified on the basis of their morphological and physiological properties. As a result of progress in bacteriological technique, particularly the introduction of solid media, the isolation of bacteria in pure culture became easy. In the light of observations on large numbers of pure bacterial cultures, the theory of monomorphism rapidly won the acceptance of bacteriologists. One can thus regard this first period, which extends to the beginning of the 20th century, as having been mainly concerned with the descriptive study of bacteria and with the investigation of the diverse properties which could be used for the identification of species.[1]

General acceptance of the concept of monomorphism was the first essential step for the establishment, not only of bacterial genetics, but also of bacteriology as a science. However, like many other doctrines, monomorphism soon became dogmatic. Having performed a vital service by making possible the identification of bacterial species, it was illegitimately extended to assert the constancy of bacterial form and function, and to deny to bacterial species all possibility of variation.

II. BACTERIAL VARIATIONS

As the number of known bacterial species increased and as more and more of their specific properties were recognized, the variability of these properties became increasingly evident. Morphological characters, biochemical characters, antigenic properties, virulence—in fact, every one of the attributes that can be studied in bacteria—were found to be subject to variation. During the period between 1900 and 1940, the dogma of immutability was seriously challenged, and variability became recognized as one of the most important phenomena of microbiology.

With few exceptions, however, bacterial variations were the subject of observation rather than of experimentation. The most diverse kinds of variation were reported, and the proposed interpretations were not less numerous. Variations were described as being either slow or abrupt, reversible or irreversible, spontaneous or induced. For the most part, such distinctions depended on the conditions under which the variations were observed. The variation appeared slow or abrupt, continuous or discontinuous, depending on whether liquid cultures or isolated colonies were studied. If the variation was detected under normal cultural conditions (a morphological variation for instance), it appeared to be spontaneous; if its demonstration required the use of special methods (utilization of a sugar, for instance), it appeared to be induced.

Quite early, however, examples of sudden hereditary variations affecting easily recognizable characteristics were described. There were,

---

[1] The various systems proposed for the classification of bacteria are nothing more than arbitrary and empirical groupings designed to facilitate identification. This contention is particularly well documented by Van Niel (1946). The taxonomy of higher plants and animals can lay claim to being something more than an arbitrary arrangement of convenience because the fundamental taxonomic unit (the species) can be defined in objective scientific terms. A similar basis for defining bacterial species has not yet been discovered.

notably, Beijerinck's observations, reported as early as 1900 (and extended in a paper published in 1912), in particular those concerning the color of colonies of *Bacillus prodigiosus*. Another case in point is the classical strain of *Escherichia coli mutabile* described by Massini (1907) which, unable to ferment lactose, gives rise to variants that possess this property. The rarity, discontinuity, and stability of these variations were so evident to their discoverers that they did not hesitate to recognize them as "mutations" in the sense of de Vries. As early as 1912, Dobell defined bacterial variation as "a permanent change, however minute, occurring in a microorganism, and from then on transmitted to successive generations."

As for the *mechanism* of bacterial variation, the most diverse and contradictory interpretations were offered. The literature of this period leaves an impression of extraordinary confusion (see Hadley, 1927; Arkwright, 1930). This confusion can be attributed to several main causes.

1. *The lack of an adequate experimental method.* Most of the reports on variations in microorganisms were rather the result of casual observation than of true experimentation. Consequently, the examples given by different authors could hardly be compared. Bacteriologists, accustomed to working with cultures, i.e., with large populations, were generally unable to distinguish between the properties of a population as a whole, and those of its individual members. The concept of the clone (i.e., the population of individual organisms descended from a single individual) spread rather slowly among bacteriologists (Rippel, 1929; Van Loghem, 1929).

2. *The difficulty of establishing a distinction between genotype and phenotype.* This difficulty is at the root of interminable discussions between the partisans of mutational theories and those who wanted to see in bacterial variations a proof of the plasticity or physiological adaptability of these microorganisms to the changes occurring in their environmental conditions. Some workers doubted even the possibility of making such a distinction and believed that, in bacteria, genotype and phenotype were blended.

3. *The ignorance concerning the physiology of bacterial growth.* Many observations, above all morphological ones, were carried out on old cultures. From this practice arose the various theories of complex "developmental cycles," which revived, in a number of different forms, Naegeli's pleomorphism. Only in 1928 did the investigations of Henrici establish the limits of "normal" morphological variation in bacteria.

4. *The use of selective agents for the isolation of variants.* The most remarkable examples of hereditary variations were those produced by

the action of selective agents. Here again two classes of hypotheses were proposed. According to some, the only effect of the agent used was to select rare *spontaneous mutants* already present in the bacterial culture *before* treatment. Others believed that the treatment itself *induced* the modification which subsequently permitted a certain fraction of the population to be selected by the agent. Among the studies, outstanding for their experimental rigor, which pointed to the mutational nature of the variations investigated, it is worth mentioning that of F. M. Burnet (1929), who established that, in some cases, bacteriophage-resistant bacteria were unlike the original sensitive type in their antigenic constitution; and that of I. M. Lewis (1934), who showed that, in a culture of *E. coli mutabile* grown in a synthetic glucose medium, i.e., in the absence of lactose, about one bacterium in 10^5 was able to use lactose.

It seems, moreover, that as the complexity of genetic systems in sexually reproducing organisms became increasingly apparent, it appeared even less permissible to geneticists and bacteriologists alike, to extend the concepts of classical genetics to bacteria.

A few quotations will serve to illustrate the diversity of opinion on the nature of variations in bacteria, as well as the evolution of ideas in this field during the period under consideration.

". . . We should perhaps regard as mutants only those hereditary variations whose mode falls outside the limits of the species; and this should be construed as meaning outside the range of types represented by the normal changes (cyclic or otherwise) characteristic of the organism in question. Until, therefore, we train ourselves to detect the limits and range of cyclogenic variation characteristic for each bacterial species, we are scarcely in a position to recognize a mutation when it appears. It is safe to say, however, that at the present moment we do not know of one unequivocal or authentic case of mutation among the bacteria . . . . In the meantime it might be well if the term "mutation" were banished from the vocabulary of the bacteriologist." (Hadley, 1927, pp. 270–273).

". . . The view that bacteria, since they are unicellular and without any definite nucleus, are simple forms which can comparatively easily be modified by the environment and can pass on such changes to their offspring appears to be the most acceptable view . . . . (Arkwright, 1930, p. 369).

". . . Distinction between soma and germ plasm is (in bacteria) purposeless. When a bacterium divides, the two elements born of this fission are but two fragments of the original individual . . . . It is only as a convention that they can be spoken of as descendants . . . . Irreversible constitutional changes can happen spontaneously or be induced by external means. The persistence and suddenness of such "mutations" tend naturally to suggest factorial changes: however, they could also be due to unequal divisions of the other constituents of living matter. Consequently, the word mutation should be used only with qualifications in the case of bacteria, and it should be remembered that this word is here synonymous with irreversible transformation, and there is no possibility of indicating precisely which parts of the organism are more markedly modified." (Guyénot, 1930, pp. 148–152).

". . . The subject of bacterial variation and heredity has reached an almost hopeless state of confusion. Almost every possible view has been set forth and there seems no reason to hope that any uniform consensus of opinion may be reached in the near future. There are many advocates of a Lamarckian mode of bacterial inheritance while others hold to the view that it is essentially Darwinian. The early workers regarded variation in so-called mutable strains as mutations in the sense of de Vries. Some more recent workers have explained this behavior as due to Mendelian segregation, while others have regarded it as evidence of a cyclogenic life history.

The experiments reported above support the view that variation occurs spontaneously, in some cases at least, and without regard to environmental influences. Variation, when beneficial, may be preserved by selective action of the medium. Non-beneficial variation . . . would be eliminated by overgrowth of the more vigorous original cells." (I. M. Lewis, 1934).

". . . In microbiology, more than anywhere else, it is very difficult to define systematic categories because of the practically unlimited polymorphism of bacteria . . . , of the modifying influence, more or less durable and sometimes definitive, of the culture medium and of the absence of sexual processes.

. . . Microbes display a phenomenon with few equivalents in more evolved animals and plants: it is the modification or mutation determined by the more or less prolonged action of the culture medium." (Cuénot, 1936, pp. 92 and 118).

". . . Independent variation in three sets of characteristics does not appear to be consistent with any theory of cyclic change in organisms. It seems more likely that, in these cases at least, the inheritance of individual characteristics has been subject to some irregularity.

. . . It therefore seems more in line with current genetic opinion to assume that the independent variation in several characteristics . . . is the result of change in individual genes or "gene mutation." (Reed, 1937).

". . . The first step (in the development of a genetic system) may have been the differentiation of genes that are still undifferentiated in viruses and bacteria." (Darlington, 1939, p. 124).

". . . Most (bacterial) transformations can be simply accounted for on the assumption that a variety of mutations arise, each with a certain frequency, in bacterial strains. In any given environment a certain biotype or biotypes are selected to become the dominant components of the culture.

". . . Since a mutation is usually reversible, the bacterial transformations are likewise reversible in most cases. Although some bacteriologists are prone to believe that the behavior of bacteria is incompatible with established concepts of genetics and evolution theory, there are valid reasons to think that bacteria may prove to be the best available material for exact studies on mutation and natural selection." (Dobzhansky, 1941, p. 189).

". . . (In bacteria) the entire organism appears to function as both soma and germplasm, and evolution must be a matter of alteration in the reaction-system as a whole." (Huxley, 1942, p. 131).

It is evident from these quotations that, although the existence of sudden hereditary variations in bacteria was generally recognized, the significance of these variations and their interpretation in genetic terms remained a controversial subject.

III. BACTERIAL MUTATIONS AND THEIR CHARACTERISTICS

Any real progress in knowledge of bacterial genetics therefore seemed dependent on two main factors: (1) the development of experimental methods and habits of thought better adapted to the study of bacterial variation; (2) the acquisition of facts that would allow the bacteria to be brought into relation with other organisms which were accessible to Mendelian analysis.

The date of 1940 marks approximately the beginning of this third period, when bacteria entered the domain of genetics. Since then, the importance of bacterial genetics as a discipline has grown continuously. In this chapter, we shall consider only the data concerning bacterial variation.

A. Characters Used in the Study of Bacterial Mutations

Even though all the recognizable properties of bacteria can vary, some are easier to analyze quantitatively than others and have therefore played an important role in the study of bacterial mutations.

1. *Resistance to antibacterial agents.* When a bacterial culture is exposed to the action of an antibacterial agent (chemical, physical, or biological), one can select individuals which possess the hereditary property of specific resistance to the agent in question. The rapid elimination of bacteria of the original sensitive type makes it possible, not only to isolate, but also to count such resistant variants. Particular mention should be made here of virulent bacteriophages the action of which is remarkably rapid: as soon as bacteria are infected with such phages, their metabolism is blocked and the infected bacteria are irretrievably destined to die (S. S. Cohen and Anderson, 1946; Monod and Wollman, 1947).

2. *Use of carbon sources.* The ability to utilize certain carbon compounds is widely employed in classifying bacteria. This property is linked to the presence of specific enzymes the activity of which can, in some cases, be easily investigated. Monod and Audureau (1946) were thus able to demonstrate that the lactose positive variants (Lac^+) from a strain of *E. coli mutabile* produced an enzyme (β-galactosidase) only in the presence of a specific inducer of this enzyme, such as lactose. In this case, accordingly, the genotypic property of the strain (the ability to synthesize a specific enzyme) can be distinguished from its phenotypic expression (the actual synthesis of the enzyme).

3. *The ability to synthesize some essential metabolites.* This is also a valuable criterion in bacterial taxonomy. The classical studies of Knight (1936) and Lwoff (1938) showed that closely related bacterial species differed in their ability to synthesize one or more essential metabolites. There were good reasons to believe that these losses of metabolic functions by bacteria were the results of a physiological evolution (Lwoff, 1932, 1943), itself the consequence of mutations. One of the first recognized examples of an hereditary variation in the requirement for a growth factor was discovered in *Eberthella typhosa* (Fildes, Gladstone, and Knight, 1933). Strains isolated from nature require tryptophan for growth, but can be "trained" to grow without this amino acid after several passages in a synthetic medium containing low concentrations of the growth factor. These conditions allow the selection of bacteria which no longer require tryptophan, i.e., which are capable of synthesizing it.

B. Spontaneous Mutations in Bacteria

The experimental study of hereditary variations involves the use of methods of selection. One is thus faced with the problem of the origin of the selected variants; are they spontaneous mutants which have arisen prior to the treatment, or is the variation induced by the treatment itself? The whole subsequent development of bacterial genetics depended on the answer to this question. The view that the variations were induced by changes in environmental conditions was widespread among bacteriologists; as Luria (1947) remarked, bacteriology was the last stronghold of Lamarckism. The demonstration of the spontaneous character of bacterial mutations was to indicate that there is no fundamental difference between the variations which occur in bacteria and those which occur in organisms accessible to Mendelian analysis.

The work of Luria and Delbrück (1943) provided this vital demonstration, and at the same time introduced into microbiology the statistical methods required for the study of large populations. Their analysis is based on the following reasoning. If bacterial mutation is a rare event, discontinuous and random, there should be a marked fluctuation in the number of mutants present, at a given time, in a large number of *independent cultures,* each of which has grown from a small inoculum. Conversely, in separate samples taken from a *single culture* inoculated under the same conditions, the distribution of mutants should be much more homogeneous. On the hypothesis that mutations are induced by the agent used for selection, the distribution of the number of mutants present in the different samples should be independent of the previous history of the culture. For their study, Luria and Delbrück chose a particularly favorable system, the acquisition of resistance to a virulent bacteriophage.

This statistical *fluctuation test* was later applied with the same success to many examples of variation (Demerec, 1945; Witkin, 1947; Oakberg and Luria, 1947; Newcombe and Hawirko, 1949). Other, more direct, methods have been more recently developed (Newcombe, 1949; J. and E. M. Lederberg, 1952). In every case studied, the spontaneous character of bacterial mutations can be demonstrated. It should be noted, however, that this demonstration has not convinced all workers in the field and that some have continued to support the hypothesis of an "adaptation" of bacteria to modifications of environmental conditions (Sevag, 1946; Hinshelwood, 1946; Dean and Hinshelwood, 1953; Timakov, 1959).

The characteristics of spontaneous mutations in bacteria are exactly the same as those which mark mutations in higher organisms: an abrupt and discontinuous change in a particular hereditary property, the mutation occurs at random and affects only a small fraction of the individuals present in a given population. Every mutation occurs at a characteristic rate and affects specifically one (or sometimes several) phenotypic characters. When different properties can be altered by different mutations, it can be demonstrated that these mutations occur independently of one another; more precisely, the probability that mutation A will occur is unaffected by the preceding occurrence of mutations B or C (Demerec and Fano, 1945). Lastly, the mutants formed are usually as stable as the types from which they are derived.

Bacterial mutations, thus have the same factorial character as the mutations that occur in organisms which reproduce sexually. There was accordingly every reason to suppose that, in bacteria as in higher organisms, mutations affect hereditary determinants which are themselves factorial.

C. Induced Mutations and Physiological Genetics

The evolution of bacterial genetics was deeply influenced by advances in other branches of genetics, particularly by advances in the genetics of other microorganisms. The existence of typical sexual phenomena in fungi such as the ascomycete *Neurospora* (Dodge, 1935) and in yeasts (Winge, 1935), made it possible to extend genetic analysis to organisms related much more closely to bacteria than the classical objects of genetic research. By means of physical mutagenic agents (X-rays, ultraviolet light) or chemical ones (mustard compounds), one can induce in these microorganisms various mutations, especially mutations affecting metabolic properties. By such methods, Beadle and Tatum (1941) were able to isolate a great variety of mutants of *Neurospora crassa* deficient in their ability to synthesize essential metabolites ("biochemical" mutants) and to demonstrate that each loss of function was under the control of a specific genetic determinant.

Those agents which are effective mutagens in organisms accessible to Mendelian analysis are also mutagenic for bacteria (Croland, 1943; Gray and Tatum, 1944; Roepke, Libby and Small, 1944). A variety of biochemical mutations may be induced in bacteria. The deficient mutants so obtained are comparable in every respect to the mutants of *Neurospora* in which the genetic "block" affects the same biosynthetic reactions (Tatum, 1946).

The possibility of obtaining fairly easily a great variety of biochemical mutants has also made possible the systematic investigation of the relations between the mutations and their physiological effects. Physiological genetic studies, notably those of Ephrussi and Beadle (1937) on the synthesis of eye pigments in *Drosophila,* had already shown that some mutations prevent the formation of specific chemical substances. The investigations of the school of Beadle and Tatum greatly extended knowledge in this field, and gave rise to a true "biochemical genetics" (Beadle, 1945). A given biochemical mutation results in the interruption, at a definite point, of the chain of reactions leading to the biosynthesis of a specific essential metabolite. This interruption is in most cases related to the absence of a specific enzyme (see Horowitz and Fling, 1956). There is consequently a close relationship between genes and enzymes: each gene appears to control the synthesis of a particular enzyme.

As a result of improvements in the methods of selection of biochemical mutants (Davis, 1950a; J. Lederberg, 1950a; Adelberg and Myers, 1953) bacteria provide a particularly favorable material for studies of this kind (Davis, 1950a, 1952). The methods of biochemical genetics have contributed much to the clarification of the biosynthetic pathways of a large number of essential metabolites: amino acids, vitamins, purines, and pyrimidines. They have also made possible a start on the study of the relations between the structure of genetic determinants and their function.

The common characters of mutations in bacteria and in organisms subject to Mendelian analysis, the fact that mutations affecting the same properties exist in both groups, and finally the fact that these mutations are inducible in both groups by the same mutagenic agents, all suggest a basic similarity of hereditary mechanisms. Not only are the hereditary properties in both cases controlled by factorial hereditary determinants; even more, these determinants must be of the same nature and possess analogous properties.

IV. THE GENETIC APPARATUS OF BACTERIA

In animals and plants the genetic determinants of Mendelian characters are located on the chromosomes, which are themselves contained in the cellular nuclei. An essential constituent of chromosomes is deoxyribonucleic acid (DNA), which is responsible for their special affinity for basic dyes and which can be stained specifically by the Feulgen method.

Like many cytological problems, the problem of the bacterial nucleus has given rise to heated arguments (see Dubos, 1945). In bacteria, structures exhibiting the characteristics of nuclear formations can be demonstrated either by the Feulgen or the Piekarski technique (Badian, 1933; Piekarski, 1937; Delaporte, 1939; Robinow, 1942). These structures contain practically all the DNA present in bacteria and disappear after treatment with the enzyme deoxyribonuclease (Boivin, Tulasne, Vendrely, and Minck, 1947). Their division is coordinated with that of the bacteria, and, for a given species, their number varies with physiological conditions. Recent investigations have shown that it is possible to follow the development of these structures during the course of bacterial growth by direct observation under the phase contrast microscope (Tulasne, 1949; Mason and Powelson, 1955). Although some authors contend that the term *nucleus* should be restricted to structures having certain morphological properties (see Robinow, 1956), it seems justifiable to give this word a *functional* definition, and to term *bacterial nuclei* those structures that are the functional equivalents in bacteria of the cellular nuclei of more highly developed organisms.

Apart from the fact that bacterial nuclei, like those of other cells, consist essentially of DNA, there is ample evidence that they contain the hereditary determinants of bacteria. Some of the evidence will be examined in the next chapter. We shall mention here only the relationship between the delays in expression or segregation of some mutations and the average number of nuclei per bacterium. Since most bacteria are multinucleate, one may expect (if the nucleus is actually the seat of the hereditary factors) that pure clones of mutants will appear only after some delay when, owing to nuclear and bacterial division, the mutated nuclei have segregated from the other nuclei of the bacterium. This phenomenon was demonstrated experimentally by Witkin (1951), who studied segregation of the ultraviolet induced mutation lactose$^+$ → lactose$^-$ in populations of *E. coli* characterized by different average numbers of nuclei per cell.

* * *

The bacteria are not a primitive group of organisms in which soma and germplasm are blended, contrary to the general belief some twenty years ago. They possess a nuclear apparatus comparable to that in the cells of other organisms and one which, likewise, contains the determinants of hereditary characters. These bacterial determinants possess the individuality and specificity accorded to the genes of higher organisms. They control phenotypic characters the biochemical mechanisms of which have been analyzed with precision in many cases. Accordingly, the study of bacterial mutations has contributed to demonstrating the universality of genetic mechanisms and of the metabolic reactions they control.

The domain of genetics has furthermore been extended beyond the bacterial world. In viruses (notably the bacteriophages) just as in bacteria, mutations that alter a variety of hereditary traits have been discovered (Luria, 1945; Hershey, 1946). These hereditary variations exhibit all the general characteristics of mutations. It must therefore be admitted that they too are under the control of factorial hereditary determinants.

Thus, in all "organisms," whatever their degree of organization and their evolutionary level, hereditary properties are under the control of factorial determinants whose nature, mutual relations, and mode of distribution during reproduction must be fundamentally similar since their role is to ensure the remarkable stability of the hereditary properties of these organisms as well as their variability.

CHAPTER II

The Modes of Transfer of Hereditary Characters in Bacteria and the Genetic Problem of Lysogeny

A serious disadvantage which long existed in the study of bacterial variations was the impossibility of analyzing these phenomena by genetic methods, i.e., by experimental hybridization. Conversely, the prevalent confusion of ideas concerning the nature of bacterial variability considerably delayed the demonstration and interpretation of processes of genetic exchange in bacteria.

In this chapter, we shall briefly describe the various phenomena of exchange or transfer of genetic characters now known to occur in bacteria. Disregarding historical order, we shall first give an account of the discovery of genetic recombination in bacteria. We shall consider next the different kinds of transfer and acquisition of genetic characters which occur without cellular contact. The last part of this chapter will be devoted to lysogenic bacteria and to the genetic problem which they present.

I. GENETIC RECOMBINATION IN BACTERIA

Although the study of bacterial mutations pointed to the existence of a homology between the hereditary determinants of bacterial characters and the genes of higher organisms, it did not permit any conclusion concerning the eventual relationship between these genetic determinants. There were, however, good reasons to believe that the organization of the genetic apparatus of bacteria could not be fundamentally different from that of the other organisms.

The hereditary characters of bacteria are as stable as those of higher organisms. If bacterial variability may formerly have appeared to be greater than that of other organisms, it was because neither the size of the bacterial populations concerned, nor the infinite possibilities of selection created by the slightest changes in environmental conditions, were taken into account. Quantitative measurements have, in fact, shown that the mutation rates in bacteria are comparable to those in other organisms. The stability of bacterial characters can be explained only by the assumption of a mechanism which ensures an even distribution of the genetic determinants at each division, and which operates with a precision comparable to that of mitosis. It is difficult to imagine a model which fulfills better these requirements than that offered by other biological systems: the precise order of genetic determinants on one or more structures whose duplication and segregation occur regularly at each cellular division. Bacteria have sometimes been thought of as "bags of genes." It should be noted, however, that any model which would suppose random distribution of the genetic determinants would be bound, *a priori*, to run into serious difficulties if it were to account both for the stability of bacterial characters and for their variability. The presence of each genetic determinant in limited number (e.g., one per nucleus) would permit variation but would preclude stability. Conversely, the existence of a large number of copies of each genetic determinant would ensure stability, but would be incompatible with the established characters of bacterial mutations.

Only hybridization experiments could provide definitive information about this important problem; but until 1946, such experiments could not be undertaken with bacteria. Prior to this time, sexual phenomena in bacteria had been repeatedly looked for, described, and even imagined, usually on the basis of simple microscopic observations on stained preparations (see Bisset, 1950; Hutchinson and Stempen, 1954). But even when such microscopic preparations strongly suggested the occurrence of conjugation or fusion, the lack of genetic data precluded evaluation of their real significance. Attempts to cross bacteria were made by Sherman and Wing (1937), followed by Gowen and Lincoln (1942), who stated clearly the conditions and the possible results of experiments designed to demonstrate the existence of sexual processes in bacteria. But these experiments gave negative results. At best, however, they could have detected only frequent genetic recombinations, since the characters used did not lend themselves to the selection of possible genetic recombinants.

We owe to J. Lederberg and Tatum (1946a and b) the discovery of genetic recombination in bacteria, and it should be stressed that this important discovery was the fruit of a carefully planned investigation and not of casual observations. Lederberg and Tatum were guided by the following principles.

(1) If phenomena of recombination occur in bacteria, they are probably rare. This could be inferred both from the small number and dubious character of the claims for fusion based on microscopic observa-

tions and from the failure of previous attempts to demonstrate genetic recombination experimentally. To establish the formation of rare genetic recombinants, it is thus essential to *select* them. One must also be able to distinguish them from spontaneous mutations.

(2) The use of strains which differ in their growth factor requirements appears particularly favorable for the selection of possible genetic recombinants. As already mentioned, it is possible to induce in bacteria a great variety of metabolic deficiencies. By successive mutagenic treatments, one can accumulate several metabolic deficiencies in a single strain. These characters are usually stable, and different nutritional characters revert independently to the wild type (Tatum, 1946). A simultaneous mutation of two characters is thus most improbable: it would occur with a frequency of about 10^{-14}. Finally, the work of Beadle and Tatum on the fungus *Neurospora crassa* had shown that each nutritional character is under the control of a specific genetic determinant, and that the power of synthesizing a given essential metabolite is dominant over the inability to do so.

The bacterium chosen by Lederberg and Tatum was a typical *Escherichia coli,* labeled K12, which had been used for many years as a laboratory strain in bacteriology courses at Stanford University. This strain, which grows in a simple synthetic medium without the addition of growth factors, had already been used by Tatum (1945) in his work on induction of biochemical mutations in bacteria.

The first strains used by Lederberg and Tatum were double or triple mutants, i.e., strains in which several biochemical mutations had been induced by successive mutagenic treatments. One of these strains required biotin (B^-), phenylalanine (Ph^-) and cystine (C^-); another needed threonine (T^-), leucine (L^-), and vitamin B_1 (B_1^-).* When cells of either strain were spread in large numbers (10^8) on plates of a synthetic agar medium without growth factors (minimal medium), no colonies developed. On the other hand, when the same numbers of cells of the two strains were spread *together* on a plate of minimal medium, about a hundred colonies appeared. These colonies consisted of bacteria which could be subcultured on a minimal synthetic medium. Such bacteria are termed *prototrophs,* according to the nomenclature proposed by Ryan and Lederberg (1946). Conversely, mutants requiring growth factors are termed *auxotrophs.*

The wild strain, capable of synthesizing all essential metabolites may be represented by the factorial symbols $B^+Ph^+C^+T^+L^+B_1^+$ and the

---

* In bacterial genetics, the ability to synthesize an essential metabolite is usually symbolized as +, the loss of this ability as —.

two polyauxotrophic mutants by the symbols $B^-Ph^-C^-T^+L^+B_1^+$ and $B^+Ph^+C^+T^-L^-B_1^-$, respectively. The prototrophic colonies formed after mixing are apparently composed of $B^+Ph^+C^+T^+L^+B_1^+$ individuals, in which the genetic characters of both parental types have been reassorted. In other words, they are *genetic recombinants* (Fig. 1). When the same experiment was repeated, but with selection for only two characters of each parental type instead of three (the B^+Ph^+—T^+L^+ char-

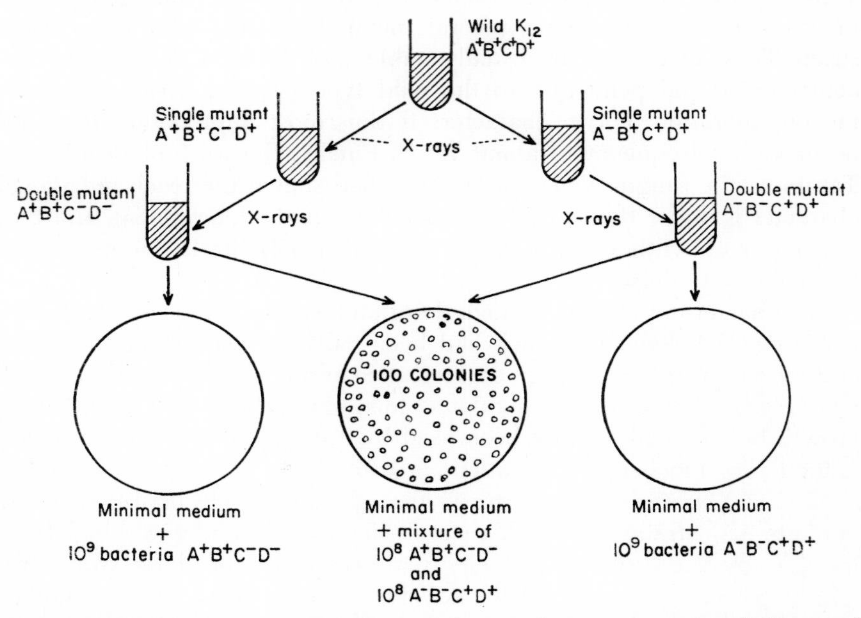

FIG. 1. Diagrammatic representation of the initial experiment of Lederberg and Tatum.

acters for instance), segregation of the nonselected characters C and B_1 was observed among the genetic recombinants $B^+Ph^+T^+L^+$ that were formed (J. Lederberg and Tatum, 1946a and b).

As for the mechanism of this reassortment of genetic characters, it was soon shown to be a true sexual process. Not only did genetic recombination require that the bacteria from both strains be intact and alive (Tatum and Lederberg, 1947), but actual cellular contact was also necessary (Davis, 1950b). Hypotheses which presupposed a more or less persistent association of genetic material from the two parental types, such as the formation of aggregates, of heterokaryons, or of diploid heterozygotes were soon excluded. In fact, as will be shown in the next chapter, when the two strains involved in a cross differ by a number of genetic characters which play no part in the selection of recombinants, these characters segregate among the recombinants, and it is possible to demonstrate the existence of linkage relationships between these unselected characters and the characters used for the selection of recombinants (Tatum and Lederberg, 1947; J. Lederberg, 1947).

Accordingly, genetic recombination is the result of conjugation between bacteria of different genotypes, a conjugation that is followed by a process comparable to crossing-over, and by the segregation of hybrid bacteria possessing properties inherited from each of the two parental types.

The phenomenon discovered by Lederberg and Tatum consequently proved that, during recombination, the genetic determinants of bacteria show the same factorial character as had already been revealed by the study of variability. It also showed that these genetic determinants are linearly arranged in a structure comparable to the chromosomes of the cells of higher organisms.

In the year which saw the discovery of genetic recombination in bacteria, analogous phenomena were reported in bacteriophages (Delbrück and Bailey, 1946). As mentioned in Chapter I, mutations can be observed that affect any of the recognizable properties of these viruses: the appearance or size of the plaques, host range, etc. If sensitive bacteria are infected with two related bacteriophages which differ in two genetic characters, these bacteria release not only phages of both infective types, but also phages of recombinant types. For instance, when bacteria are mixedly infected with phages $T2rh^+$ and $T2r^+h$ (in which r and r^+ represent differences in plaque morphology and h and h^+ differences in the activity of the bacteriophages on two different hosts), they produce particles of the two parental types and of the recombinant types T2rh and $T2r^+h^+$. The proportions of these recombinant types in the progeny permit calculation of the distances which separate the genetic determinants in question. Thus in bacteriophages, just as in bacteria, genetic maps can be constructed in recombination units (Hershey and Rotman, 1948).

In sum, among the simplest living organisms, the bacteria and even the viruses, one can also find the fundamental properties which characterize the hereditary material of animals and plants: the individual and factorial character of genetic determinants, and the organization of these determinants on linear structures.

II. THE TRANSFER OF HEREDITARY CHARACTERS IN BACTERIA

Long before the discovery of bacterial conjugation, some cases of the transmission of hereditary properties in bacteria had been described (see J. Lederberg, 1948). As early as 1909, Kuhn and Woithe observed and designated by the term para-agglutination the acquisition, by strains of *E. coli* grown in mixed culture with *Shigella* or *Salmonella*, of the property of agglutinating following exposure to anti-*Shigella* and anti-*Salmonella* sera (see Kuhn and Ebeling, 1916). In some cases, the transmission of characters from one strain of bacteria to another could be observed only in mixed cultures (E. Wollman and Mme Wollman, 1925); in other cases, the phenomenon occurred when one of the strains had been grown in a filtrate of the other strain (F. M. Burnet, 1925; Cantacuzène and Bonciu, 1926; Legroux and Genevray, 1933).

It is also known that some strains of bacteria, called lysogenic bacteria, possess the hereditary property of producing bacteriophages which are active against other bacterial strains. When such bacteriophages infect sensitive bacteria, they can give rise to new lysogenic systems (Bordet, 1925; Bail, 1925). In this case, an hereditary property is unquestionably acquired through infection.

As early as 1925, Eugène Wollman proposed "to designate by the term paraheredity all these phenomena of the acquisition of characters by some kind of contagion." This "transmission of characters from one cell to another through the external medium" seemed to him to indicate that "the bearers, or factors, of the characters in question must reproduce inside the affected cells, since the properties acquired by them are maintained for many generations" (E. Wollman, 1927).

The validity of this concept has been verified by the investigations of the past fifteen years, which have established the mechanisms of gene transfer in bacteria.

A. Transformation

The most remarkable example of a transfer of hereditary characteristics was described by Griffith in 1928. After injecting mice simultaneously with viable, noncapsulated, and therefore avirulent, pneumococci of type II and with heat-killed encapsulated pneumococci of type I, Griffith observed, to his great surprise, that the inoculated animals died of septicemia. From the blood of these animals he isolated viable, encapsulated pneumococci of type I, namely of the antigenic type to which the killed cells had belonged.

These results were confirmed and extended by several workers, notably Dawson and Sia (1931), who were able to reproduce this transformation *in vitro,* and Alloway (1932) who obtained a transformation *in vitro* not with killed cells, but with bacterial extracts. However, it was the investigations of Avery, MacLeod, and McCarty (1944) that revealed the true importance of this phenomenon and elucidated its mechanism. These workers in fact showed that pneumococcal transformation could be produced by purified preparations of deoxyribonucleic acid (DNA) extracted from encapsulated donor bacteria. The preparations of "transforming principle" were active at extremely low concentrations. The "transformed" bacteria were not only able to transfer their new antigenic properties to their descendants, but could also serve as a source for the extraction of a DNA able, in its turn, to induce the transformation of non-capsulated strains. "It is evident, therefore," wrote the authors of this discovery, "that not only is the capsular material reproduced in successive generations but that the primary factor, which controls the occurrence and specificity of capsular development, is also reduplicated in the daughter cells."

This discovery had great repercussions. In fact, it showed for the first time the specific role of a nucleic acid in a biological phenomenon, and the importance that this idea has since acquired scarcely needs to be stressed. The real meaning of the phenomenon was not immediately apparent, however. It was hard to visualize what relation there could be between the synthesis of a capsular polysaccharide and of a nucleic acid. Pneumococcal transformation was compared to induced mutations and to the reproduction of viruses, until in 1947 Muller proposed the following interpretation: ". . . parts of chromosomes . . . might . . . have penetrated the capsuleless bacteria and in part at least have taken root there, perhaps after having undergone a kind of crossing-over with the chromosomes of the host."

Since the fundamental work of Avery, MacLeod, and McCarty, transformation has been extensively studied (see reviews by Austrian, 1952; Ephrussi-Taylor, 1955; Hotchkiss, 1955). It has been shown that many different characters can be transmitted from a donor strain to a recipient strain by DNA extracted from the donor bacteria, and transformation has been discovered in a variety of other bacterial species. When donor and recipient bacteria differ in several hereditary characters, each character of the donor bacteria is acquired independently of the others. Only in exceptional cases has linkage been observed and described (Hotchkiss and Marmur, 1954). Transformation thus appears to represent a transfer of small segments of genetic material.

Since the original discovery of Avery and his co-workers, information about the role in heredity of nucleic acids, and DNA in particular, has increased considerably. DNA, a universal constituent of the genetic apparatus of animals and plants, is also a major constituent of many viruses, particularly bacteriophages. Experiments carried out by Hershey and Chase (1952) have shown that when bacteria are infected by virulent bacteriophage T2, it is almost exclusively the DNA of the infecting phage which enters the bacteria and consequently ensures the multiplication of the bacteriophage and the perpetuation of its genetic specificity.

Paradoxically, therefore, and such paradoxes are not rare in the evolution of scientific knowledge, it was the study of bacteria and viruses, organisms long thought to lack a true genetic apparatus which revealed the role of the nucleic acids as bearers of genetic information.

B. Lysogenization

A second way in which hereditary properties can be acquired through infection is by the formation of lysogenic systems. The bacteriophages capable of forming such systems are called *temperate* (Jacob, Lwoff, Siminovitch, and Wollman, 1953). When sensitive bacteria are exposed to the action of a temperate bacteriophage (itself produced by a lysogenic strain), some cells lyse while others survive and, in turn, become lysogenic. Once established, the lysogenic character is extremely stable, as stable as the other hereditary properties of the bacterial strain in question (Bordet, 1925; Bail, 1925).

Lysogenic strains obtained in the laboratory by lysogenization of sensitive bacteria have the same properties as lysogenic strains isolated from nature. They perpetuate hereditarily the capacity to produce phage, and the phage that they produce is of the type with which they were lysogenized. They also acquire a specific resistance, or *immunity*, to the type of phage used to lysogenize them. This immunity results not from an inability to adsorb the phage, but from an inability to reproduce it.

Thus lysogenization leads to a stable association between a virus, the bacteriophage, and a bacterium; the lysogenic system so established thereafter behaves as a single reproductive unit. The parallel, frequently drawn, between lysogenization and transformation is an obvious one.

Production of phage and immunity to the homologous phage are properties common to all lysogenic strains: they are the very expression of lysogeny (see Lwoff, 1953; Jacob, 1954a). Sometimes, however, lysogenization results in the acquisition of properties whose relationships to lysogeny are not immediately evident: for example, changes in the appearance of colonies (Dooren de Jong, 1931; Ionesco, 1953) and in the morphology of the cells (E. Wollman and Mme Wollman, 1938). During the past few years, other examples, even more striking, have been described, such as the synthesis of surface antigens (Iseki and Sakai, 1953) or the production of toxin by diphtheria bacilli (Freeman, 1951). In every case, lysogenization by certain temperate bacteriophages results in the acquisition by the bacteria of new hereditary properties, and there is a perfect correlation between the acquisition of these properties and the establishment of lysogeny.

The problems raised by lysogenic bacteria will be examined in more detail in a later section of this chapter. Lysogeny indeed represents a peculiar situation in which the genetic material of a virus and that of the bacterial host are integrated.

C. Transduction

More recently, a third mode of transfer of genetic characters in the absence of cellular contact has been described by Zinder and Lederberg (1952). Hoping to extend the demonstration of genetic recombination to species other than *E. coli,* Zinder and Lederberg chose for study a group of strains of *Salmonella typhimurium.* When certain strains that differed in nutritional characters were mixed, the formation of genetic recombinants could be observed. Contrary to what happens with *E. coli* K12, however, the phenomenon could be reproduced when cells of one strain were suspended in culture filtrates of the other strain. It was then shown that the agent responsible for the transfer of genetic characters was a temperate bacteriophage. The phenomenon was termed *transduction.*

A great variety of genetic characters can be transduced from donor bacteria to recipient bacteria: nutritional characters, utilization of sugars, resistance to inhibitors, motility, surface antigens, etc. Only those characters present in the donor bacteria; i.e., the bacteria used in the preparation of a lysate of the transducing phage, can be transmitted to given recipient bacteria. The frequency of transduction of a given character from donor bacteria is low (only one particle of bacteriophage in a million can transmit the character), and as a rule different characters are independently transmitted. In certain cases, however, the simultaneous transfer of several characters has been observed (Stocker, Zinder, and Lederberg, 1953). Transduction and lysogenization are two distinct phenomena. Only certain types of temperate bacteriophages have the ability to transduce. On the other hand, transduction can occur without concomitant lysogenization of the transduced bacteria (Zinder, 1953).

The phenomenon of transduction can thus be visualized in the following way: during the multiplication of certain temperate phages, small segments of bacterial genetic material are included at random within the phage particles. When these bacteriophages infect bacteria of a different genotype (recipient bacteria), the genetic segments from the donor bacteria, brought in by the infecting bacteriophage, can undergo recombination with the genetic material of the recipient. The size of the segments capable of being transported by a phage particle is small, in all probability limited by the size of the carrier phage itself, and consequently different genetic characters are as a rule independently transduced.

Transduction of genetic characters has been studied in a great many *Salmonella* strains (J. Lederberg and Edwards, 1953), in *Shigella* and in *Escherichia coli* (Lennox, 1955). In the case of *E. coli* K12, the genetic data obtained by conjugation and by transduction can be compared. The simultaneous transduction of characters which are known to be linked can thus be shown (Lennox, 1955; Jacob, 1955). Transduction permits the accurate analysis of the fine structure of short genetic segments (Demerec and Demerec, 1956; Demerec, 1956; P. E. Hartman, 1957).

In addition to this mode of transduction which is generalized and nonspecific, another mode of transduction, characteristically specific and restricted to certain genetic characters of the donor has been described more recently (Morse, Lederberg, and Lederberg, 1956a). In this case, only a limited segment of genetic material of a donor bacterium can be transferred to a recipient. As will be seen later, this mode of genetic transfer may be in some way considered as intermediate between generalized transduction and conversion of genetic properties as sometimes observed after lysogenization.

* * *

Three modes of "para-hereditary" acquisition of new properties have so far been recognized in bacteria: one, transformation, involves the penetration into recipient bacteria of DNA "molecules" extracted from donor bacteria; the second, lysogenization, brings about the formation of a stable association between a recipient bacterium and a virus; the third, transduction, appears to be a combination of the first two, since some genetic material from a donor bacterium is transported into a recipient by means of a bacteriophage. As Eugène Wollman wrote in 1928, "the two notions of heredity and infection which seemed so completely distinct and in some ways incompatible, . . . almost merge under certain conditions."

In transformation as well as in transduction, one is admittedly confronted by unusual mechanisms of genetic exchange between individuals of the same race or species. However, they are without any doubt phenomena of hybridization; perhaps at first sight disconcerting for the geneticist, but in no way opposed to the basic concepts of genetics. In lysogenization, on the other hand, it is the genetic material of a virus which becomes associated with that of a bacterium. The very existence of such an association raises major problems, which must next be considered.

III. LYSOGENY AND ITS GENETIC DETERMINATION

Lysogeny represents a situation in which, as Bordet wrote in 1925, "the power of reproducing the bacteriophage is woven into the hereditary web of the bacterium." Although this definition is still valid today, the facts about lysogeny were given the most varied interpretations. The true nature of this phenomenon became evident only in 1950, thanks to the studies of Lwoff and his collaborators. An experimental analysis of lysogeny was indeed dependent upon the possibility of distinguishing between the various relationships which can be established between bacteria and bacteriophages.

In the extreme case of the so-called virulent bacteriophages, infection invariably culminates in the death of the bacterium and the production of new infectious particles. This process has been the object of the classic investigations of Delbrück (1946), Luria (1953), Hershey (1957a), and their schools.

In the other extreme case of the lysogenic bacteria, a stable association exists between bacteriophages and bacteria. Seemingly harmless for the bacteria, this association nevertheless manifests itself by the production of bacteriophages which are active on other bacterial strains, the sensitive so-called indicator strains. A description of the evolution of ideas concerning lysogeny and a general account of knowledge in this field can be found in the review of Lwoff (1953) and the monograph of Jacob (1954a). Other reviews have been published more recently (Jacob and Wollman, 1957a, 1959b; Bertani, 1958; Jacob, 1960).

A. The Concept of Prophage

Lysogeny is, by definition, the hereditary ability to produce bacteriophage in the absence of external infection. A lysogenic bacterium accordingly possesses and transmits to its descendants the power of producing a bacteriophage (Lwoff, 1953). Since production of bacteriophage leads to destruction of the cell in which it takes place, the ability of lysogenic bacteria to produce phage is a potentially lethal character (Lwoff and Gutmann, 1950). Lysogenic bacteria do not contain infectious particles of bacteriophage (F. M. Burnet and McKie, 1929; E. Wollman and Mme Wollman, 1936). The noninfectious form in which lysogenic bacteria perpetuate the ability to produce the phage has been called *prophage* by Lwoff and Gutmann.

In a culture of lysogenic bacteria, only a small portion of the population undergoes lysis with the concomitant release of infectious particles. For reasons still unknown, the balance between the prophage and the bacterium in these cells has been upset. With some lysogenic strains, such treatment as irradiation with small doses of ultraviolet light induces the

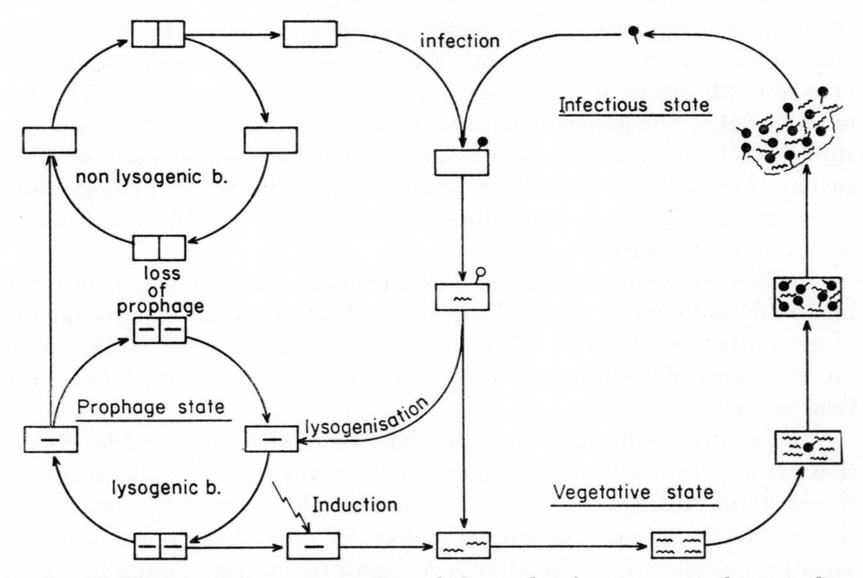

FIG. 2. Diagrammatic representation of the cycle of a temperate bacteriophage in inducible lysogenic bacteria (after Lwoff, 1953).

development of bacteriophage and the release of infectious particles in almost all members of the treated population. This is the phenomenon of *induction*, discovered by Lwoff, Siminovitch, and Kjeldgaard (1950). Agents capable of producing this effect are known as inducing agents. With other lysogenic strains, however, no means of increasing the rate of spontaneous phage production are known. The inducible or noninducible character of a lysogenic strain is usually determined by the kind of prophage it carries.

It is known that after infection of sensitive bacteria, bacteriophages enter a noninfectious phase (E. Wollman and Mme Wollman, 1937; Doermann, 1948). As shown by Hershey and Chase (1952), this loss of infectivity reflects the fact that only the nucleic acid of the infecting particles enters the bacteria, whereas the infective power (i.e., the ability to become specifically adsorbed on sensitive bacteria) is a property of the protein coat of bacteriophages. During the reproduction of bacteriophage, be it after infection of sensitive bacteria or after induction of lysogenic bacteria, the phage genome is therefore in a noninfective or *vegetative state* (see Jacob, 1954a).

These two noninfective states, the vegetative state and the prophage state, differ fundamentally. In the *vegetative state,* the phage genome multiplies actively and controls the synthesis of the material necessary for the production of infective particles. This phase of multiplication is, therefore, essentially transient and leads to the lysis of the bacterium and the release of infective particles. In the *prophage state,* on the other hand, the phage genome behaves like a normal bacterial constituent, whose reproduction is closely coordinated with that of the bacterium. Normally, there is a very low probability that it can evolve toward the vegetative state. In the inducible lysogenic strains, this transition can, as we have seen, be induced with high efficiency. The reproductive cycle of a temperate bacteriophage is shown in Fig. 2.

B. The Prophage as a Genetic Unit

Lysogeny is a stable hereditary character. Consequently, the properties that distinguish a lysogenic strain from the homologous nonlysogenic strain can be regarded as the phenotypic expression of a special genetic determinant, the prophage. The prophage can, therefore, be defined as *the structure which, in lysogenic bacteria, carries the genetic information necessary for the production of a given type of bacteriophage and which confers on these bacteria certain specific hereditary properties.*

In some lysogenic bacteria, a genetic lesion of the prophage prevents one of the reactions necessary for the formation of infectious particles (see Jacob and Wollman, 1956a; Jacob, 1960). In these *defective lysogenic bacteria,* the presence of a prophage is manifested only by phenotypic properties other than the production of bacteriophage. If it were not possible to compare the properties of the lysogenic and nonlysogenic derivatives, it would obviously be extremely difficult, in such cases, to differentiate a prophage from a bacterial genetic determinant.

The existence of lysogenic bacteria thus poses problems of great genetic interest. Specifically, it may be asked whether the number of prophages contained in a lysogenic bacterium is large or small, and whether the properties of the prophage are those of a cytoplasmic constituent or those of a nuclear constituent. It may further be asked whether the prophage is the only genetic determinant of lysogeny, or whether lysogeny may not also be under the control of bacterial factors. One can obtain indirect information about these problems by the special techniques for the study of bacteriophage (Jacob, 1954a; Jacob and Wollman, 1957a); but it is obvious that only genetic experiments can provide definitive answers.

The existence of genetic recombination in bacteria should provide the means of making such a study. In fact, the strain of *E. coli,* in which genetic recombination was discovered, is lysogenic, and nonlysogenic mutants of this strain have been isolated (E. M. Lederberg, 1951). It thus became possible to cross lysogenic and nonlysogenic bacteria and to study the behavior of the lysogenic character in these crosses. As will be seen in a later chapter, this study has elucidated the genetic determination of lysogeny. Conversely, genetic analysis of crosses between lysogenic and nonlysogenic bacteria has helped a great deal to refine our understanding of the mechanism of conjugation and genetic recombination in bacteria.

* * *

The existence in bacteria of mechanisms for the exchange or transfer of hereditary properties, barely surmised some fifteen years ago, has permitted the extension of the methods of genetic analysis to these microorganisms. These mechanisms of genetic transfer and exchange range from what seems to be the equivalent of a conjugation process to hitherto unknown modes of transfer of chromosomal segments or even of "purified genetic material." Although their evolutionary significance is still difficult to evaluate, it seems that they could be considered as rudimentary sexual processes. This is especially true in the case of the phenomenon discovered by Lederberg and Tatum, where genetic recombination requires cellular contact. Lastly, lysogeny raises both the question of the determination of hereditary characters by elements possessing a much higher degree of autonomy than the purely bacterial genetic factors, and that of the relations between cells and viruses.

CHAPTER III

Genetic Recombination at Low Frequencies

The experiments of Lederberg and Tatum, described in the preceding chapter, demonstrated the existence of phenomena of genetic recombination in bacteria. This genetic recombination appeared to be the result of a conjugation process, since it occurred only if the parental bacteria had actually been in contact. A brief summary of the characteristics of genetic recombination in *E. coli* K12 as observed in these early crosses will be given in this chapter.

I. THE GENETIC ANALYSIS OF CROSSES

The number of recombinants formed in the experiments reported by Lederberg and Tatum was always very small. Although this number might vary with the strains used and with the selection methods employed, it never exceeded one recombinant in 10^5 bacteria. This low frequency of recombination imposes a special methodology and greatly complicates the analysis of the results.

A. Methods of Genetic Analysis

The methods commonly used in genetics involve the analysis of all the offspring of several identical crosses, or of samples chosen at random among all the products of a large number of identical crosses. The extremely low frequency of recombination observed in the crosses of *E. coli* K12 made obligatory the use of the original method devised by Lederberg and Tatum, which consists in the selection of certain types of recombinants. Such a method has several special features.

(1) Among all the possible matings, only those which yield a certain type of recombinant are detected.

(2) Among all the products of such a mating, only the type of recombinant that is selected can be analyzed.

(3) It is not the immediate product of conjugation which is analyzed but its progeny, since one colony of recombinants contains about 10^7 individuals.

In spite of these peculiarities, the essential characteristics of genetic recombination in *E. coli* K12 were quickly established, thanks to the work of Tatum and Lederberg (1947) and of J. Lederberg (1947).

Among the genetic characters, the behavior of which is followed in a cross, it is necessary to distinguish: *selected characters,* which are used to select the recombinants on the one hand and *unselected characters* or markers on the other. When strains which differ by a large number of characters are crossed, it is possible, in a given selection, to study how the various markers are distributed among the selected recombinants. When several characters can be independently used as selectors, one can analyze in the same cross various types of recombinants. It is by such methods that J. Lederberg (1947) could establish that the various genetic characters of *E. coli* K12 appear to be arranged in a single linkage group and was thus able to draw the first genetic map of a "bacterial chromosome."

B. The Bases of Genetic Analysis

A few simple examples, borrowed from J. Lederberg (1947) will help to illustrate these methods and to establish the essential characteristics of the process of genetic recombination in *E. coli* K12.

Let us consider a cross between a doubly auxotrophic strain, unable to synthesize two essential metabolites, biotin (B) and methionine (M), and a triple auxotroph, unable to synthesize threonine (T), leucine (L), and vitamin B_1. These two strains can be symbolized as $T^+L^+B_1{}^+M^-B^-$ (type A) and $T^-L^-B_1{}^-M^+B^+$ (type B), respectively. If both parental strains are sensitive to the virulent bacteriophage T_1 ($T_1{}^s$) all prototrophic recombinants $T^+L^+B_1{}^+M^+B^+$ will be, like the parental strains, $T_1{}^s$. If both parental strains are resistant to T_1 ($T_1{}^r$) all prototrophic recombinants will be $T_1{}^r$.

Let us now examine the outcome of reciprocal crosses in which the parental strains differ with respect to this character:

$$(1)\quad T^+L^+B_1{}^+M^-B^-T_1{}^r \times T^-L^-B_1{}^-M^+B^+T_1{}^s$$

and

$$(2)\quad T^+L^+B_1{}^+M^-B^-T_1{}^s \times T^-L^-B_1{}^-M^+B^+T_1{}^r$$

In cross (1), 75 per cent of the prototrophic recombinants have the character $T_1{}^r$ of the parental type (A) and 25 per cent the character $T_1{}^s$ of the parental type (B). In cross (2) the proportions are reversed: 64 per cent of the prototrophic recombinants have the character $T_1{}^s$ of the parental type (A) and 36 per cent the character $T_1{}^r$ of the parental type (B). It should be added that analysis of a large number of bacteria from the same recombinant colony indicated that the component cells were identical, with respect not only to the prototrophic character, but also to the character of resistance or sensitivity to bacteriophage T_1.

From these results Lederberg drew the following conclusions:

(1) Bacteria are *haploid*, as shown by the fact that segregation of the T_1^r and T_1^s alleles occurs in the selected recombinants (clones derived from F_1 hybrids), and that the ratios in which these alleles appear are reversed, depending on the parental type which carries them.

(2) The diploid stage formed by conjugation does not persist. Segregation of haploid recombinants from the zygotes occurs *early*, since the recombinant colonies are composed of individuals with the same genotype.

(3) Linkage relations exist between the genetic determinants studied, the character (T_1) tending to be linked more closely with the selected markers $T^+L^+B_1^+$ than with the selected markers M^+B^+.

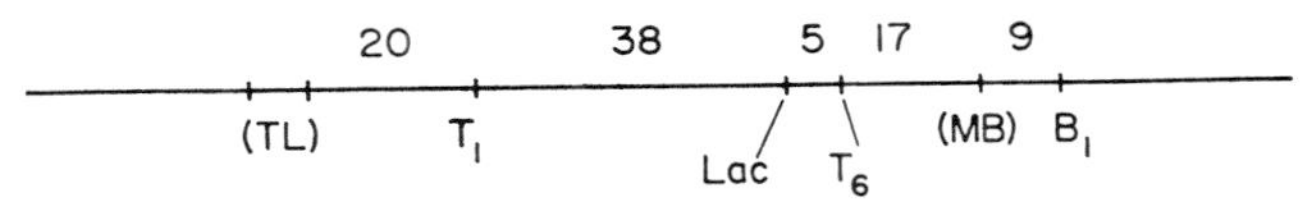

FIG. 3. The first genetic map of *E. coli* K12, established by Lederberg (1947). The figures given correspond to the relative frequencies of recombination between the genetic characters indicated.

Lederberg extended these results by using successively as unselected markers each of the nutritional characters which had been used as selected markers in the previous crosses, and subsequently by differential labeling of the strains used for crosses with new characters, such as ability to ferment lactose (Lac) or resistance to bacteriophage T_6. He was thus able to show that the various characters studied were all linked, and could be arranged in linear order. The first genetic map prepared by J. Lederberg (1947) is shown in Fig. 3.

It should be mentioned that in the strains used by Lederberg, the selected markers T and L on the one hand, and M and B on the other, are close enough so that their simultaneous use does not unnecessarily complicate genetic analysis when recombinants $T^+L^+M^+B^+$ are selected.

Thus, shortly after the discovery of genetic recombination in bacteria, the brilliant work of Lederberg proved that segregation and recombination of numerous characters takes place in bacterial crosses, and that the genetic determinants of these characters can be arranged in linear order. Consequently, it seems justifiable, by analogy with what is known of other organisms, to designate the material structure which carries this genetic linkage group as the "bacterial chromosome."

The results of the genetic analysis of crosses seemed to confirm the validity of the hypothesis proposed by Lederberg and Tatum to account for the phenomenon of genetic recombination in bacteria. According to this hypothesis, recombination is the consequence of a cellular fusion followed by nuclear fusion, and of "crossing-over" during meiotic reduction of the zygote. This hypothesis, besides being the simplest one, was also the only one which could provide a basis for genetic analysis and make possible the interpretation of the results. Because of the low frequency of recombination, the genetic analysis of a particular class of selected recombinants is justified only if these recombinants come from similar zygotes, formed during similar acts of conjugation, i.e., if they are samples of an homogeneous population.

II. THE SUBSEQUENT DEVELOPMENT OF GENETIC ANALYSIS

Genetic analysis has been extended to a large number of genetic characters, especially those which are relatively easy to score: capacity to synthesize essential metabolites, ability to utilize various carbohydrates, sensitivity or resistance to various bacteriophages or inhibitors. Some of these characters can be used to select recombinants in addition to their use as unselected markers; others can be used only as unselected markers. Table 1 gives a list of some of the characters which have been used in early studies of genetic recombination in *E. coli* K12.

Special mention must be made of the characters of resistance to antibiotics and other antibacterial agents. The use of such characters as selective markers makes it possible to prevent the residual growth of one of the parental types which is impossible when selection of genetic recombinants is based on the use of nutritional characters (J. Lederberg, 1950b). This technique also permits crosses in which one of the strains is auxotrophic and resistant to the antibacterial agent, whereas the other is prototrophic and sensitive. This greatly extends the field of operation, since it eliminates the necessity for a tedious "marking" of strains whose fertility or behavior in crosses is to be analyzed.

All the characters studied have proved to be under the control of determinants which recombined or segregated in crosses in more or less close association with the determinants of the genetic characters that were initially investigated. These results reinforced the assumption of a single linkage group, and hence of a single chromosome, in *E. coli* K12.

Table I

Some Characters Used in Early Investigation of Genetic Recombination in *E.coli* K12

Biosynthesis	Symbol	References	Utilization	Symbol	References	Resistance	Symbol	References
Amino acids			Sugars			Inhibitors		
Threonine	T	3, 7, 9	Lactose	Lac	3, 8, 9, 11, 14	Sodium Azide	Az	3, 10
Leucine	L	11, 14, 15	Galactose	Gal	1, 3, 8, 13, 16	Valine	Val	2, 12
Phenylalanine	Pa	9, 15				Norleucine	Nl	5
Cystine	C	9, 15, 16	Arabinose	Ara	3, 13			
Histidine	H	16				Antibiotics		
Methionine	M	3, 5, 7, 9, 11, 13	Maltose	Mal }		Streptomycin	Sm	3, 10, 13
			Xylose	Xyl }	3, 5, 11, 13	Chloromycetin	Cm	4
Proline	Pr	2, 5, 9	Mannitol	Mtl }		Terramycin	Tm	4
						Polymyxin	Pm	3
Vitamins						Phages and colicins		
Biotin	B	9, 15				T_1—T_5	T_1	1, 11, 14, 15
Thiamine	B_1	3, 9, 11, 15				T_3	T_3	7
						T_6	T_6	9, 11
						λ	λ	16
						Colicins	Col	6

References for Table I (for complete citation see List of References at end of book).

1. Cavalli-Sforza, 1950.
2. Cavalli-Sforza and Calef, 1955.
3. Cavalli-Sforza and Jinks, 1956.
4. Cavalli-Sforza and Lederberg, 1953.
5. Clowes and Rowley, 1954a.
6. Frédéricq and Betz-Barreau, 1952.
7. Hayes, 1953a.
8. E. Lederberg, 1952.
9. J. Lederberg, 1947.
10. J. Lederberg, 1950b.
11. J. Lederberg, Lederberg, Zinder and Lively, 1951.
12. Manten and Rowley, 1953.
13. Newcombe and Nyholm, 1950b.
14. Rothfels, 1952.
15. Tatum and Lederberg, 1947.
16. E. L. Wollman, 1953.

A. Genetic Recombination and Allelic Relationships

The fact that genetic recombination comparable to crossing-over occurs in bacteria has made it possible to extend to these organisms the analysis of allelic relations between genetic determinants which appear to affect the same phenotypic character. For instance, among the mutants resistant to bacteriophage T_1, some are resistant to T_1 alone, others to both T_1 and T_5. Crosses between bacteria of these two types give rise to recombinants sensitive to T_1, a result which indicates that the two mutations are not allelic (J. Lederberg, Lederberg, Zinder, and Lively, 1951). In the same way, early analysis of Lac^- mutations showed that the genetic system which controls the ability to ferment lactose, is rather complex and comprises several loci (E. M. Lederberg, 1952). For some of these loci, multiple alleles were found, which could be distinguished by the rate at which the corresponding strains return to the initial Lac^+ phenotype, whether by reverse mutations at the same locus or by mutations at suppressor loci.

This type of analysis has also been applied to the study of resistance to antibiotics. It is well known that the acquisition by spontaneous mutations of resistance to antibiotics or inhibitors can occur in different ways. In some cases, for example with streptomycin, a high level of resistance can be acquired in a single mutational step; in other cases, for example with penicillin, the level of genetically acquired resistance increases with succeeding mutational steps (Demerec, 1948). By appropriate crosses, Newcombe and Nyholm (1950a) were able to show that resistance to streptomycin apparently depends on one single locus. At least three different alleles are known to exist at this locus, responsible respectively for streptomycin-sensitivity, streptomycin-resistance, and streptomycin-dependence. On the other hand, Cavalli-Sforza and Maccacaro (1950, 1952) were able to show that resistance to chloramphenicol, which is acquired in successive steps, is under polygenic control.

The study of allelic relationships, which is one of the basic methods of Mendelian analysis, provided additional evidence for the close homology between the genetic system of bacteria and that of sexually reproducing organisms. Such studies also permit the establishment of the relationships between the genetic determinants and the characters they control, i.e., between the genes and their functions.

B. Diploid Heterozygotes and the Functional Analysis of Allelism

Analysis of crosses had indicated that segregation of the recombinant types occurs early, and that the "zygotes" formed during conjugation have a transient existence. In some cases however, J. Lederberg (1949b) succeeded in isolating prototrophs which seemed to have the properties of permanent diploid heterozygotes. During their multiplication, these prototrophic bacteria gave rise to cells of the same genotype as one or the other parental types, as well as to recombinant types. The existence of these diploid heterozygotes verified by isolating individual cells by techniques of micromanipulation (Zelle and Lederberg, 1951), furnished another proof of the sexual character of genetic recombination in *E. coli* K12. It seemed also to open new possibilities for the genetic analysis of this phenomenon.

The formation of diploid heterozygotes is the result of a mutation (Het), which appeared in one strain of *E. coli* K12. It soon proved to have extremely complex consequences. Genetic analysis revealed that these permanent diploid heterozygotes were not actually true heterozygotes: although both parental alleles for certain characters were present, other characters were represented by only one allele. In general, the characters of *one* of the parents predominate in these aberrant forms (J. Lederberg, Lederberg, Zinder, and Lively, 1951).

In spite of these peculiarities to which we shall return later, the existence of diploid heterozygotes has made possible the analysis of dominance. In diploid heterozygotes carrying both the wild type and the mutant alleles governing a single character, it could be shown that ability to synthesize an essential metabolite is dominant over inability, ability to utilize or to ferment a sugar is dominant over inability, sensitivity to a bacteriophage is dominant over resistance (J. Lederberg, 1949b), and sensitivity to streptomycin is dominant over resistance to this antibiotic (J. Lederberg, 1951a).

Another type of analysis not feasible with haploid bacteria which becomes possible with diploid heterozygous forms is the functional analysis of mutations which affect the same character. It is known that if mutations with the same phenotypic expression occur at different loci, the diploid heterozygotes (or heterokaryons) which carry these two mutant genes on the two members of a homologous chromosome pair (i.e., in the *trans* position) will have the wild phenotype and not the mutant phenotype (see E. B. Lewis, 1951; Pontecorvo, 1956). This indicates that the two mutations affect two different reactions which are both involved in the expression of the same phenotype. If, on the other hand, the diploid heterozygotes (or heterokaryons) in *trans* position exhibit the mutant phenotype and not the wild phenotype, this is taken to indicate that the two mutations affect the same function. These findings lead to a functional definition of allelism: those mutations which affect the same function are considered to be allelic even though recombination between the determinants under study may be possible (see Chapter XIV).

Analyses of this type can be performed with *E. coli* K12 thanks to the existence of diploid heterozygotes. For instance, two mutations, which were found both to confer resistance to bacteriophage T_1 but to be undissociable by recombination, were revealed as nonallelic by functional analysis. The diploid heterozygotes for these mutations in position *trans* have the wild phenotype, sensitive to phage T_1 (J. Lederberg *et al.*, 1951). These mutations therefore are not considered to be multiple alleles at the same locus, but to have occurred at different, although closely linked, loci. Another example of this type of analysis is the study by E. M. Lederberg (1952) of a series of mutations affecting the utilization of lactose. Three of these mutations, Lac_{1a}^-, Lac_{1b}^-, and Lac_4^-, although closely linked, can be dissociated by recombination. The diploid heterozygotes $Lac_{1a}^-\ Lac_4^+/Lac_{1a}^+\ Lac_4^-$ or $Lac_{1b}^-\ Lac_4^+/Lac_{1b}^+\ Lac_4^-$ exhibit the Lac^+ phenotype, whereas the diploid heterozygotes $Lac_{1a}^-\ Lac_{1b}^+/Lac_{1a}^+\ Lac_{1b}^-$ exhibit the Lac^- phenotype. This result indicates that the mutations Lac_{1a}^- and Lac_{1b}^- have occurred at different sites in a single locus (heteroalleles), whereas the mutation Lac_4^- has occurred at another locus (see Beadle, 1957).

C. Crosses between Lysogenic and Nonlysogenic Strains of *Escherichia coli* K12

The lysogenic character of *E.coli* K12 was discovered quite accidentally by E. M. Lederberg (1951). After exposure of K12 to ultraviolet light, she isolated a nonlysogenic mutant which was sensitive to the bacteriophage produced by the other strains of *E.coli* K12. This temperate bacteriophage was given the name λ.* The lysogenic K12 strain, represented by the symbol K12(λ), is inducible by ultraviolet light (Weiglé and Delbrück, 1951); owing to this property, it has become one of the strains most widely used for the study of lysogeny. The fact that *E.coli* K12 is lysogenic plays no part in the phenomenon of genetic recombination; genetic recombinants are formed just as well in crosses between lysogenic strains as in crosses between nonlysogenic ones. When the parental strains are both lysogenic, all the genetic recombinants formed are likewise lysogenic; conversely, when the parental strains are both nonlysogenic, all genetic recombinants are likewise nonlysogenic (E. M. Lederberg, 1951).

* It may be noted in passing that this designation in itself stated a hypothesis about the genetic determination of lysogeny, since it is conventional to use a Greek letter as a symbol to designate cytoplasmic particles.

The possibility of performing crosses between lysogenic and nonlysogenic strains should clearly shed some light on the genetic determination of lysogeny. Before discussing the results of such crosses, we shall describe briefly the few simple models that could be entertained *a priori*, in order to compare the actual results with the predictions derived from these models (Fig. 4).

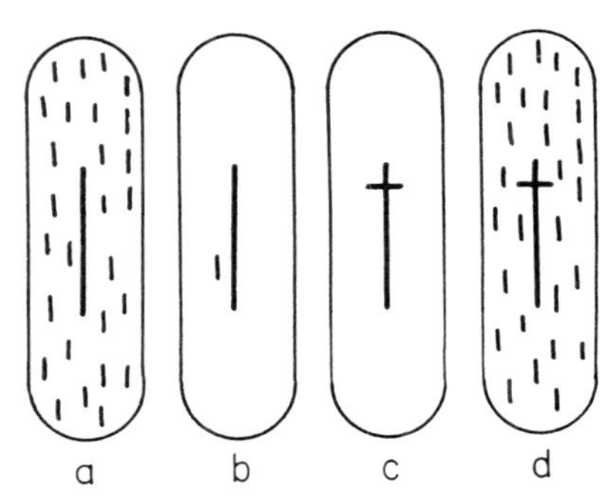

FIG. 4. Diagrammatic representation of the hypotheses concerning the genetic determination of lysogeny.

(1) In every bacterium, there might exist a large number of prophages distributed at random at the time of bacterial division (Fig. 4 *a*).

(2) In every bacterium, there could be a very limited number of prophages (one per nucleus for example). In this case, the division of the prophage should be strictly coordinated with that of the bacterial genetic material. The prophage could exist either independently of the bacterial chromosome (Fig. 4 *b*), or closely associated with it (Fig. 4 *c*).

(3) Lastly, whatever the nature of the prophage itself, lysogeny could be controlled in addition by a bacterial genetic determinant, the role of which might be, for instance, to ensure the hereditary maintenance of the prophage (Fig. 4 *d*).

In crosses between lysogenic $(ly)^+$ and nonlysogenic $(ly)^-$ strains, the following results were obtained. The lysogenic character segregates: some genetic recombinants are lysogenic, others are nonlysogenic. In addition, the segregation of the characters ly^+ and ly^- of the parental types occurs in close association with certain genetic determinants of galactose utilization (E. M. and J. Lederberg, 1953; E. L. Wollman, 1953).

According to the hypothesis formulated by Tatum and Lederberg (1947), genetic recombination would follow the fusion of the parent bacteria. If this were true, the results of crosses between lysogenic and nonlysogenic bacteria would eliminate a purely cytoplasmic determination of lysogeny, such as that schematized in diagram *a* of Fig. 4. Lysogeny would seem to depend on a chromosomal factor, and this factor would be linked to the determinants of galactose utilization. However, the results did not permit the decision as to whether the prophage is the *only* hereditary determinant of lysogeny (diagram *c*), or whether a purely bacterial determinant is also involved (diagram *d*).

The results of experiments with diploid heterozygotes led to similar conclusions (E. M. and J. Lederberg, 1953). Although the diploids isolated from crosses between lysogenic and nonlysogenic bacteria were never heterozygous for the character "lysogeny," it was possible to obtain diploids heterozygous for this character in crosses between haploid nonlysogenic Gal^- bacteria and lysogenic Gal^+ diploids. When segregation of these diploid heterozygotes occurred, the characters lysogeny and galactose were found to segregate in close association.

D. Genetic Recombination in the *Escherichia coli* Group

The studies summarized above were all carried out with mutants of a single strain, *E.coli* K12. The obvious question then arose: is genetic recombination an exceptional phenomenon, peculiar to this strain, or can comparable phenomena be observed in other bacterial strains? For some time, studies of this question were rare and, for the most part, fruitless, because of the technical difficulties involved in demonstrating genetic recombination by the method of Lederberg and Tatum. However, it is possible to find, both among natural isolates and among stocks from culture collections, certain strains of *E.coli* that cannot grow in synthetic minimal medium, and rarely mutate to prototrophy. Among seven strains with such properties, Cavalli-Sforza and Heslot (1949) found one that could be crossed with *E.coli* K12.

The technique of crossing prototrophic bacteria sensitive to streptomycin (sensitivity is almost universal in the *E.coli* group) with resistant auxotrophs, and selecting the prototrophic streptomycin-resistant recombinants allowed J. Lederberg (1951b) to make a systematic study of "fertility" in the *E.coli* group. Among some 2000 different strains of *E.coli*, he found about 50 able to form recombinants when crossed with a $T^-L^-B_1^-Sm^r$ strain of *E.coli* K12. Thus fertility no longer appeared to be an exceptional phenomenon. However, its relative rarity (possibly due to the fact that production of antibiotics of the colicin type and lysogeny are common in the *E.coli* group) could also be explained by the existence of phenomena of sexual compatibility, which will be described in the next chapter (J. Lederberg and Tatum, 1953).

Genetic recombination is not therefore restricted to one particular strain of *E.coli.* In spite of the small number of strains in which this phenomenon could be demonstrated, and of the small number of recombinants formed in a given cross, genetic recombination in bacteria indeed appeared to be equivalent to a sexual process. It opened the way for the study of numerous problems, previously unapproachable, in the field of bacterial genetics. The results from such studies indicated that the organization of bacterial genetic determinants is basically similar to that found in higher organisms. However, difficulties were not slow to appear. We shall now summarize them briefly.

III. THE DIFFICULTIES OF GENETIC ANALYSIS

A. Crosses between Haploid Bacteria

As the number of characters studied increased and the means of selecting recombinants became more varied, the difficulties of interpreting the results became ever greater. Even though linkage relations within certain groups of characters were clear, it was often difficult to establish the order with respect to one another, of the various linkage groups so defined, and to arrange them on a single chromosome (Cavalli-Sforza, 1950; Newcombe and Nyholm, 1950b; J. Lederberg *et al.*, 1951; Fried and Lederberg, 1952). Analysis of the experimental results led to the formation of such hypotheses as the existence of a branched chromosome (J. Lederberg *et al.*, 1951) or even of two chromosomes having some reciprocal interactions (Fried and Lederberg, 1952).

Even for characters located in the same linkage group, it was extremely difficult to determine order and relative distances. Thus for a group of five characters (S, Mal, Xyl, Gal, Ara) (see Table I), Newcombe and Nyholm (1950b), upon analyzing their experimental results by four different methods, obtained five possible solutions. They concluded that there was a high degree of negative interference.

Similarly, in a remarkable analysis of the linearity of the TL T_1 Lac M segment, Rothfels (1952) also observed a detectable excess in the number of double recombinants formed; nonetheless, he was able to establish without ambiguity the order of the characters under study. The hypothesis which he thought could best explain the observed anomalies was defective or irregular pairing between homologous structures.

Even more striking anomalies were observed when the results of crosses between different strains were compared, or even when the results of crosses between two given parental types were compared with those of back-crosses (recombinant $\times$ parental type).

B. Segregation of Diploid Heterozygotes

While the analysis of the genetic recombinants formed at low frequency was difficult to interpret, difficulties no less serious appeared when analysis of the behavior of the heterozygous forms isolated by J. Lederberg (1949b) was attempted. As previously mentioned, these diploid forms are apparently hemizygous for a certain number of characters. In the great majority of cases, the missing alleles in these heterozygotes are all of one parental type, and the parental type which is thus unrepresented in the heterozygote is always the same one. This phenomenon was interpreted as the consequence of chromosomal aberrations (J. Lederberg *et al.*, 1951).

Segregants with the same characters as one of the parental types B can be isolated from the diploid heterozygotes. When these segregants are back-crossed with the other parental type A, the distribution of unselected characters among the recombinants differs considerably from that found in recombinants obtained in a control cross between parental bacteria A and B. The genetic maps that one would be led to construct in the two cases would, consequently, likewise differ considerably.

* * *

Accordingly, the genetic composition of the haploid recombinants formed at low frequency, as well as the patterns of segregation of the unstable diploid heterozygotes presented a whole series of anomalies, which made recombination in *E.coli* K12 an example of genetic teratology. There was no doubt about the reality of conjugation, as confirmed by the kinetic experiments of Nelson (1951). The reality of genetic recombination and of linkage phenomena was equally firmly established. However, the anomalies which have been briefly summarized in preceding paragraphs appeared so substantial that Lederberg was eventually led to question the basic homology between the genetic system of *E.coli* and higher organisms: "It may be pertinent to enquire at this point whether the entire approach to the analysis of *E.coli* segregations in chromosomal or cytogenetic terms may not be fallacious—whether there may not be an entirely unique genetic mechanism involved." It seemed, in fact, that certain special features must exist in the mechanism of conjugation in *E.coli;* and that these features, still unrecognized, were responsible for the difficulties in interpreting the results of crosses.

CHAPTER IV

Sexual Differentiation and Its Genetic Consequences

We have indicated the fruitfulness of the hypothesis formulated by Lederberg and Tatum, that the process of conjugation in bacteria involves, as in most other organisms, cellular fusion (*syngamy*) followed by nuclear fusion (*karyogamy*). Since all the strains used in crosses were derived from the single wild strain *E.coli* K12, it was also generally assumed that bacterial conjugation did not involve sexual differentiation and consequently that these bacteria were *homothallic*. Subsequent observations were to show, however, the falsity of this assumption. Not only do distinct sexual types exist in bacteria, but this sexual differentiation has important genetic implications.

William Hayes deserves much of the credit for the progress made in recent years in our knowledge of bacterial conjugation. By concerning himself with the mechanism of conjugation, rather than with the formal analysis of the results of crosses, Hayes first showed that the anomalies revealed by genetic analysis might well reflect the peculiarities of the conjugation process itself.

I. THE POLARITY OF BACTERIAL CROSSES

Most of the crosses of *E.coli* K12 have been made between bacteria derived from two main lines. These two lines, originally isolated by Tatum (1945), were chosen for two reasons: because of the comparatively high fertility of the crosses between them; and because the recombinants selected made it fairly easy to locate other genetic characters. One of these strains, (A), is unable to synthesize methionine and biotin (M^-B^-), the other, (B), is auxotrophic for threonine, leucine, and vitamin B_1 ($T^-L^-B_1^-$). As we shall presently see, it happens that these two classical strains belong to distinct sexual types.

A. Sexual Polarity

The first evidence for sexual differentiation in *E.coli* was presented by Hayes. In a study of the kinetics of conjugation, Hayes (1952a) performed reciprocal crosses between strains (A) and (B), differentially marked by streptomycin sensitivity (Sm^s) and streptomycin resistance (Sm^r). In the cross (A) $Sm^s \times$ (B) Sm^r, roughly the same number of recombinants was formed, when the mixture of bacteria was immediately spread on a medium containing streptomycin and when it was spread on a medium without streptomycin. On the contrary, in the cross (A) $Sm^r \times$ (B) Sm^s, no recombinants were formed when the mixture of bacteria was spread on a medium with streptomycin. Thus, the antibiotic did not prevent genetic recombination when the bacteria of strain (A) were streptomycin-sensitive, but rendered the cross sterile when the bacteria of strain (B) were sensitive to its action.

The polarity revealed by this experiment was independent of the presence of streptomycin in the selection medium, and consequently, of the segregation or expression of the genetic determinant controlling streptomycin-resistance. In fact, if bacteria of strains (A) and (B), sensitive to streptomycin, were individually treated with this antibiotic, and then crossed with untreated bacteria of the opposite strain on a medium containing no streptomycin, the same phenomenon occurred: when bacteria of strain (A) had been treated with the antibiotic, the number of recombinants $T^+L^+M^+B^+$ formed was not markedly smaller than that formed in a control cross; but when bacteria of strain (B) had been so treated, no recombinants were formed.

These experiments showed that the roles of the two types of bacteria used in the cross were not identical. It appeared as if the formation of recombinants took place in the bacteria of strain (B) whose survival was consequently indispensable. As for the bacteria of strain (A), whose survival was not necessary, it seemed that their role was in some manner to "fertilize" the bacteria of strain (B) by the transfer to them of genetic material. It thus became necessary to distinguish between *donor bacteria* —i.e., those able to transfer genetic characters—and *recipient bacteria*—i.e., those able to receive genetic characters (Hayes, 1952a).

Another evidence of this sexual polarity is provided by the differential effect of ultraviolet light on the two types of bacteria involved in a cross. It had already been observed (Haas *et al.*, 1948; Clark *et al.*, 1950) that small amounts of U.V. light increase the number of recombinants formed in a cross. When the treatment with U.V. light is applied not to the mixture of bacteria, but to the individual strains used in the cross (Hayes, 1952b), irradiation of bacteria of strain (A) noticeably increases the frequency of recombination, whereas irradiation of bacteria of strain (B) decreases the number of recombinants formed.

These phenomena seemed clearly to show the existence of a sexual differentiation in *E.coli* K12. Additional evidence was soon forthcoming.

Certain mutants, isolated by chance from the strain (A) B^-M^-, when mixed under the usual conditions with bacteria of the strain (B) $T^-L^-B_1^-$, did not form recombinants. However, these mutants, which seemed to have lost their fertility (F^- mutants), could be crossed successfully, with a $T^-L^-B_1^-$ segregant from a "diploid" (J. Lederberg, Cavalli, and Lederberg, 1952), or with the wild type or a prototrophic recombinant of *E.coli* K12 (Hayes, 1953a). A distinction could thus be made between F^- strains, which could not be crossed with one another, and F^+ strains which were fertile in crosses with F^- strains. The F^- strains corresponded to "recipient" bacteria and the F^+ strains to "donor" bacteria in the terminology of Hayes.

TABLE II
INFLUENCE OF MATING TYPE ON THE FERTILITY OF A CROSS

Cross	Example: A × B	Results
$F^- \times F^-$	$B^-M^-F^- \times T^-L^-B_1^-F^-$	Sterile 0
$F^+ \times F^-$	$B^-M^-F^- \times T^-L^-B_1^-F^+$ $B^-M^-F^+ \times T^-L^-B_1^-F^-$	Fertile ++
$F^+ \times F^+$	$B^-M^-F^+ \times T^-L^-B_1^-F^+$	Fertile +

The results of the various possible crosses between strains of the two sexual types, F^+ and F^-, are shown in Table II.

B. THE FERTILITY FACTOR, F

The wild type of *E.coli* K12 and most of the mutants derived from it are F^+, whereas the strains descended from the polyauxotroph $T^-L^-B_1^-$ are F^-. It seems that in the course of the treatments (especially X-ray irradiations) which led to the isolation of this mutant, a mutation from the F^+ to the F^- state occurred. Other mutations of this type have since been observed on rare occasions.

F^+ and F^- bacteria accordingly appear to differ by virtue of the fact that the former contain an hereditary factor which is not present in the latter. This fertility factor, F, has the remarkable property of being *transmissible,* with great efficiency, by contact between F^+ and F^- bacteria (J. Lederberg, Cavalli, and Lederberg, 1952; Hayes, 1953a; Cavalli-Sforza, Lederberg, and Lederberg, 1953).

In a cross between F^+ and F^- bacteria, the recombinants are F^+. Bacteria arising from the segregation of diploid heterozygotes are also F^+. When F^+ and F^- bacteria are brought in contact in a medium favorable to growth, there occurs a "conversion" of the F^- bacteria to the F^+ state. This conversion is extremely rapid since about 70 per cent of the F^- cells may thus be transformed in less than an hour. The bacteria which have acquired the F^+ character transmit it hereditarily to their offspring and the strains obtained can in turn transmit the F^+ character to other F^- cells. These properties, and particularly the facility with which the F^+ character can be transmitted, have contributed to the view that the F factor is "infective." However, all attempts to transform F^- bacteria into F^+ bacteria by means of culture filtrates, extracts, lysates, grindings, or even whole killed F^+ cells, have failed completely. Although the acquisition of the F^+ character at first appeared to be another example of "heredity by infection," it nonetheless requires, like genetic recombination itself, cell to cell contact between intact and metabolically active bacteria.

One of the phenotypic expressions of the F "factor" is the ability of F^+ bacteria to form recombinants when they are mixed with F^- bacteria. Under certain physiological conditions (when bacteria have reached the stationary phase of growth), this expression may disappear, F^+ bacteria then behaving phenotypically like F^- bacteria (J. Lederberg *et al.*, 1952; Cavalli-Sforza *et al.*, 1953). Such bacteria are phenocopies, since they remain genotypically F^+; when they are again placed in favorable conditions, they can once more form recombinants when mixed with F^- bacteria, and also transmit the F^+ character to them.

Sexual differentiation between F^+ donor and F^- recipient bacteria is thus under the control of a hereditary factor the properties of which differ from those of the other bacterial genetic determinants. The sexual types, F^+ and F^-, do not segregate during crosses; and, even more remarkable, the efficiency with which the F factor is transmitted from F^+ to F^- bacteria is some 10^5 to 10^6 times greater than the frequency of recombination observed in crosses between these same bacteria.

C. Genetic Polarity

The facts which have just been described show that sexual differentiation exists in bacteria. They also show that the roles played in mating by the two sexual types are not equivalent, since the transfer of the genetic characters seems to occur from the F^+ donor bacteria to the F^- recipient bacteria. Hayes (1953a) was largely responsible for demonstrating the profound genetic consequences of this sexual polarity.

Let us consider again the two strains of *E.coli* K12, (A) and (B); (A) has the characters $T^+L^+B^-M^-$, and (B) the inverse characters $T^-L^-B^+M^+$ (see Tables I and II). These two strains differ also in a number of additional characters *a b c d e f* . . . which are not involved in the selection of $T^+L^+B^+M^+$ recombinants. Each of these strains exists, moreover, both in the F^+ and in the F^- state. One can consequently perform the two symmetrical crosses:

$$(A)F^+ \times (B)F^- \quad \text{and} \quad (A)F^- \times (B)F^+$$

and, select in both cases the same type of recombinants $T^+L^+M^+B^+$. It is then possible to analyze the *genetic constitution* of these recombinants, by determining the frequency of appearance among them of the alleles for the unselected characters *a b c d e f* . . . . Such a genetic analysis reveals that the genetic constitution of the selected $T^+L^+M^+B^+$ recombinants differs considerably in the two crosses, and consequently depends on the sexual types of the strains involved in the cross. In every case, the genetic constitution of the recombinants resembles that of the F^- parental type much more closely than that of the F^+ parental type. *The frequency with which a given allele of an unselected character appears among the recombinants depends on whether this allele is carried by the F^+ or by the F^- bacteria.*

The genetic polarity thus revealed by the analysis of $F^+ \times F^-$ crosses was also observed by Cavalli-Sforza *et al.* (1953). It accounts to a great extent for the difficulties encountered previously in the interpretation of the results of crosses.

The differences which had been observed between the results of the usual crosses $(A)F^+ \times (B)F^-$ and those of the back crosses (F_1 recombinants or segregants of diploid heterozygotes $\times$ parental type) may be explained by the fact that the back crosses were of the type $(A)F^+ \times (B)F^+$. It should be noted in this connection, that the results of $F^+ \times F^+$ crosses are particularly hard to interpret: indeed, it seems that the bacteria of both strains act both as donors and as recipients. A cross of the type $(A)F^+ \times (B)F^+$ in fact represents a mixture of two component crosses, $(A)F^+ \times (B)F^-$ and $(A)F^- \times (B)F^+$, the relative frequencies of these two crosses depending both on the strains used and on the experimental conditions (Hayes, 1953a).

The anomalies observed in the genetic constitution of the diploid heterozygotes isolated from certain crosses also seem to be a consequence of genetic polarity. In the incomplete diploids, the characters which exist in the hemizygous state are, in general, those of the F^- parental type. It occurs as if, during formation of these aberrant diploids, a chromosome segment of the F^+ parent had been eliminated (J. Lederberg *et al.*, 1952; Nelson and Lederberg, 1954).

Lastly, the difficulties encountered in attempting to localize genetic characters are due also, in some part, to genetic polarity. Linkage relations can be established with validity only for those genetic characters which come from donor bacteria. A genetic recombinant possesses primarily the genetic characters of the recipient bacteria, and only a small number of characters derived from the F^+ parent: characters used for the selection of recombinants and ones which are linked to them. The fact that, in a given selection, genetic characters of the F^- bacteria segregate together is not sufficient evidence that these characters are closely linked. It merely indicates that, in this selection, the corresponding alleles from the donor parental type are only exceptionally transmitted to recombinants. One may deal here only with a pseudo-linkage (E. L. Wollman, 1953).

* * *

Genetic recombination in *E.coli* K12 occurs between bacteria belonging to different mating types. This system is, therefore, *heterothallic* and not homothallic, as was at first supposed. This sexual differentiation has functional consequences, as shown by the fundamental experiment of Hayes on the differential effect of streptomycin: the transfer of genetic material is a one way transfer from donor bacteria to recipient bacteria. Thus in contrast to the general situation in other organisms, the sexual differentiation of *E.coli* influences genetic events, since the two parental types involved in a cross do not contribute equally to the genetic constitution of the recombinants.

These essential facts were to lead, as will be shown later, to a modification of the simple working hypothesis which had been adopted by Lederberg and Tatum in their study of genetic recombination in bacteria.

II. SEXUAL POLARITY AND LYSOGENY

In crosses between lysogenic $(ly)^+$ and nonlysogenic $(ly)^-$ bacteria, it had been observed that the lysogenic character segregated among the recombinants. Moreover, there seemed to be a linkage between the lysogenic character and certain determinants which control the utilization of galactose: gal_4^- (E. M. and J. Lederberg, 1953), gal_a^- (E. L. Wollman, 1953). On the hypothesis of cellular fusion, these facts spoke in favor of a chromosomal location for the genetic determinant of lysogeny. It was therefore necessary to examine the influence of sexual differentiation and of its genetic consequences on the results of these crosses, in order to verify the validity of this interpretation.

Although the sexual type of the strains used by E. M. and J. Lederberg (1953) is not mentioned, it seems that most of the crosses performed by these authors were, like ours (E. L. Wollman, 1953), either of the type F^+

$(ly)^- \times F^+(ly)^+$, or of the type $F^+(ly)^- \times F^-(ly)^+$. In crosses of the first type, in which lysogenic and nonlysogenic recombinants may be formed in comparable proportions, each of the parental types can act alternatively either as donor or as recipient, as mentioned previously. It is thus extremely difficult to interpret the results of such crosses, particularly when the characters under study do not show obvious linkage with the characters used for the selection of recombinants, as was the case for the characters lysogeny λ and galactose.

In crosses of the type $F^+(ly)^- \times F^-(ly)^+$, the proportion of the recombinants which have the characters ly^- and gal^- of the F^+ parental type is generally small (it never exceeded 6 per cent in our experiments). It was necessary, therefore, to make sure that a reversal of polarity, due to the acquisition of the F^+ character by a fraction of the F^- bacteria, had not occurred (E. L. Wollman, 1953).

To overcome these difficulties, one can perform crosses between streptomycin-sensitive donor strains and streptomycin-resistant recipient strains: the elimination of donor bacteria by streptomycin ensures that the recombinants formed really do arise by the transfer of genetic characters from this donor strain to the streptomycin-resistant strain which behaves solely as the recipient. In the crosses $F^+gal_a^-(\lambda)^-S^s \times F^-gal_a^+(\lambda)^+S^r$ or $F^+gal_a^-(\lambda)^-S^s \times F^+gal_a^+(\lambda)^+S^r$, about 5 per cent of the recombinants formed had the $gal_a^-(\lambda)^-$ characters of the donor parental type. Conversely, in the crosses $F^+gal_a^+(\lambda)^+S^s \times F^+gal_a^-(\lambda)^-S^r$ no recombinant having both the characters gal^+ and $(\lambda)^+$ of the donor bacteria was found (E. L. Wollman, 1953, and unpublished results).

The asymmetry observed in the results of the crosses between lysogenic and nonlysogenic bacteria, depending on whether the prophage λ was carried by the donor or by the recipient bacteria, made difficult the interpretations of such crosses. It seemed that the "nonlysogenic" character could be transmitted from donor bacteria to genetic recombinants, whereas the "lysogenic" character could not. In order that the linkage observed between lysogeny and galactose should be fully significant in allowing the conclusion that lysogeny was determined by the prophage itself, behaving as a nuclear locus, it was necessary to show a concurrent transfer of the characters lysogeny and galactose from an F^+ to an F^- strain (E. L. Wollman, 1953).

Crosses between bacteria of known sexual types were also performed by Frédéricq (1953a) and by Appleyard (1954a), who confirmed the existence of a genetic linkage between the characters lysogeny λ and gal_a. In a study of the segregation of lysogeny for a particular temperate phage α, Frédéricq (1953a) observed that this character, lysogeny α, segregated independently from the character lysogeny λ and seemed linked to a determinant controlling the utilization of xylose.

Having obtained nonlysogenic F^+ and F^- strains on the one hand and different mutants (λs and λcl) of the temperate phage λ on the other, Appleyard was able to perform the following types of crosses:

1. $F+(\lambda)- \times F-(\lambda)-$
2. $F+(\lambda)- \times F-(\lambda)+$
3. $F+(\lambda)+ \times F-(\lambda)-$
4. $F+(\lambda)+ \times F-(\lambda)+$

in which the strains involved are lysogenic for different mutants of phage λ. In the crosses of types 1, 2, and 4, the character gal_a^- of the F^+ parental type was transmitted to about 3 per cent of the prototrophic recombinants. In the crosses of types 2 and 4, the characters $(\lambda)^-$ and $(\lambda)^+$ of the F^+ parental type were found in identical proportions among the recombinants formed, and in close association with the character gal_a^-. From these experiments, Appleyard could therefore conclude that lysogeny was under chromosomal control, the only determinant being the prophage itself. In the crosses of type 3, however, the proportion of recombinants which had received the character λ^+ and gal_a^- from the F^+ parental type was considerably smaller (about 0.1 per cent).

These findings, on the whole, appeared to favor the hypothesis of a chromosomal determination of lysogeny. Particularly the work of Appleyard which showed that the characters nonlysogeny $(\lambda)^-$ and lysogeny $(\lambda)^+$ of the F^+ parental type are both transmitted to the recombinants with comparable frequency and in association with the character gal_a^- of the donor bacteria when the recipient bacteria are lysogenic, seemed to indicate that the chromosomal determinant of lysogeny was the prophage itself. Similarly, the fact that in strains obtained by lysogenization of sensitive bacteria, the character lysogeny λ was always linked to the genetic determinants controlling galactose utilization, seemed to show that there exists a specific locus for the prophage (Appleyard, 1954a; Frédéricq, 1954a; E. M. Lederberg, 1954). However, the ambiguity inherent in the $F^+ \times F^-$ crosses, the ignorance concerning the mechanism of genetic recombination, the difficulties in locating various genetic characters (especially the gal characters), and, above all, the asymmetry observed in the results of reciprocal crosses depending on which of the parental types was lysogenic, still left some doubt as to the validity of these conclusions. If the prophage λ was actually located on the bacterial chromosome, it did not behave like other genetic factors, since apparently, in some crosses, it could not be transmitted from the donor bacteria to recombinants. One might imagine that, in this case, conjugation caused the induction of the prophage λ, which behaved as a lethal factor. This hypothesis, later confirmed experimentally (see Chapters VI and VII) in crosses with high frequency of recombination (Jacob and Wollman, 1954a; E. L. Wollman and Jacob, 1954a) was formulated independently by Frédéricq (1954a, 1955a) to account for the anomalies observed in the results of crosses between lysogenic F^+ and nonlysogenic F^- bacteria.

III. SEXUAL POLARITY AND BACTERIAL FERTILITY

The only systematic search for fertile strains in the *Escherichia coli* group was carried out by Lederberg (see Chapter III). Of almost 2,000 strains isolated from nature, about 5 per cent were capable of giving recombinants when mated with an F^- strain of *E.coli* K12 (J. Lederberg and Tatum, 1953). These strains accordingly seem to be F^+, like the wild *E.coli* K12. The technique used in this search consisted of the selection of prototrophic, streptomycin-resistant recombinants. It cannot be applied to crosses between F^+ strains of K12 and strains of *E.coli* isolated from nature, which explains why no investigations of this kind have yet been carried out. It seems likely, however, that most of the wild strains of *E.coli* are F^-. This is true of certain strains currently used in various laboratories, the fertility of which has, therefore, been investigated. In particular, the strain studied by Cavalli-Sforza and Heslot (1949), the W strain used by Davis (1950a) in his work on biochemical genetics (Cavalli-Sforza *et al.*, 1953), strain C (Lieb *et al.*, 1955) and, lastly, strain B of *E.coli* used in classic investigations of virulent bacteriophages (Haan, 1954a, b, 1955) are all F^-. These strains can all be crossed with K12 F^+, and can acquire from it the F^+ character. They can subsequently be crossed with F^- bacteria of the homologous strain.

The behavior of the *Shigella* group is somewhat different. A large number of *Shigella* strains, studied by Luria and Burrous (1957), are F^-. They can be mated with F^+ strains of *E.coli* K12 or *E.coli* C. By contact with these F^+ strains, they can acquire the F^+ character and transmit it to F^- *E.coli.* The F^+ *Shigella,* however, do not form recombinants when they are mixed with either F^- *Shigella* or F^- *E.coli.*

Finally, genetic recombination has recently been demonstrated between *E.coli* and various *Salmonella* strains (Miyake and Demerec, 1959; Baron, Carey, and Spilman, 1959a). Thus, intercrosses have now become possible between the *Escherichia, Shigella,* and *Salmonella* groups (Baron *et al.*, 1959b).

Phenomena of genetic recombination which also involve a system of sexual compatibility have been described in *Pseudomonas aeruginosa* (Holloway, 1955, 1956; Holloway and Fargie, 1960) and in *Serratia marcescens* (Belser and Bunting, 1956). On the other hand, there is no sexual differentiation in *Streptomyces coelicolor*, where phenomena of genetic recombination have been demonstrated (Sermonti and Spada-Sermonti, 1956). The indications of a system of genetic recombination in *Achromobacter fischeri* (McElroy and Friedman, 1951) have not yet been confirmed.

The existence of conjugation and of genetic recombination is therefore not exceptional in bacteria. The difficulties in demonstrating their existence, which have hitherto limited such studies, are due mainly to the low frequency of recombination and to the existence of more or less complex systems of sexual compatibility. In the *E.coli* group as well as in the *Shigella* and *Salmonella* groups, the ability to participate in the process of conjugation seems fairly widespread.

Since these phenomena were discovered less than fifteen years ago, it is not surprising that most of the work has been concerned with the characteristics and the mechanism of the conjugation process in a single strain of *E.coli*. The knowledge thus acquired has only recently made possible the extension of such studies to other related groups of bacteria. It remains for the future to determine whether comparable phenomena can also be demonstrated in groups of bacteria that are more distant taxonomically.

IV. THE HYPOTHESES CONCERNING THE MECHANISM OF GENETIC RECOMBINATION

Sexual differentiation in bacteria and its genetic consequences have been interpreted in different ways. Lederberg and Cavalli interpreted bacterial genetic recombination as the consequence of a classical sexual process; Hayes, on the other hand, proposed that the mechanism of the conjugation process itself in bacteria is distinctive and different from the classical one.

These differences of interpretation may be attributed to differences in outlook of the authors concerned: Hayes examined mainly the results of $F^+ \times F^-$ crosses, whereas Lederberg focused his attention on the formation and segregation of the aberrant heterozygotes previously mentioned.

A. The Hypotheses of Lederberg and Cavalli

1. *Sexual differentiation.* The fertility of a given cross is dependent on a system of sexual compatibility. F^- strains are not compatible with

each other and various F^+ strains possess different "degrees of fertility" in the sense of M. Hartmann's concept of relative sexuality (1929). The fertility of a cross increases with the difference in the "degree of fertility" of the strains involved (J. Lederberg, Cavalli, and Lederberg, 1952; Cavalli-Sforza, Lederberg, and Lederberg, 1953).

2. *Formation of zygotes.* Conjugation leads to the formation of a complete zygote containing all the genetic material of both parents. This zygote was at first believed to be formed by the fusion of the parental cells, and subsequently considered to be constituted mainly by the F^- bacterium which, as a consequence of conjugation, is fertilized by a complete nucleus from the F^+ parent (J. Lederberg, 1955a).

3. *Genetic polarity.* The formation of a zygote is followed by karyogamy and meiosis. All the zygotes formed are thus identical. The genetic polarity is the result of a *post-zygotic* elimination, which generally, but not necessarily, bears on genetic characters of the F^+ parental type. This hypothesis is principally based on the study of certain diploid heterozygotes in which elimination affects principally a particular chromosomal segment, containing the characters maltose (Mal) and streptomycin (Sm). In some cases, however, it is the characters of the F^- parental type which appear to be eliminated. Less frequently, the elimination may affect characters from both parental types. Elimination is thus not only postzygotic, but also postmeiotic, i.e., secondary to the recombination and disjunction of the chromosomes of the zygote (Nelson and Lederberg, 1954; J. Lederberg, 1955a). This chromosomal elimination is under the control of a specific locus, E, located on the chromosome of F^+ bacteria, which acts as a lethal factor (Cavalli-Sforza and Jinks, 1956).

B. The Hypothesis of Hayes

The original interpretation proposed by this author involved three aspects, of which only the first two now appear to be essential (Hayes, 1953a, b).

1. *One-way transfer.* The difference between F^+ and F^- bacteria is more than a difference of mating type, since it introduces polarity into the conjugation process; as shown by the differential action of streptomycin, the transfer of genetic material is a one way transfer from F^+ donor to F^- recipient bacteria.

2. *Partial transfer of genetic material.* Only a portion of the genetic material of the F^+ bacteria is transferred to the F^- bacteria during conjugation, which explains the unequal contribution of the parental types to the genetic constitution of the recombinants. The zygotes formed are thus incomplete and heterogeneous. The selection of recombinants which

have inherited one or another character of the F^+ donor bacteria also results in a selection among the zygotes, since the analysis is restricted to those zygotes which have received from the donor bacteria a genetic segment carrying the selected characters.

Watson and Hayes (1953) thought that the results of crosses could be interpreted by the existence of three distinct linkage groups. Since interreactions can be demonstrated between these supposedly independent linkage-groups, Clowes and Rowley (1954b) proposed the hypothesis that ruptures may occur at random along a single chromosome. In this view, the contribution of the F^+ bacteria to the zygotes consists of chromosomal fragments whose length and genetic constitution can vary from one zygote to another. This hypothesis accounts both for the existence of a single linkage group and for the incomplete contribution of the F^+ bacteria.

3. *Mechanism of transfer.* Hayes (1953a, b) had formulated the hypothesis that the one way transfer of genetic segments could be carried out by a subcellular "vector," resistant to the action of streptomycin. This hypothetical "gamete" was interpreted as being the sexual factor F, which could occasionally become associated with a genetic segment. This ingenious representation appeared to account for a great many facts (low frequency of recombination, peculiar behavior of the F character, one-way transfer and partial transfer, "inducing" action of U.V. light). It also suggested the analogous nature of genetic recombination in *E.coli* K12 and of the phenomena of transduction which had been just discovered. There was one major difficulty about this hypothesis, however: the impossibility of dissociating the hypothetical gamete from the donor cell itself. There was no alternative but to accept these two elements as identical.

The alternative hypotheses formulated to explain the peculiarities of genetic recombination in bacteria by Lederberg and Cavalli on the one hand, and by Hayes on the other, thus lead to entirely distinct representations of the phenomenon. According to the concept of Lederberg and Cavalli, bacterial recombination is not fundamentally different from the sexual processes that occur in other organisms, since it results in the formation of complete zygotes in which the genomes of both parental types are represented equally. The peculiarities revealed by the analysis of the crosses must then result from anomalies in the process of genetic recombination itself; namely, from the postmeiotic elimination of chromosomal segments.

According to Hayes' concept, the anomalies result from the very process of conjugation, and not from the subsequent steps which, in the zygotes, lead to the formation of genetic recombinants. The mechanism of conjugation differs markedly from the usual sexual processes, since it leads to the formation of incomplete zygotes which have received only chromosomal fragments from the donor bacteria. Bacterial conjugation thus resembles somewhat the other processes of genetic transfer in bacteria described in Chapter II.

The genetic effects of sexual differentiation led, therefore, to representations of conjugation and of genetic recombination in *E.coli* K12 which were conceptually very different, but which had similar formal implications for the interpretation of the numerical results of crosses. These results have been explained in a number of different ways. We have already mentioned the analysis of Watson and Hayes (1953), who concluded that there were three independent linkage groups. The linkage-group proposed by Clowes and Rowley (1954b) is represented in Fig. 5.

(Nl Gal_5 Ara_1) (Sm Mal_1) (Xyl Man) Isol M_1 M_2 B_1 TL Pr Lac

FIG. 5. The linkage group of *E. coli* K12 (after Clowes and Rowley). For explanation of the symbols, see Table I, p. 33.

Finally, special mention must be made of the remarkable analysis of Cavalli-Sforza and Jinks (1953, 1956). These authors interpreted the results of many crosses by assuming the existence of "a single linear linkage group, which carries in its middle a region or locus having a unique property, namely, that the majority of recombinants will inherit such a chromosome segment, or locus, from only one of the parents, i.e. the F^- parent. In addition, chromosome pairing is poor and irregular." The genetic map drawn by Cavalli and Jinks is represented in Fig. 6.

T Ara_2 L Az T_1 Lac_1 T_6 Gal_2 (E) Sm Mal_1 Xyl M B_1

FIG. 6. Chromosome map of *E. coli* K12 (after Cavalli and Jinks). The meaning of the symbols is given in Table I.

* * *

The discovery of a sexual differentiation in bacteria shed new light on the phenomenon of genetic recombination. It emphasized the sexual character of this phenomenon, and brought bacteria into closer analogy with other organisms in which exchange of genetic characters and sexuality are closely associated. It also showed that there is a relationship between sexual polarity and the genetic anomalies which characterize bacterial crosses.

However, this discovery raised more questions than it answered. In contradistinction to what is observed in other organisms, crosses that are reciprocal with respect to the sexual type of the bacteria involved do not give the same result. In last analysis, any interpretation of the phenomena of recombination in bacteria was dependent on an understanding of the mechanism of the genetic polarity. The proposed hypotheses, different as they were, attempted to relate the results obtained by analysis of rare recombinants formed in enormous bacterial populations to the events that occur during a single conjugational act. Accordingly, the difficulty of choosing between the two hypotheses can be readily imagined. In particular, there seemed little hope of elucidating the mechanism of conjugation as long as genetic recombination remained such a rare event.

As will be seen in the second part of this monograph, it was the discovery of donor strains exhibiting a "high frequency of recombination" that made possible the analysis of the process of conjugation in bacteria.

PART II

Bacterial Conjugation and Its Mechanism

"Le sexe n'est autre chose que la différence du masle et de la femelle."

AMBROISE PARÉ
(*De l'invention et excellence de la médecine et chirurgie*).

CHAPTER V

The Characteristics of Crosses with High Frequency of Recombination

Genetic recombination in bacteria, as so far described, is an extremely rare phenomenon. Even under the most favorable conditions, the number of genetic recombinants which can be selected in a cross between F^+ and F^- bacteria is never greater than 1 per 100,000 parental cells. Such a low frequency of recombination seemed to preclude the possibility, not only of directly observing bacterial conjugation, but also of arriving at a satisfactory representation of the events that take place at the level of individual bacteria.

The discovery of donor strains with a high frequency of recombination (Hfr strains), made independently by Cavalli and by Hayes, opened the way to the quantitative study of bacterial recombination, and has been indispensable for progress in this field.

I. THE DISCOVERY AND PROPERTIES OF Hfr STRAINS

The first known Hfr strain was found by Cavalli-Sforza (1950) among mutants of *E.coli* K12 resistant to nitrogen mustard. One of these resistant mutants (derived from the classic $F^+M^-B^-$ strain) produced 1000 times more recombinants when mated with an $F^-T^-L^-B_1^-$ strain than did the F^+ strain from which it was derived: hence the name "Hfr" to denote high frequency of recombination. This Hfr strain was fairly unstable and reverted to the initial F^+ type. There was no relation between the Hfr character and resistance to nitrogen mustard, since the other mutants resistant to nitrogen mustard were not Hfr, and the F^+ strains obtained by reversion of the Hfr strain were still resistant to nitrogen mustard.

Although Cavalli's Hfr strain (Hfr C) arose from an F^+ strain and was very fertile when crossed with F^- bacteria, the recombinants formed were F^-. Moreover, the Hfr C cells did not transmit to the F^- bacteria either the Hfr or the F^+ character. "Thus, in spite of its capacity to yield F^+ after back mutation to Nfr (normal frequency of recombination), Hfr should be classed as F^- so far as its activity in infection experiments is concerned and as strongly F^+ in relation to its activity in recombination." (Cavalli-Sforza, Lederberg, and Lederberg, 1953). For Cavalli, therefore, the $F^+ \rightarrow$ Hfr mutation resulted in an increase of the "fertility" of the cross. The fact that the Hfr bacteria did not transmit either the F^+ or the Hfr character to F^- bacteria could indicate that the "F factor" had mutated to a new form or that it was present in a masked, noninfective form.

Most of our knowledge of the properties of the Hfr strains is derived from the work of Hayes. From the F^+ strain used by Cavalli (strain 58-161), Hayes isolated, also by chance, an Hfr strain (Hfr H) which, when crossed with a given F^- strain, produced 1000 times more recombinants than did the original F^+ strain (Hayes, 1953b). Hayes confirmed Cavalli's observations and showed that the Hfr H bacteria possessed all the properties of donor bacteria. For instance, a streptomycin treatment which left only 10^{-6} to 10^{-7} surviving Hfr bacteria, did not reduce noticeably the frequency of recombination, whereas the same treatment applied to F^- bacteria completely sterilized the cross.

Most important of all, Hayes made the remarkable discovery that a *high frequency of recombination was observed only when some types of recombinants were selected.* When other types were selected, the recombination frequency was low, being comparable to that of the $F^+ \times F^-$ crosses. For instance, in a cross between bacteria Hfr H $T^+L^+B_1{}^+M^-S^r$ and $F^-T^-L^-B_1{}^-M^+S^s$, recombinants $T^+L^+M^+$ were formed with high frequency and recombinants $T^+L^+B_1{}^+M^+$ with low frequency.* When the two parental strains also differed in other characters—such as ability to ferment lactose (Lac) or sensitivity to sodium azide (Az)—the characters Az and Lac of the Hfr parental type could be found among the $T^+L^+M^+$ recombinants formed with high frequency, but the $B_1{}^+$ or S^r alleles of the same parental type could not. When prototrophic and streptomycin-sensitive (S^s) Hfr H bacteria were crossed on the one hand with $F^-T^-L^-B_1{}^-S^r$ bacteria, and on the other hand with $F^-M^-S^r$ bacteria, the same phenomenon was observed: recombinants $T^+L^+B_1{}^+S^r$ or M^+S^r were formed only with low frequency. It appeared as if, in an Hfr H $\times$ F^- cross, *only certain genetic characters* (T, L, Az, Lac) *could be transmitted to recombinants with high frequency, whereas other characters* (B_1, M, S) *were transmitted with low frequency* (Hayes, 1953b).

* The symbols used have the following meaning (see Table I): T (threonine), L (leucine), B_1 (vitamin B_1), M (methionine), S (streptomycin). Additional information concerning both experimental methods and nomenclature will be found in the following section of this chapter.

Hayes also made the following observations. (1) The genetic recombinants formed with high frequency are generally F^-, whereas, among the genetic recombinants formed with low frequency, some are F^- and others Hfr. (2) Irradiation of Hfr bacteria by ultraviolet light does not increase the number of recombinants formed with high frequency. On the other hand, it increases the number of recombinants formed with low frequency to an extent comparable to that observed in an $F^+ \times F^-$ cross when the F^+ parental type is irradiated. (3) The frequency of recombination is one-tenth as high in an Hfr $\times$ F^+ cross as in the homologous Hfr $\times$ F^- cross.

The properties of Hfr strains illustrate the two essential characteristics of the conjugation process in *E.coli* K12, as established by Hayes' investigations. (1) The one-way transfer of the genetic characters of donor bacteria to recipient bacteria is even more evident than in $F^+ \times F^-$ crosses. (2) The fact that only certain characters can be transmitted with high frequency to recombinants can be explained without difficulty by the hypothesis of a partial transfer of genetic material during conjugation.

In the following paragraphs, we shall examine more closely the main aspects of genetic recombination in crosses between Hfr and F^- bacteria. After describing the experimental methods and the material that we have used in our own investigations, we shall consider the characteristics which can be established from the quantitative analysis of crosses with a high frequency of recombination.

II. EXPERIMENTAL METHODS

In a cross between bacteria, and more specifically between Hfr and F^- bacteria, the transfer of genetic characters appears to take place from *donor bacteria* (Hfr or F^+) to *recipient bacteria* (F^-). The choice of strains and the methods employed are largely determined by this fact.

A. Bacterial Strains

1. *Source.* The various strains of *Escherichia coli* K12 which we have used came from three main lines: F^- strains from the $T^-L^-B_1^-$ line (strain Y10); F^+ strains from the wild type or the double mutant 58-161 (see Tatum and Lederberg, 1947); and finally derivatives of strain Hfr H isolated by Hayes (1953b). These strains were "marked," either by nutritional characters (requirement for a growth factor or inability to utilize a sugar) or by characters of resistance to antibiotics or to bac-

teriophages. The usual procedures for the isolation of mutants were employed (J. Lederberg, 1950a).

The principal strains which will be discussed are described in Table III.

The wild K12 strain and most of the mutants derived from it are lysogenic for phage λ. In order to perform crosses between lysogenic and nonlysogenic bacteria in all possible combinations, it was necessary to devise a technique for "curing" lysogenic bacteria.

The bacteria to be "cured" are subjected to a strong dose of ultraviolet light, which leaves only about 10^{-5} survivors. After irradiation, the suspension of bacteria is placed in liquid nutritive medium to which anti λ serum has been added and is incubated at 37° for about 3 hours, which time is sufficient for the expression of the "nonlysogenic" character. Samples are spread on nutrient agar. The lysogenic or nonlysogenic character of the colonies formed is determined by the technique of "replica plating," by means of a velvet pad (J. and E. M. Lederberg, 1952), on agar plates seeded with bacteria sensitive to phage λ. The proportion of colonies which do not produce phage ranges from 1 in 500 to 1 in 1000. These colonies are re-isolated and their nonlysogenic or defective character is determined (see Jacob and Wollman, 1956a).

Among the strains listed in Table III, strain P678 is the one which will be mentioned most often in the following account. It was obtained from strain W677 by "reversion" of the character Gal_5^-, selection, after ultraviolet irradiation, of a galactose$^-$ mutant whose Gal_b^- character is linked to prophage λ [this Gal_b^- character is different from the Gal_a^- character of strain 112 (E. L. Wollman, 1953)], and lastly, by isolation of a nonlysogenic mutant through use of the method just described. From strain P678(λ)$^-$, a variety of auxotrophic derivatives have been obtained of which strains PA209 and PA260 (Table III) are representative.

2. *Nomenclature.* As is customary in bacterial genetics, characters are represented by the first letters of their names (see Tables I and III). In the case of nutritional or fermentative characters, the ability to synthesize an essential metabolite or to utilize a certain sugar is represented by the symbol of this character followed by the plus sign; lack of such ability is indicated by the minus sign (e.g., $T^-L^-B_1^-$, inability to synthesize threonine, leucine, vitamin B_1; Lac^-, Gal_b^-: nonutilization of lactose, galactose). Similarly, sensitivity to an antibiotic (S, streptomycin; Az, sodium azide) or to a bacteriophage (T_1, T_3, T_6) is indicated by s and resistance to the same agent by r.

In order to simplify nomenclature, when a single strain is frequently used in different forms (lysogenic or nonlysogenic, streptomycin-sensitive

TABLE III
STRAINS USED[a]

Designation	Characters	Origin	Reference
E.coli K12			
Hfr H strains			
HfrH $(\lambda)+$	Prototroph	Hfr H	Hayes, 1953b
HfrH $(\lambda)-$	Prototroph	$HfrH(\lambda)+$	Jacob and Wollman, 1956b
HfrH (λd)	Prototroph	$HfrH(\lambda)+$	Jacob and Wollman, 1956b
F+ strains			
58–161	$M- \ (\lambda)+$		Tatum and Lederberg, 1947
112	$C-H-Gal_a- \ (\lambda)-$		E. L. Wollman, 1953
F− strains			
Y10	$T-L-B_1-T_1{}^r \ Lac-(\lambda)+$	Y10	Tatum and Lederberg, 1947
C600	$T-L-B_1-T_1{}^r \ Lac-(\lambda)-$	Y10	Appleyard, 1954a
P14	$T-L-B_1-T_1{}^r \ Lac-(\lambda d)$	Y10	Jacob and Wollman, 1956a
P678 $(\lambda)-$ and P678 $(\lambda)+$	$T-L-B_1-Az^rT_1{}^r \ Lac-Gal_b-$ $Mal-Xyl-Man-Ara-B_1-\lambda^r$	W677	Jacob and Wollman, 1956b
PA 209	$T-L-B_1-H-Tr-Az^rT_1{}^rLac-$ $Gal_b-Mal-Xyl-Mtl-Ara-\lambda^r$	P678	Jacob and Wollman, 1958c
PA 260	$T-L-B_1-H-S\text{-}G-Az^rT_1{}^r$ $Lac-$ $Gal_b-Mal-Xyl-Mtl-Ara-\lambda^r$	P678	Jacob and Wollman, 1958c
E.coli C	Prototroph		Weiglé and Bertani, 1953

[a] The symbols refer to (see Table I): inability to synthesize methionine (M−), cystine (C−), histidine (H−), threonine (T−), leucine (L−), tryptophan (Tr−), serine-glycine (S-G−), vitamin B_1 (B_1-); nonfermentation of galactose (Gal−), lactose (Lac−), maltose (Mal−), xylose (Xyl−), mannitol (Mtl−), arabinose (Ara−); resistance to phages T_1 ($T_1{}^r$), λ (λ^r); lysogeny for phage λ $(\lambda)+$, nonlysogeny $(\lambda)-$, defective lysogenic strain $(\lambda d)+$.

or -resistant), the name of the strain is kept unchanged: for instance, P678 S^s, P678 S^r, P678(λ)+, P678(λ)− designate strains having essentially the same genotype and differing from one another by those characters explicitly mentioned. The lysogenic character for a particular phage is represented by the symbol of the phage between brackets followed by a plus sign, the nonlysogenic character being represented by the same symbol followed by the minus sign.

B. Bacterial Cultures

1. *Culture media.* The culture media used are all derived from two basal media.

a. Complete medium: meat extract, 100 ml; peptone Uclaf, 10 g; NaCl, 10 g; water Q.S. to 1000; adjusted to pH 7. This medium is solidified by the addition of agar (CA medium): 12 g per liter for the preparation of plates used for counting bacteriophages; 20 g per liter for plates intended for enumerating or characterizing bacteria. The soft agar used for double layer plating contains 7 g of agar per liter.

b. Minimal medium. KH_2PO_4, 6.8 g; $MgSO_4 \cdot 7H_2O$, 0.1 g; $(NH_4)_2SO_4$, 1 g; $Ca(NO_3)_2$, 0.01 g; $FeSO_4 \cdot 7H_2O$, 0.0005 g; doubly distilled water to bring the total to 1000 ml. Adjusted to pH 7 with KOH. All the dilutions are carried out in this medium diluted to 1/20 with doubly distilled water. This diluted minimal medium will be referred to as buffer.

This same medium is solidified by addition of 15 g of Difco agar per liter (MA medium). The soft agar used for platings contains 7 g of Difco agar per liter.

2. *Culture methods.* All experiments are carried out with exponentially growing cultures. The culture media, distributed either in Erlenmeyer flasks or in test tubes, are inoculated with a 1 per cent inoculum of an overnight culture prepared in the same medium. In order to achieve proper aeration, the cultures are shaken in thin layers in a water bath at 37°C. The course of bacterial growth is followed by measuring the optical density in an electrophotometer (see Monod, 1942).

In every experiment, the number of viable cells is determined by plating on nutrient agar.

C. Bacterial Crosses

Since the transfer of genetic characters takes place from the Hfr to the F^- bacteria, it is usually desirable to use conditions in which *a fixed number of Hfr bacteria is mixed with an excess of F^- bacteria.* The evaluation of the number of recombinants formed, for instance, will be made with reference to the input number of Hfr bacteria.

1. *Technique of crosses.* All the crosses are carried out in liquid media, usually in nutrient broth.

Cultures of the bacteria to be crossed are harvested during the exponential phase of growth in broth, centrifuged, resuspended in broth and mixed so as to obtain a final concentration of 4.10^8 F^- bacteria and of 2.10^7 Hfr bacteria per milliliter; i.e., a ratio of one Hfr to twenty F^-. The mixture is aerated gently in a water bath at 37°C. Samples are removed, diluted in buffer, and plated on the appropriate medium. Unless otherwise indicated, the platings are made after 60 minutes of contact. Modifications of this basic technique will be indicated in the text.

2. *Selection of recombinants.* As the transfer of genetic characters takes place from the donor to the recipient F^- bacteria, it is necessary to choose an F^- strain carrying the minus alleles of such characters (e.g., T^-L^-), in order to make possible the selection of recombinants that have acquired from the parental Hfr type the corresponding plus alleles. On a synthetic medium lacking the required growth factors, the F^- bacteria are incapable of forming colonies. As for the donor Hfr bacteria, whose role consists only in transferring genetic material to the recipient F^- bacteria, they must be also prevented from growing, i.e., *counter-selected.* This can be achieved either by using an Hfr strain that is auxotrophic for a character distinct from those of the F^- strain, or by treating with an antibacterial agent (inhibitor, antibiotic, or phage) to which the F^- bacteria are resistant. Whatever the character used for counter-selection, the genetic determinant of this character itself should not be transmitted with high frequency, if grossly distorted results are to be avoided.

For instance, in a cross between bacteria Hfr H $T^+L^+M^-S^s$ and $F^-T^-L^-M^+S^r$, in which the characters T^+L^+ are transmitted with high frequency, the frequency of recombination observed is identical, whether the recombinants $T^+L^+M^+$ or $T^+L^+S^r$ are selected, because neither the M character (methionine), nor the S character (streptomycin) is transmitted with high frequency by Hfr H bacteria (Hayes, 1953b). Most of the crosses described below are carried out between bacteria Hfr H S^s and F^- P678 S^r, streptomycin being used as the counter-selective agent against the Hfr bacteria.

When the Hfr and the F^- bacteria differ in several characters which can be used independently for the selection of recombinants, it becomes possible to achieve several selections in the same cross. For instance, in a cross Hfr H $S^s \times F^-$ P678 S^r, both $T^+L^+S^r$ recombinants and Gal^+S^r recombinants are generally selected. The $T^+L^+S^r$ recombinants are obtained by plating samples of the mixture of bacteria on MA medium containing glucose (10 g per liter), thiamine (1 μg per milliliter) and streptomycin (150 μg per milliliter); the Gal^+S^r recombinants, by plating on MA medium containing galactose (10 g per liter), *l*-threonine, *dl*-leucine (80 μg per milliliter of each), thiamine and streptomycin. It is worth noting that the characters T (threonine) and L (leucine) are located so close to one another that they are generally used simultaneously for selection of recombinants. In contrast to most of the characters controlling utilization of sugars, the character Gal_b can be safely used as sole selector: the presence of galactose inhibits the residual growth of the Gal_b^- bacteria and reversion of this character is extremely rare.

Platings are carried out by adding a carefully measured volume of a suitable dilution of the bacterial mixture, to 3 ml. of 0.7 per cent agar kept in the melted state in a waterbath at 42°C. The content of the tube is then poured into a plate containing the solidified selective MA medium. After solidification of the second layer of agar, the plates are put in an incubator at 37°C where they are kept 48 hours. The colonies of recombinants are then counted.

The results of a cross are evaluated by relating the number of recombinants obtained, in a given selection, to the input number of bacteria of the minority parental type. We shall thus apply the term *frequency of recombinants* to the relationship, "*number of recombinants per 100 initial bacteria of the minority type.*" In most cases, this will mean number of recombinants per 100 initial Hfr cells.

3. *Genetic analysis of recombinants.* Genetic analysis of recombinants is carried out in order to determine the ratios in which the unselected characters of the Hfr donor bacteria appear in the recombinants.

The recombinants are first re-streaked on the same medium as that used for their selection. Individual colonies are then transferred to form the pattern of a grid, regularly arranged on the surface of a plate containing the same medium. After growth, this plate is replicated by means of velveteen pads (J. and E. M. Lederberg, 1952) to plates containing a variety of media which allow the determination of the genetic characters of the recombinants. The following media are employed: for determining nutritional characters, an appropriate selective MA medium; for determining fermentation of sugars, CA medium containing the sugar in question (10 g per liter), together with an appropriate indicator dye; for determining resistance or sensivitity to sodium azide, CA medium + Na N_3 (M/850); for determining resistance or sensitivity to a bacteriophage, CA medium with the phage spread on its surface.

In any given selection, from 100 to 400 recombinants are thus analyzed, the exact number depending on the precision desired for analysis of the cross and on the frequency of transmission of the character under study.

The results are expressed in "percentage of the selected recombinants having inherited from the parental Hfr type each of the genetic characters analyzed." We will call "*genetic constitution of recombinants*" the frequency with which various unselected characters from the Hfr bacteria are transmitted to the recombinants formed in a given selection.

III. CHARACTERISTICS OF THE CROSSES BETWEEN Hfr H AND F$^-$ BACTERIA: THE TL-Gal CHROMOSOMAL SEGMENT

In the following chapters, we shall discuss the mechanism of conjugation as it occurs between Hfr and F$^-$ bacteria and analyze the various steps of the process which leads to the formation of recombinants. As shown by Hayes, in such crosses, only some of the characters from the Hfr donors are transmitted to recombinants with high frequency whereas others are transmitted with low frequency. The formation of a genetic recombinant is a complex process which involves a series of successive steps, the emergence of a recombinant bacterium being only the end product of the sequence. As will be discussed in the following chapters, experimental criteria may be obtained which allow the recognition of the intermediate steps and their quantitative determination. Such a quantitative analysis, however, is simple only when applied to those characters of the Hfr donor which are transmitted to recombinants with high frequency. To begin with, this analysis will therefore be restricted to such characters. After having described the conjugation process with the characters transmitted with high frequency, we shall extend the analysis to the whole bacterial chromosome and show that in fact, there is no fundamental difference in the mechanism of recombination with high or with low frequency in Hfr $\times$ F$^-$ crosses but rather that the very mechanism of genetic transfer involves a continuous gradient of transmission from one end to the other of the Hfr chromosome.

In a cross between Hfr H and F$^-$ bacteria, one may determine both the *frequency of recombinants* (i.e., the number of recombinants formed in one of several selections) and the *genetic constitution of recombinants* (i.e., the distribution, among the recombinants, of the various unselected characters of the parental Hfr type). We shall first examine the characteristics of crosses between nonlysogenic bacteria, in which complications due to the presence of a prophage cannot occur.

A. The $T^+L^+S^r$ Recombinants and the Genetic Characters Transmitted with High Frequency by Hfr H Bacteria

Among the characters which are transmitted with high frequency by Hfr H bacteria are the characters T, L, Az, Lac (Hayes, 1953b). Let us consider a cross between F^- P678 marked with the characters $T^-L^-B_1^-$ Az^r T_1^r Lac^- Gal_b^- Mal^- Xyl^- Man^- S^r λ^r $T3^r$, and prototrophic Hfr H bacteria having the opposite characters. Both strains involved are nonlysogenic. After 60 minutes of contact, samples of the mating mixture are plated on MA medium containing glucose, vitamin B_1, and streptomycin, in order to select for the $T^+L^+S^r$ recombinants formed with high frequency. In repeated crosses of this kind, the frequency with which $T^+L^+S^r$ recombinants are formed is of the order of 10 per cent.

Genetic analysis of the recombinants reveals that they all possess certain characters of the parental F^- type: specifically, Mal^- Xyl^- Man^- B_1^- λ^r $T3^r$. The corresponding alleles from the Hfr type do not appear among the $T^+L^+S^r$ recombinants. Other characters of the Hfr parent are transmitted to the $T^+L^+S^r$ recombinants in remarkably constant proportions, from one cross to another: e.g., the character Az^s is transmitted in 90 per cent of the cases, the character T_1^s in 70 per cent, the character Lac^+ in 45 per cent and the character Gal_b^+ in 25 per cent. Consequently, this experiment defines *two groups of genetic characters*: those which are capable of being transmitted with high frequency from the Hfr H bacteria to the recombinants $T^+L^+S^r$, and those which cannot be transmitted with high frequency to these recombinants.

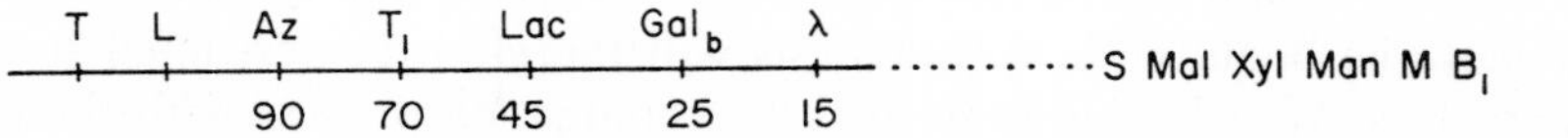

T L Az T_1 Lac Gal_b λ .... S Mal Xyl Man M B_1
90 70 45 25 15

FIG. 7. The TL-Gal chromosomal segment. The characters are arranged on this segment according to their frequency of appearance among the recombinants $T^+L^+S^r$. The characters not transmitted with high frequency (less than 1 per cent among the recombinants $T^+L^+S^r$) are arranged according to the order indicated by Cavalli and Jinks (1956) on a dotted line.

Genetic characters which are transmitted with high frequency from the Hfr H bacteria to the $T^+L^+S^r$ recombinants are found among these recombinants in different proportions, the proportions being characteristic for each character. Such characters can therefore be ordered according to their relative frequency of transmission to $T^+L^+S^r$ recombinants. In all likelihood, this order reflects their relative distances from the selected characters T^+L^+. *A linear linkage group of the characters transmitted with high frequency by the Hfr H bacteria* is thus defined.

Among the characters that distinguish Hfr H from P678 F− bacteria, the most distant on this group are the characters TL and Gal_b. The chromosomal segment which carries these characters will be called the TL-Gal segment (Fig. 7).

B. The Gal+Sr Recombinants and the Polarity of the Chromosomal TL-Gal Segment

In a cross between strains Hfr H S^s and F− P678 S^r, both nonlysogenic, one can select both $T^+L^+S^r$ and Gal^+S^r recombinants, and compare the frequency at which they are formed as well as their genetic constitutions. In samples taken after 1 hour of contact between the strains being crossed, the frequency of Gal^+S^r recombinants is of the order of 2.5 per cent, whereas the frequency of $T^+L^+S^r$ recombinants is about 10 per cent (Table IV). Thus, in the same cross, different recombinant types are formed with different frequencies.

Table IV
Kinetics of the Formation of Recombinants in Crosses
Hfr H(λ)−S^s × F−(λ)− S^r

Samples taken and plated at time *t* (minutes)	Frequencies of recombinants in crosses		
	Hfr H(λ)− × P678(λ)− Recombinants		Hfr H(λ)− × C600 Recombinants
	$T^+L^+S^r$	Gal^+S^r	$T^+L^+S^r$
10	1.9	0.34	3
20	4	1	6.3
40	8.4	2.3	15.6
60	9.3	2.4	18

Growing cultures of Hfr H(λ)− and F−(λ)− bacteria are mixed at time 0 (2.10^7 Hfr and 4.10^8 F− bacteria per ml). The mating mixture is aerated at 37°. At various times, samples are taken, diluted out, and plated on glucose MA medium containing thiamine and streptomycin (selection of $T^+L^+S^r$ recombinants) or galactose MA medium containing threonine, leucine, thiamine, and streptomycin (selection of Gal^+S^r recombinants). At time 0, Hfr bacteria are also plated on CA medium for a determination of the input number of the minority parent.

Genetic analysis of Gal^+S^r recombinants shows that like the $T^+L^+S^r$ recombinants, they do not inherit certain genetic characters of the parental Hfr type, such as the characters Mal^+ or Xyl^+. As for those unselected characters that are transmitted to $T^+L^+S^r$ recombinants, they are found among Gal^+S^r recombinants in comparable and high proportions (Table V). While it is easy, therefore, in analyzing the $T^+L^+S^r$ recombinants, to establish the relative order of the characters carried by the TL-Gal segment, this no longer is the case for Gal^+S^r recombinants, since among them the various characters carried by this segment are found with comparable frequencies.

TABLE V

GENETIC CONSTITUTION OF THE RECOMBINANTS FORMED IN A CROSS BETWEEN Hfr(λ)−S^s AND P678(λ)−Sr BACTERIA

Type of recombinants	Frequency of recombinants	Frequency (per cent) of the Hfr characters							
		T+L+	Az^s	T_1^s	Lac+	Gal+	Mal+	Xyl+	Man+
$T^+L^+S^r$	9.3	100	91	72	48	27	0	0	0
Gal^+S^r	2.4	83	78	79	81	100	0	0	0

[a] The "genetic constitution" of a given type of recombinants corresponds to the distribution, among this class of recombinants, of the genetic characters from the Hfr parent (see text, page 65). The "frequency of recombinants" given in the second column is the fraction of the minority Hfr parent which have produced a given type of recombinants after 60 minutes of mating. Notice among the $T^+L^+S^r$ recombinants, the decreasing proportion of the Hfr alleles from Az to Gal. Notice, in contrast, among the Gal^+S^r recombinants, the high and almost constant proportion of the Hfr alleles for the unselected characters. In the latter case, the frequencies with which the Hfr alleles appear among the Gal^+S^r recombinants may vary according to the conditions of crosses and of plating, but they are always higher than 50 per cent and essentially the same for the different unselected characters of the TL-Gal segment.

There seems to be a relationship between the differences observed in the frequency at which $T^+L^+S^r$ and Gal^+S^r recombinants are formed, and the differences shown by genetic analysis of these recombinants. In fact, the Gal^+S^r recombinants are about one-fourth as numerous as the $T^+L^+S^r$ recombinants, but over 50 per cent of them possess also the characters T^+L^+ of the Hfr parental type. Transmission of the character Gal^+ from Hfr bacteria to recombinants is thus less likely to occur than is transmission of the characters T^+L^+; accordingly, when a recombinant has inherited the character Gal^+, it is highly probable that it has also inherited the T^+L^+ characters. A *genetic polarity* exists, therefore, along the TL-Gal segment, a polarity that may be expressed numerically by the ratio of the number of $T^+L^+S^r$ recombinants to the number of Gal^+S^r recombinants formed in the same cross (E. L. Wollman and Jacob, 1957).

C. THE KINETICS OF FORMATION OF GENETIC RECOMBINANTS

The preceding observations were made on recombinants derived from samples removed after 1 hour of contact between the parental types. We shall now consider how the number of recombinants formed varies as a function of the time elapsed after mixing the parental strains.

Strains Hfr H S^s and F− P678 S^r, both nonlysogenic, are mixed under the usual conditions of crosses (4.10^8 F− bacteria and 2.10^7 Hfr bacteria per milliliter). At variable intervals after mixing, samples are taken, diluted, and plated on selective media in order to evaluate the number of $T^+L^+S^r$ recombinants on the one hand and of Gal^+S^r recombinants on the other. The results of such an experiment are given in Table IV and Fig. 8.

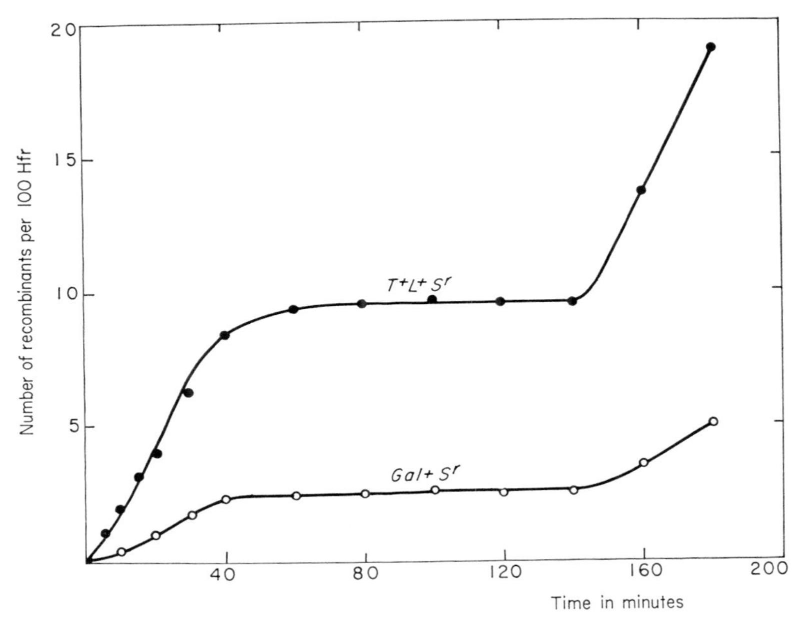

FIG. 8. The kinetics of formation of genetic recombinants in a cross between nonlysogenic Hfr H S^s and F− P678 S^r bacteria. This experiment is similar to those reported in Table IV, but 70 minutes after the bacteria were mixed, the mating mixture (tube 1) is diluted 50 times in 1/10th strength broth. This dilution (tube 2) is shaken gently at 37°C like the initial tube. Up to 120 minutes, samples are taken from both tubes and after 120 minutes only from tube 2. Aliquots are plated on selective media. Abscissa: Time in minutes after the initial mixing. Ordinate: Number of genetic recombinants related to the initial number of Hfr bacteria.

It may be seen that the number of $T^+L^+S^r$ recombinants and of Gal^+S^r recombinants increases regularly from the moment the parent cells are put together until about the 50th minute. This number then remains constant for more than an hour. Only after the experiment has proceeded for about 140 minutes, does the number of recombinants again increase. From this point on, it doubles every 40 minutes or so.

The initial ascending phase of the curves expresses the kinetics of conjugation; the second ascending phase after the intervening plateau corresponds to the multiplication of the recombinants formed. The significance of these three phases will be considered in more detail in Chapter VIII, but several points should be made here.

1. The curves representing the kinetics of formation of $T^+L^+S^r$ and Gal^+S^r recombinants extrapolate to the origin, which indicates that *conjugation begins to take place as soon as the parental cells are mixed.*

2. Both these curves reach a plateau, at approximately the same time. Once the plateau is reached, the number of recombinants remains constant for more than an hour. This indicates that, 50 minutes after they have been mixed, *all the cells capable of taking part in conjugation have effectively mated.*

3. The levels of the plateaus are very different. The frequency of $T^+L^+S^r$ recombinants is about 10 per cent, whereas the frequency of Gal^+S^r recombinants is about 2.5 per cent. Since, in the course of a single cross, the frequency of recombinants differs with the method of selection used, this frequency of recombinants *constitutes only an imperfect indication of the frequency of conjugation.* It can give, at best, only a minimal estimate (E. L. Wollman and Jacob, 1955; Jacob and Wollman, 1955a).

Under the experimental conditions chosen, the maximum number of genetic recombinants is reached in less than an hour of contact. This fact justifies the choice of method, i.e., the enumeration of the $T^+L^+S^r$ and Gal^+S^r recombinants in samples taken after 1 hour of contact between the parent cells.

D. Variations Depending on the Nature of the Strains Involved in Hfr H $\times$ F^- Crosses

When Hfr H $\times$ F^- crosses are made between a number of different strains, certain variations in the results are observed. Such variations have to be taken into account when the results of different crosses are to be compared.

1. *Variations in the frequencies of recombinants.* a. When a particular Hfr H strain is crossed with various F^- strains, the frequency of recombinants can vary with the F^- strain involved. For instance, in the cross Hfr $H(\lambda)^- \times C600(\lambda)^-$, the frequency of occurrence of $T^+L^+S^r$ recombinants is twice as great as in the cross Hfr $H(\lambda)^- \times P678(\lambda)^-$ (Table VI).

As may be seen from Table VI, the frequencies of recombinants are, in the cases observed, independent of the character lysogenic or non-lysogenic of the F− strain when these strains are closely related. This is the case for strains P678(λ)+ and P678(λ)− (crosses 1 and 2). It is true also for strains Y10(λ)+, C600(λ)−, and P14(λd)+ (crosses 3, 4, and 5).

TABLE VI
FREQUENCIES OF RECOMBINANTS OBSERVED IN VARIOUS CROSSES Hfr H S^s × F− S^r

Number	Crosses	Frequency of recombinants[a] T+L+S^r	Gal+ S^r	Ratio $\frac{\text{T+L+S}^r}{\text{Gal+ S}^r}$
1	Hfr(λ)− × P678(λ)−	9.3	2.4	3.9
2	Hfr(λ)− × P678(λ)+	9.8	2.1	4.7
3	Hfr(λ)− × C600(λ)−	18	—	—
4	Hfr(λ)− × Y10(λ)+	18.8	—	—
5	Hfr(λ)− × P14(λ*d*)+	17.8	—	—
6	Hfr(λ)+ × P678(λ)+	16.8	3.9	4.3
7	Hfr(λ)+ × P678(λ)−	6.8	0.13	52
8	Hfr(λ)+ × Y10(λ)+	38.9	—	—
9	Hfr(λ)+ × P10(λ*d*)+	37.2	—	—
10	Hfr(λ)+ × C600(λ)−	18	—	—

[a] The frequencies of recombinants have been determined in samples taken after 60 minutes of mating.

b. When two different Hfr H strains are crossed with the same F− strain, the frequencies of recombinants may vary with the Hfr H strain involved. For instance, when the lysogenic strain Hfr H(λ)+ is crossed with a lysogenic F− strain, the frequencies of recombinants are twice as high as when the nonlysogenic strain Hfr H(λ)− is crossed with the same lysogenic F− strain. This is true (Table VI) irrespective of the selection method (crosses 2 and 5) and of the F− strain (crosses 4 and 8, 5 and 9).*

When comparing the results of crosses involving different strains, it is therefore necessary to take into consideration these differences in the frequencies of recombinants due to the nature of the strains used.

2. *Variations in the genetic constitution of recombinants.* These variations are much less important than the variations in frequency of recombinants. In particular, the ordering of the different characters carried by the TL-Gal segment and the relative distances between them as de-

* We will not discuss here crosses between lysogenic Hfr H bacteria and non-lysogenic F− bacteria (crosses 7 and 10). This subject will be considered at length in Chapter VII.

termined by analysis of $T^+L^+S^r$, vary only slightly (Table V). Likewise, analysis of Gal^+S^r recombinants shows that the various characters of the TL-Gal segment always appear with similar frequencies although these frequencies may vary from 50 to 80 per cent.

* * *

The facts described above illustrate the principal characteristic of crosses with a high frequency of recombination: its asymmetry, of which several expressions have already been mentioned in this chapter.

The first expression of such asymmetry is *sexual polarity.* When Hfr H and F^- bacteria are placed in contact, the transfer of genetic material is unidirectional, taking place from the Hfr H donor cells to the F^- recipient cells, as shown by the fact that sterilization of the Hfr H bacteria by streptomycin or even their destruction, after conjugation, by a virulent bacteriophage (Hayes, 1955) does not prevent the formation of genetic recombinants.

A second expression of asymmetry is *genetic polarity*: only certain characters from the Hfr H cells can be transmitted with high frequency to genetic recombinants. Consequently a distinction can be made between two categories of genetic characters: those for which the frequency of recombination is high, and those for which it is low (Hayes, 1953b).

The third is the *polarity of the TL-Gal segment,* i.e., the polarity existing along the linkage group on which are located the genetic characters transmitted with high frequency. It seems as if a gradient exists, along the TL-Gal segment. This gradient is of such a nature that the further a genetic character is situated from the TL characters, the less chance it has of being transmitted to a recombinant. For convenience, we shall apply the term *proximal* to a character located near TL and *distal* to a character such as Gal_b, located further from TL.

Both the genetic polarity and the polarity of the TL-Gal segment could result from one or the other of the mechanisms analyzed at the end of the preceding chapter. According to the hypothesis formulated by Lederberg and Cavalli, the two polarities could be purely genetic: the whole chromosome from an Hfr H cell is *transferred* to an F^- bacterium, only certain characters are thereafter *transmitted* to recombinants, as a result of defective pairing between two homologous structures and postzygotic elimination of a chromosomal segment from the Hfr cell.

According to Hayes' hypothesis, on the contrary, only a segment of the chromosome of the Hfr cell is transferred during conjugation, and this would explain why the high frequency of recombinants is limited to one group of characters. As for the polarity of the segment TL-Gal, it could be a consequence of the incompleteness or the unevenness of the transferred chromosomal segments.

We shall now attempt to analyze the evidence in favor of one or the other of these hypotheses and to look for the possible solutions to the problems thus raised.

It is necessary, at the outset, to stress the importance of distinguishing between the *transfer* of genetic characters from donor to recipient cells and the *transmission* of these same characters from Hfr bacteria to genetic recombinants. This distinction, which is equally necessary whatever the hypothesis, appeared difficult to establish experimentally as long as the formation of genetic recombinants was the only known expression of the process of bacterial conjugation. These genetic recombinants, in fact, represent the final products of a series of events which take place between the moment when bacteria of opposite mating types are placed in contact and the moment when a clone of genetic recombinants has been formed.

The crosses involving lysogenic strains, which will be now considered, have helped to give a concrete meaning to this distinction between the transfer and the transmission of genetic characters.

CHAPTER VI

The Chromosomal Location of Prophages

Analysis of the genetic determination of lysogeny, by means of crosses with low frequency of recombination, had provided strong presumptive evidence for the hypothesis that prophage λ is located on the bacterial chromosome. However, the intrinsic difficulty of interpreting the results of such crosses still left some uncertainty. Although the lysogeny λ and galactose characters behaved in such crosses as if they were genetically linked, their location on the bacterial linkage group remained questionable. Furthermore, the segregation of these characters did not occur in the same way in reciprocal crosses between lysogenic and nonlysogenic strains (see Chapter IV).

The possibility of performing crosses with a high frequency of recombination allowed this problem to be taken up again, this time with greater accuracy. The Gal_b character, to which the lysogeny λ character is linked, as shown by $F^+ \times F^-$ crosses, is actually located on the linkage group which is transferred with high frequency by strain Hfr H. The high frequency of recombination made it possible, moreover, to analyze quantitatively the causes of the asymmetry observed in reciprocal crosses between lysogenic and nonlysogenic bacteria.

These studies, which will be described in the present chapter, have established unambiguously the chromosomal location of prophages. They have also shown that a prophage such as λ behaves differently from other bacterial genetic determinants, since its transmission to genetic recombinants is affected by the parental strain—whether recipient or donor—which carries it.

I. THE TEMPERATE BACTERIOPHAGE λ

As mentioned earlier, the K12 strain of *E. coli,* and most of the mutants derived from it, are lysogenic. The bacteriophage λ produced by these bacteria can multiply on certain nonlysogenic substrains of K12 or on other strains of *E. coli,* such as *E. coli* C (see Table III). When the two strains in a cross are both lysogenic for λ, the lysogenic character of these strains has no effect on the outcome of the cross. For instance, the two

Hfr strains of Cavalli (Hfr C) and of Hayes (Hfr H), are both lysogenic and the investigations of these authors, reviewed in the preceding chapter, were carried out with lysogenic strains.

Before describing the work on the localization of prophage λ by means of high frequency crosses, it seems desirable to recall briefly some properties of the lysogenic bacteria K12(λ) and of phage λ, as well as some methods the knowledge of which may be useful for an understanding of the experiments reported.

A. Lysogenic Strains K12(λ) and Defective Lysogenic Strains K12(λd)

A culture of K12(λ) bacteria contains about one particle of free phage per one hundred bacteria. Under the influence of agents such as ultraviolet light, it is possible to induce phage production in almost all the bacteria of a culture. Every induced bacterium yields on the average one hundred infective particles (Weiglé and Delbrück, 1951). Bacteria of the lysogenic K12(λ) type are generally capable of adsorbing phage λ, but are not affected by its action: they are immune. Certain strains—whether nonlysogenic or lysogenic—are resistant to phage λ because they are incapable of adsorbing it. This is the case for strain P678, for instance (Table III).

Several defective lysogenic strains have been isolated (E. M. and J. Lederberg, 1953; Appleyard, 1954b; Jacob and Wollman, 1956a). Various treatments were used to produce these strains; most of them were obtained among the survivors after subjection to high doses of ultraviolet irradiation. Defective lysogenic strains no longer produce phage λ, either spontaneously or even after induction, but retain nonetheless the specific immunity of K12(λ) bacteria and, in most cases, also the same high sensitivity to killing by ultraviolet radiation. These defective strains perpetuate a mutant λ prophage, unable to perform one of the reactions necessary for the formation of infectious particles of bacteriophage λ (see Chapter XV).

B. The Genetic System of Bacteriophage λ

When spread on susceptible bacteria, the wild type bacteriophage λ, produced by K12(λ), forms small uniformly turbid plaques the diameter of which is about 0.5 mm. From this phage, it is possible to isolate a variety of mutants which differ from the original type in size or appearance of plaques, capacity for lysogenization, or host range. All retain the antigenic specificity of wild type λ. Among these mutants, those which form clear plaques are unable to lysogenize and most of them are unable to grow on K12(λ) bacteria, lysogenic for anyone of the mutants. A certain class of clear mutants, however, called virulent inducers, are capable of overcoming the immunity of lysogenic bacteria K12(λ) and of developing within these cells. The plaque morphology of some mutants of phage λ is illustrated in Fig. 9 (Jacob and Wollman, 1954b).

The genetics of bacteriophage λ is fairly well known. By appropriate crosses (Fig. 10), it has been possible to arrange all the known characters of this phage in a single linkage group (Jacob and Wollman,

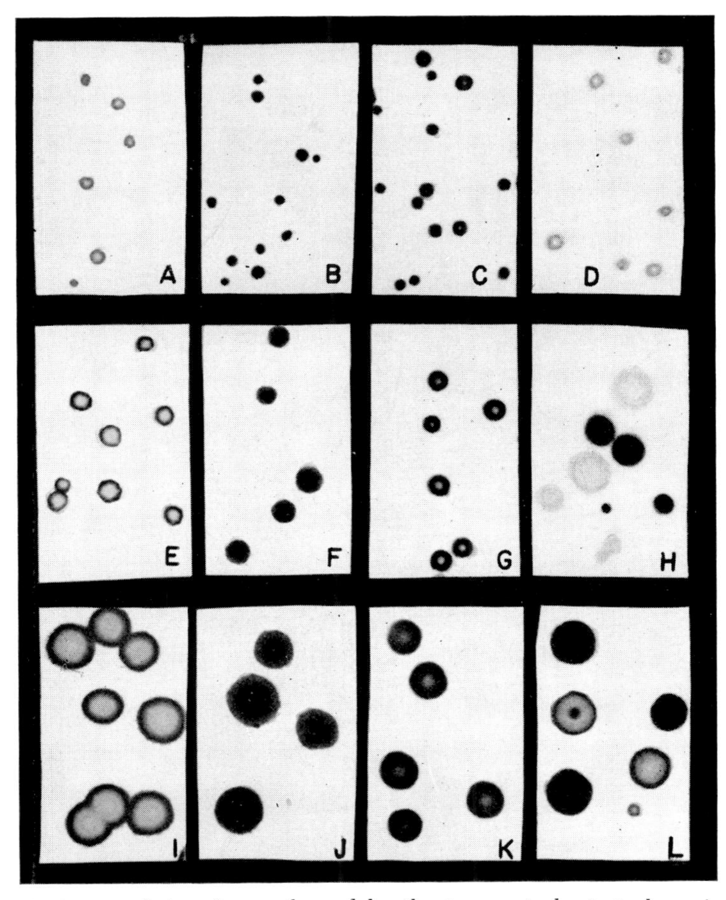

FIG. 9. Aspect of the plaques formed by the temperate bacteriophage λ and by some of its mutants. A, wild type; B, small clear; C, small centered; D, small uniformly turbid; E, medium turbid; F, medium clear; G, medium centered; H, clear and virulent phages spread over a mixture of indicator bacteria. (The clear plaques are formed by the virulent phages, the turbid plaques by the clear phages); I, large turbid; J, large clear; K, large centered; L, plaques formed in a cross wild type × large virulent.

1954b; E. L. Wollman and Jacob, 1954b; Kaiser, 1955). Similarly, by superinfecting with genetically marked λ phages, defective lysogenic bacteria, previously induced by ultraviolet light, it has been possible to locate in this linkage group a variety of prophage mutations responsible for the defective character (Jacob and Wollman, 1956a; Jacob, Fuerst,

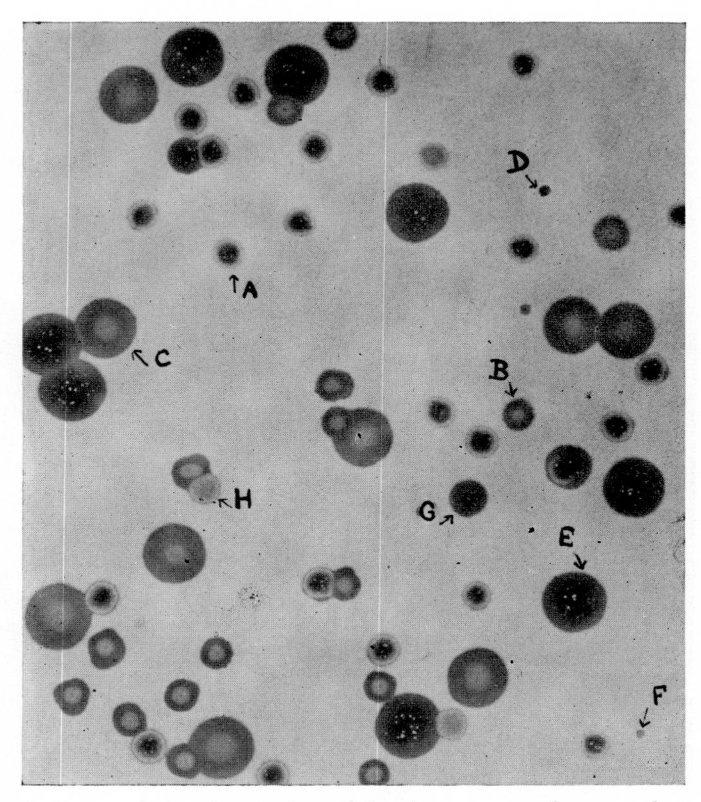

FIG. 10. Aspect of the plaques formed by the progeny of a cross between two strains of phage λ differing by three characters.

Parental types	A : m_5+cmi (small clear) B : m_5c+mi+ (medium turbid)
Single recombinants	C : m_5+c+mi+ (large turbid) D : $m_5$cmi (minute clear) E : m_5+cmi+ (large clear) F : m_5c+mi (minute turbid)
Double recombinants	G : $m_5$cmi+ (medium clear) H : m_5+c+mi (small turbid)

and Wollman, 1957). A diagram of the linkage group of bacteriophage λ is given in Fig. 11.

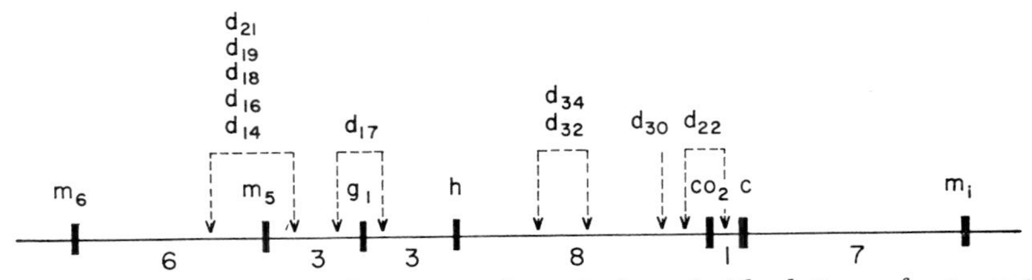

FIG. 11. Linkage group of temperate bacteriophage λ. The letters refer to mutations affecting characters of the plaques. The *d* symbols refer to various defective mutations. The figures represent the fraction of recombinants formed in two factor crosses by mixed infection of sensitive bacteria.

C. METHODS USED IN BACTERIAL CROSSES INVOLVING LYSOGENIC STRAINS

The general techniques for the study of bacteriophage are too well known to require description here (see Adams, 1950, 1959). Similarly, the description of the techniques appropriate to the study of lysogenic bacteria is beyond the scope of the present work (see Jacob, 1954a). Only those technical aspects that are essential to an understanding of the present discussion will be briefly described.

1. *Enumeration of infective centers.* The term "infective center" designates any particle capable of giving rise to a plaque on an agar plate seeded with sensitive indicator bacteria. It may arise from a free phage particle, an infected sensitive bacterium, or an induced lysogenic bacterium. It is often necessary to distinguish between those infective centers which are due to free phages and those which originate from phage-producing bacteria; when samples from a culture of lysogenic bacteria are plated on agar in the presence of sensitive bacteria, some of the plaques formed result from free phages and others from lysogenic bacteria which have released phage in the course of their residual growth on the plate.

There are several ways of distinguishing between the two kinds of infective centers. The free phages may be eliminated either by centrifugation and washing of the bacterial pellet, or by neutralization with a specific antiserum. The bacterial infective centers may be eliminated by treating the suspension with chloroform, which destroys bacteria but not bacteriophages. An even simpler method is to plate the mixture on an agar medium containing streptomycin (150 μg/ml), and inoculated with indicator streptomycin-resistant bacteria: the bacterial infective centers are inactivated, and only the free phages form plaques (Bertani, 1951).

In a bacterial cross, the last mentioned procedure can be used to distinguish the infective centers formed by one strain from those formed by the other, provided that one of the strains is streptomycin-sensitive and the other streptomycin-resistant. Samples of the mating mixture are plated onto nutrient agar containing streptomycin and inoculated with streptomycin-resistant indicator bacteria. Strain 112 S^r (Table III) has been generally used as the indicator strain.

2. *Technique of crosses and analysis of recombinants.* The general techniques of crosses do not differ from those described in the preceding chapter. The cultures of the strains to be crossed are centrifuged and washed, in order to eliminate the free phage particles; and in some cases, it may be necessary to carry out the crosses in the presence of an antiphage serum.

In crosses between lysogenic and nonlysogenic bacteria, what is looked for is the segregation of the lysogenic character among the recombinants.

The recipient strains, whether lysogenic or nonlysogenic, must consequently be *resistant to the bacteriophage under study* in order to avoid infection and lysis of the nonlysogenic recombinants by extrinsic bacteriophage. The recombinants are carefully reisolated, preferably in the presence of antiphage serum. Their lysogenic or nonlysogenic character is determined by replica plating onto CA medium previously inoculated with indicator bacteria. After incubation, the replicas of the lysogenic recombinants will be surrounded by a zone of lysis.

In crosses between bacteria lysogenic for different mutants of the same bacteriophage, what is looked for is the segregation of the two types of prophages among the recombinants.

When there is no means of detecting independently each of the mutant types, quantitative analysis becomes extremely difficult and, consequently, somewhat inaccurate. This situation arises in crosses between strains producing phages which differ in morphological characteristics, such as the appearance or the size of the plaques that they form (Fig. 9). Each recombinant must be first carefully reisolated in order to avoid contamination by phages of the other type. It must be then cultivated, after which samples of the culture are plated on indicator bacteria in order to determine the type of phage produced.

In crosses between lysogenic bacteria carrying prophages of which at least one type can be identified independently of the presence of the other type, analysis of the results is much simpler. This is the situation for crosses between lysogenic bacteria carrying certain mutant types of the same phage (phages differing in their host range, or normal and defective prophages). It is also the situation in crosses between lysogenic bacteria which carry different bacteriophages.

A mutant of λ is known which differs from the wild type in its host range. This mutant (λh) is capable of forming plaques on bacteria that are resistant to the wild type (Appleyard *et al.*, 1956). By genetic recombination between a phage λ and a related phage with a different host range, it is possible also to isolate a hybrid phage which possesses the specificity of λ, but the host range of the other phage. In this way, by crossing λ and the temperate phage 434 (see below) the hybrid (λh_{434}) was obtained (Kaiser and Jacob, 1957).

In crosses between bacteria lysogenic for phages which differ in their host range [cross K12(λ) × K12(λh_{434})], for instance, it is possible to identify independently the recombinants which yield one of the phage types and the recombinants which yield the other type. In crosses between normal lysogenic bacteria [K12(λ)] and defective lysogenic bacteria [K12(λd)], only the recombinants that produce the normal phage type can be detected. In these various cases, the recombinants are reisolated and analyzed by means of the method already described. Identification of their lysogenic character is achieved by replica plating on appropriate indicator bacteria.

II. THE LOCATION OF PROPHAGE λ

A. Hfr $H(\lambda)^- \times F^-(\lambda)^+$ Crosses and the Chromosomal Determination of Lysogeny

The results obtained in crosses between nonlysogenic Hfr H bacteria and lysogenic F^- bacteria resistant to bacteriophage λ are shown in Tables VI (p. 71) and VII (p. 82).

1. *The frequencies of recombinants* observed are, as indicated, the same in the cross Hfr $H(\lambda)^- \times F^-(\lambda)^+$ and in the corresponding cross Hfr $H(\lambda)^- \times F^-(\lambda)^-$ (Table VI, crosses 1 to 5). In particular, the ratio of the number of $T^+L^+S^r$ recombinants to the number of Gal^+S^r recombinants formed in the same cross (ratio $T^+L^+S^r/Gal^+S^r$), is close to 4 in both cases, whether or not the F^- strain is lysogenic.

2. *The genetic constitution of recombinants* is also the same in a cross $Hfr(\lambda)^- \times F^-(\lambda)^+$ as in the corresponding cross $Hfr(\lambda)^- \times F^-(\lambda)^-$, as far as the various characters (Az, T_1, Lac, Gal) carried by the TL-Gal segment are concerned (Table VII, crosses 1 and 2).

The character "lysogeny λ" segregates in the cross, since about 15 per cent of $T^+L^+S^r$ recombinants inherit the nonlysogenic character of the

TABLE VII

GENETIC CONSTITUTION OF RECOMBINANTS FORMED IN VARIOUS CROSSES BETWEEN Hfr H S^s AND F−P678 Sr BACTERIA

Crosses	Ratio $\frac{T+L+S^r}{Gal+\ S^r}$	Genetic constitution of recombinants: T+L+S^r					Gal+ S^r				
		Az^s	$T_1{}^s$	Lac+	Gal+	$(\lambda)^a$	T+L+	Az^s	$T_1{}^s$	Lac+	$(\lambda)^a$
Hfr(λ)− × P678(λ)−	4.2	91	72	48	27	—	83	78	79	81	—
Hfr(λ)− × P678(λ)+	3.7	92	73	49	31	15	75	75	74	74	84
Hfr(λ)+ × P678(λ)+	4.2	90	70	47	29	14	80	78	78	82	82
Hfr(λ)+ × P678(λ)−	54	86	60	21	2.5	0.1	82	79	78	74	1

[a] The column (λ) refers to the frequency of appearance, among the recombinants, of the (λ) character of the Hfr parent: (λ)− in the cross Hfr(λ)− × P678(λ)+, (λ)+ in the cross Hfr (λ)+ × P678(λ)−. In the cross Hfr(λ)+ × P678(λ)+ the two strains carried a different, genetically marked, λ prophage.

parental Hfr type. The frequency with which the nonlysogenic character of the Hfr parent appears among the $T^+L^+S^r$ recombinants indicates that lysogeny is under the control of a chromosomal determinant, and that this determinant is located beyond Gal_b in relation to TL, on the TL-Gal segment (Fig. 7, p. 66).

Analysis of the Gal^+S^r recombinants confirms the chromosomal location of the genetic determinant of lysogeny. It shows, furthermore, the close linkage between this determinant and the determinant of the Gal_b character: more than 80 per cent of the Gal^+S^r recombinants have also inherited the nonlysogenic character of the donor bacteria.

The crosses between nonlysogenic Hfr H bacteria and lysogenic F^- bacteria therefore establish beyond question that the determination of lysogeny is chromosomal. These crosses show further that, in the case of bacteriophage λ, the determinant of lysogeny is situated among the group of characters transmitted with high frequency by the Hfr H bacteria. This determinant is closely linked with the Gal_b character on the distal portion of the TL-Gal segment (E. L. Wollman and Jacob, 1954a, 1957).

B. Hfr $H(\lambda)^+ \times F^-(\lambda)^+$ Crosses and the Chromosomal Location of Prophage λ

Although the crosses described above permit the conclusion that lysogeny is chromosomally determined, they do not prove that the genetic determinant of this character is the prophage itself. This can be demonstrated only by crosses between bacteria both of which are lysogenic for bacteriophage λ, in which the type of prophage carried by each parental type can be readily distinguished; that is by crosses between *bacteria carrying genetically different prophages λ*.

The crosses between lysogenic Hfr H bacteria and F^- bacteria which are also lysogenic have characteristics in every respect comparable to those of the crosses already described. Let us recall that with the Hfr $H(\lambda)^+$ strain used, the frequencies of recombinants are twice as high as in the corresponding crosses involving the nonlysogenic strain Hfr $H(\lambda)^-$ (crosses 6, 8, and 9 in Table VI).* The genetic constitution of the recombinants formed in the Hfr $H(\lambda)^+ \times F^-(\lambda)^+$ crosses, is identical for all characters except lysogeny, with that of the recombinants formed in an Hfr $H(\lambda)^- \times F^-(\lambda)^-$ cross (crosses 1 and 3 in Table VII).

1. *Crosses between bacteria lysogenic for morphological mutants of bacteriophage λ.* The first high frequency crosses of this type between lysogenic bacteria were performed between Hfr H bacteria, lysogenic

* It may be that the ultraviolet light treatment that brought about the "cure" of the lysogenic Hfr H strain is responsible also for this decreased "fertility."

for the wild type phage λ, and F⁻ C600 bacteria lysogenic for a double mutant of λ. This mutant forms plaques of medium size with a turbid center whereas the plaques formed by the wild type are small and uniformly turbid (see Fig. 9, A and G). One hundred and fifty $T^+L^+S^r$ recombinants were reisolated and analyzed: 30 per cent of these produced wild type bacteriophage λ as did the parental Hfr type (E. L. Wollman and Jacob, 1954a). Among such recombinants, approximately one-third produced in addition particles of the medium-sized, centered type and a few produced particles of recombinant types.

The lack of accuracy in the analysis of such crosses has already been pointed out. These results, however, show that the genetic determinant of lysogeny transmitted with high frequency from the Hfr H bacteria to the $T^+L^+S^r$ recombinants is the prophage itself.

2. *Crosses between bacteria lysogenic for phages λ which differ in their host range.* Genetic analysis is much easier when the bacteria involved in the cross carry prophages of which at least one can be independently identified in the presence of the other. This is the case for a cross between Hfr H(λh^+), bacteria which yield a wild type phage, and F^- P678(λh_{434}), bacteria which yield a hybrid λ active on cells resistant to the wild type λ phage. The results of such a cross are reported in Table VII, from which it may be seen that 14 per cent of the $T^+L^+S^r$ recombinants and 82 per cent of the Gal^+S^r recombinants no longer produce the phage type carried initially by the recipient bacteria but yield instead the λh^+ wild type.

Comparable results are obtained in crosses between defective lysogenic Hfr H(λd) bacteria and F^- P678(λ^+) bacteria which carry a normal wild type prophage. The defective prophage of the Hfr bacteria is inherited by the $T^+L^+S^r$ and Gal^+S^r recombinants with the same frequency as was the wild type prophage in the preceding cross. It is worth mentioning that, in crosses between lysogenic bacteria which carry genetically labeled prophages, a small proportion of the recombinants (about 10 per cent of those which have acquired the prophage of the Hfr parental type) carry genetic markers of both types of prophages (Jacob and Wollman, 1957a).

The results of these crosses demonstrate unquestionably that the genetic determinant of lysogeny is actually the prophage itself. A prophage λ carried by Hfr H bacteria, regardless of whether this prophage is of the wild, mutant, or defective type, is indeed transmitted to the genetic recombinants formed in an Hfr $H(\lambda)^+ \times F^-(\lambda)^+$ cross in exactly the same way as the nonlysogenic character is transmitted to these same recombinants in an Hfr $H(\lambda)^- \times F^-(\lambda)^+$ cross. There exists, therefore, on the bacterial chromosome a defined and unique site on which a prophage λ, whatever its genotype, may be located. This specific site of the prophage λ is located beyond Gal_b on the distal portion of the chromosomal segment TL-Gal (Fig. 7). The linkage between the prophage λ and the character Gal_b is confirmed by the results of transduction experiments (Jacob, 1955). When Gal_b^- bacteria, lysogenic for λ, are infected with a transducing phage which has multiplied in Gal_b^+ bacteria, nonlysogenic for λ, a fraction of the transduced Gal_b^+ bacteria also acquire the nonlysogenic character of the donor bacteria. The inverse coupled transduction of Gal_b^+ and lysogeny for λ to Gal_b^- bacteria likewise occurs.

C. Hfr $H(\lambda)^+ \times F^-(\lambda)^-$ Crosses and the Resulting Genetic Distortions

Although in Hfr $H(\lambda)^- \times F^-(\lambda)^+$ and Hfr $H(\lambda)^+ \times F^-(\lambda)^+$ crosses, prophage λ seems to behave just like other bacterial genetic determinants, the situation is completely different in crosses between lysogenic Hfr H bacteria and nonlysogenic F^- bacteria, as may be seen in Table VI (crosses 7 and 10) and in Table VII (cross 4). Not only are the frequencies of recombinants different from those obtained in control crosses; but, in addition, the genetic constitution of the $T^+L^+S^r$ recombinants is greatly altered (E. L. Wollman and Jacob, 1954a). These alterations, as will be seen in the following chapter, are the consequences of the induction of the development of prophage λ during conjugation.

The disparity in the results of reciprocal crosses between lysogenic and nonlysogenic bacteria which had already been observed in crosses with low frequency of recombination is even more evident in the results of crosses between Hfr H and F^- bacteria. When the prophage λ is carried by the recipient F^- bacteria, the lysogenic character segregates in the crosses, and its position can be located easily on the linkage group of the genetic characters transmitted with high frequency by the Hfr H bacteria. On the contrary, when prophage λ is carried by the Hfr H bacteria, it is not transmitted to the recombinants formed in a cross with nonlysogenic recipient bacteria. It behaves, in this case, as a lethal factor, and its transfer to recipient bacteria affects significantly the results of crosses.

III. THE LOCATION OF SOME OTHER PROPHAGES

Lysogenic bacteria are resistant ("immune") to the action of the bacteriophage which they are capable of producing, but remain sensitive to the action of other temperate bacteriophages. Similarly, lysogenic bacteria cannot be lysogenized, as a rule, by mutants of the phage they produce (incompatibility), but they can be lysogenized by other temperate bacteriophages in just the same way as homologous sensitive bacteria. Thus, the presence of a prophage specifically influences the reaction of the bacterium toward the homologous phage. It seems likely that there is a relationship between this specificity and the fact that a given prophage, such as λ, occupies a definite position on the bacterial chromosome (see Chapter XV). It was consequently of great interest to extend genetic analysis to prophages other than λ. For this purpose, a series of temperate bacteriophages, all active on *E.coli* K12, were isolated.

A. Properties of Some Temperate Bacteriophages Active on *Escherichia coli* K12

From 500 strains of *E.coli* of human fecal origin, it was possible to isolate 54 temperate phages active on *E.coli* K12(λ)$^-$ or on *E.coli* C: 27 were active on both K12 and C, 5 were active only on K12, and 22 only on C. A certain number of phages active on *E.coli* K12 were chosen to prepare lysogenic clones from Hfr H(λ)$^-$ and F$^-$(λ)$^-$ strains (Jacob and Wollman, 1956b).

Some of these phages are inducible by ultraviolet light, others are not. Of the inducible phages, three could not be distinguished from λ by the criteria of cross-immunity, host range, and sensitivity to anti-λ immune serum. A number of phages, inducible as well as noninducible, were selected among those giving no cross-immunity. Some properties of these temperate phages are listed in Table VIII. It may be seen, in particular, that with the indicator strains selected, the host ranges of the inducible phages and those of the noninducible phages are clearly distinct (columns 1 to 3). The various inducible phages show a certain relationship with λ in their sensitivity to an anti-λ serum (column 5) as well as in their ability to exchange genetic characters with λ (column 6). Their frequency of induction by ultraviolet light (column 4) varies over a wide range. The significance of such differences is unclear in view of the number of factors involved. In particular, each of these phages has a different lysogenizing power, which can be modified in different ways by changes in external conditions.

B. Location of the Prophages: Crosses between Nonlysogenic Hfr H Bacteria and Lysogenic F$^-$ Bacteria

In order to determine whether or not the various prophages under study are located on the linkage group which can be transmitted with high frequency by Hfr H bacteria, a series of F$^-$ P678 strains, each lyso-

TABLE VIII
PROPERTIES OF SOME TEMPERATE BACTERIOPHAGES[a] ACTIVE ON *E.coli* K12

Phages	Plaques on K12 λ^r 1	Plaques on K12 82^r 2	Plaques on K12 62^r 3	U.V. induction maximal fraction of infective centers per 100 irradiated bacteria 4	Sensitivity to an anti-λ serum 5	Recombination with λ 6
82	+	0	+	45	+	+
λ	0	+	+	> 95	+	+
434	+	0	+	> 95	+	+
381	+	0	+	45	(*)[b]	(*)[b]
21	0	+	+	> 95	(*)[b]	+
424	+	0	+	25	+	+
466	+	0	+	25	(*)[b]	(*)[b]
18	+	+	0	< 1	0	0
370	+	+	0	< 1	0	(*)[b]
62	+	+	0	< 1	(*)[b]	(*)[b]
363	+	+	0	< 1	0	0
W	+	+	0	< 1	(*)[b]	(*)[b]
299	+	+	0	< 1	(*)[b]	0
186	+	+	0	(*)[b]	0	0

[a] These 14 temperate phages exhibit different immunity patterns: bacteria lysogenic for any one of them are still sensitive to all the others. They fall into two classes: ultraviolet (U.V.) inducible and noninducible.
[b] (*) Not investigated.

TABLE IX

LOCALIZATION OF PROPHAGES BY MEANS OF CROSSES[a] BETWEEN NONLYSOGENIC Hfr H BACTERIA AND LYSOGENIC F− BACTERIA

Inducible prophages			Noninducible prophages		
	Frequency of the (ly)− character per 100 recombinants			Frequency of the (ly)− character per 100 recombinants	
Prophage	$T+L+S^r$	$Gal+ S^r$	Prophage	$T+L+S^r$	$Gal+ S^r$
82	21	89	18	<1	<1
λ	16	82	370	<1	<1
434	11	68	62	<1	<1
381	2.5	15	363	<1	<1
21	1	10	W	<1	<1
424	<1	3	299	<1	<1
466	<1	1	186	<1	<1

[a] For each cross, 200 recombinants of each type ($T+L+S^r$ and $Gal+ S^r$) were analyzed. The figures given represent the frequency (per cent) of the nonlysogenic character of the Hfr H parental type among the recombinants analyzed.

genic for a given phage, was prepared. Each of these strains was crossed, under identical conditions, with the same nonlysogenic Hfr H strain. It has been seen that, in such crosses, the genetic analysis of the $T^+L^+S^r$ recombinants makes it possible to locate the characters borne by the TL-Gal segment of Hfr H bacteria. The results of these crosses are shown in Table IX.

When the recipient bacteria are lysogenic for certain of the *inducible prophages,* such as 82 and 434, the nonlysogenic character $(ly)^-$ of the parental Hfr type is inherited by a sizable fraction of the $T^+L^+S^r$ recombinants, which indicates that these prophages are, like λ, located beyond Gal_b on the TL-Gal segment (Fig. 12). Some other inducible

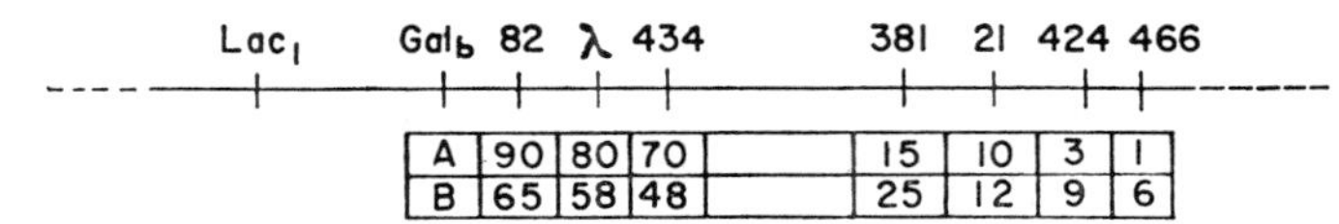

FIG. 12. Chromosomal localization of the various inducible prophages. A. Frequency (per cent) of nonlysogenic recombinants $Gal^+(ly)^-S^r$ among the total Gal^+S^r recombinants formed in various crosses between nonlysogenic Hfr H Gal^+S^s bacteria and lysogenic F− P678 $Gal_b^-S^r$ bacteria. B. Frequency of zygotic induction observed in various crosses between lysogenic Hfr H S^s bacteria and nonlysogenic F− P678 S^r bacteria.

prophages appear also to be located on this segment; but the frequency of transmission of the character $(ly)^-$ of the Hfr H parent to the 200 $T^+L^+S^r$ recombinants analyzed in each of these crosses was too low to permit accurate location in these cases. On the other hand, when the crosses involve F^- bacteria lysogenic for *noninducible prophages,* the $(ly)^-$ character of the parental Hfr H type is never transmitted to the $T^+L^+S^r$ recombinants.

These results are confirmed by analysis of the Gal^+S^r recombinants (Table IX). It is seen that certain inducible prophages are much more closely linked than others to the Gal_b character. The chromosomal sites of the different inducible prophages may thus be mapped on the distal portion of the TL-Gal segment and beyond Gal_b in respect to TL, by arranging these different prophages in order according to their apparent linkage to the Gal_b character (Fig. 12).

As for the noninducible prophages, the corresponding $(ly)^-$ determinant is never transmitted with high frequency to the Gal^+S^r recombinants.

The results of this study show that *different prophages occupy different positions on the bacterial chromosome.* The various *noninducible prophages* studied are apparently located on the portion of the chromosome of the Hfr H bacteria carrying the characters which are not transmitted with high frequency to recombinants (see Chapter X, page 174). The inducible prophages studied all appear to be located on the distal portion of the TL-Gal segment and beyond the Gal_b character. For each prophage, there is a corresponding specific locus, as evidenced, for example, by experiments in which a nonlysogenic Hfr H strain is crossed with an F^- strain doubly lysogenic for λ and 434 phages. In such crosses the $(ly)^-$ character which corresponds to each of these prophages is transmitted to $T^+L^+S^r$ and Gal^+S^r recombinants with its own specific frequency (Jacob and Wollman, 1957a, 1958a).

These results are confirmed by transduction experiments (Jacob, 1955). The same particle of transducing phage can, indeed, transmit simultaneously the character Gal_b^+ and the + or — determinants of lysogeny (82), (λ), or (434), to recipient bacteria which have the opposite characters. In the Gal_b^+ bacteria obtained by transduction of Gal_b^- bacteria, the genetic determinants corresponding to each of the prophages appear with frequencies that increase with the proximity of these determinants to the Gal_b character. From the results of transduction experiments, as well as from the results of crosses, it is possible therefore to determine the order and the relative distances of the specific loci of the three inducible prophages, 82, λ, and 434, in relation to the Gal_b character. The other inducible prophages are not closely enough linked to this locus to be accurately localized. A more precise study of their localization became possible only with the availability of additional selective nutritional markers, the determinants of which are situated beyond Gal_b on the TL-Gal segment. As will be seen in Chapter IX, the determinants that control the biosynthesis of tryptophan (Tr) and of histidine (H) meet these requirements. The inducible prophages lie in the Tr-H region.

* * *

The findings reported in this chapter show that lysogeny, a hereditary property of certain bacteria, is controlled by a chromosomal factor, this factor being indeed the prophage itself. When first envisaged, this conclusion appeared somewhat surprising, since it would seem a priori that the noninfective structure which, in lysogenic bacteria, carries the genetic information of a virus, the bacteriophage, should be cytoplasmic rather than chromosomal. Although this problem was never seriously considered before 1950, that is until the investigations of Lwoff, the hypothesis of a cytoplasmic determination of lysogeny had been accepted implicitly (see J. Lederberg *et al.*, 1951).

Since the lysogenic character can be acquired by infection, it follows that the genetic material of the infecting bacteriophage, i.e., the deoxyribonucleic acid of this phage (or a replica of this DNA), settles on the chromosome of the bacterium and thenceforth is replicated together with the genetic material of the cell itself. The linkage which is formed between the prophage and the bacterial chromosome appears to be rather an addition of the phage genome to the bacterial chromosome than a substitution of a homologous portion of this chromosome. This question will be further discussed in Chapter XV. In contrast to other genetic bacterial characters, the symbols $(\mathrm{ly})^+$ and $(\mathrm{ly})^-$ do not represent therefore two alternative conditions of the same chromosomal region but rather the presence or absence, at a specific chromosomal locus, of an additional genetic structure.

Since, for every temperate bacteriophage, there is a specific locus on the chromosome of the host bacterium where the genetic material of the phage can become attached, the lysogenic character is controlled by two factors, the genetic material of the phage and the complementary bacterial site. It is known that phage mutations may modify and even abolish the capacity of a given bacteriophage to lysogenize. It may be also assumed that bacterial mutations might affect the specific locus of attachment of a given prophage. It is not known whether bacteria that would have thus become refractory to lysogenization would still be capable of reproducing the infective bacteriophage. If this were the case, the same bacteriophage would react like a temperate phage toward the original bacterial strain and like a virulent bacteriophage toward the mutated strain.

CHAPTER VII

Zygotic Induction and Its Genetic Effects

In reciprocal crosses between nonlysogenic bacteria and bacteria which are lysogenic for a bacteriophage such as λ, the outcome depends on whether the prophage is carried by the donor or by the recipient bacteria. When the lysogenic bacteria are the F^- recipient, the lysogenic character segregates among the recombinants and can be located accurately on the bacterial chromosome. On the contrary, when the lysogenic bacteria are the Hfr H donor cells, the results of the cross are profoundly modified and the lysogenic character is not transmitted to the recombinants formed. In this case, the prophage λ is induced as a consequence of conjugation, and its development within the recipient bacteria results in their destruction. This phenomenon has been called *induction by conjugation* or *zygotic induction* (Jacob and Wollman, 1954a, 1956b).

I. ZYGOTIC INDUCTION OF PROPHAGE λ

A. Demonstration of Zygotic Induction

It was in crosses between lysogenic Hfr H bacteria and nonlysogenic F^- bacteria that zygotic induction of prophage λ was demonstrated.*

Cultures of Hfr $H(\lambda)^+S^s$ cells, carefully washed in order to eliminate free phage particles, and of F^- $P678(\lambda)^-S^r\lambda^r$ are mixed under the usual conditions of crosses (2.10^7 Hfr and 4.10^8 F^- per milliliter). The mixture is aerated in a water-bath at 37°C and samples, taken at various time intervals, are diluted and plated with indicator bacteria 112 S^r, sensitive to phage λ, on CA medium. Platings are made in duplicate in the presence and absence of streptomycin (150 μg/ml). A control tube containing only Hfr $H(\lambda)^+S^s$ bacteria is treated in the same way. The results of this experiment are given in Table X.

On the plates containing streptomycin (Sm), the number of plaques formed† by the samples taken from the Hfr $H(\lambda)^+S^s \times F^-(\lambda)^-S^r\lambda^r$ mix-

* The explanation of terms and techniques concerning the study of bacteriophage can be found in the previous chapter in the paragraph on Methods Used in Bacterial Crosses Involving Lysogenic Strains, p. 79.

† At zero time this number is about 1/1000 of the number of Hfr bacteria.

TABLE X

ZYGOTIC INDUCTION IN CROSSES BETWEEN LYSOGENIC Hfr H AND NONLYSOGENIC F− BACTERIA[a]

Plating at $t=$ (minutes)	Number of λ plaques per 100 initial Hfr						
	Control Hfr(λ)+S^s		Cross Hfr(λ)+S^s × F−(λ)−$S^r\lambda^r$		Control Hfr(λ)+S^r	Cross Hfr(λ)+S^r × F−(λ)−$S^s\lambda^r$	
	Without Sm	With Sm	Without Sm	With Sm	with or without Sm	Without Sm	With Sm
0	1.8	0.17	2	0.09	2.7	3	2.9
20	3.2	0.51	18	17.5	4.6	19	4.9
40	5.7	0.68	42	37	5.3	47	6.3
60	7.8	1.08	55	52	7.1	58	7.8

[a] Both crosses are carried under the usual conditions (see text page 93). At various time intervals, samples are taken, diluted and plated with indicator bacteria 112 S^r on agar with or without streptomycin. The controls which consist of Hfr cells alone are treated in the same way as the crosses.

ture increases steadily with time, reaching after 1 hour about 50 per cent of the initial number of Hfr cells. On the contrary, the number of plaques formed by samples taken from the control tube after 60 minutes represents only about 1 per cent of the initial number of Hfr cells. In the latter case, the plaques are small and irregular, like those formed by free phages, whereas the larger and more regular plaques arising from the samples of the cross are characteristic of those formed by bacterial infective centers.

On the plates without streptomycin, the results are essentially similar, except for the fact that, at zero time, the plates exhibit a background of small plaques of varying size due to the residual growth of Hfr cells. For the samples taken from the control, the number of these small plaques increases with time to reach, at around 60 minutes, about 10 per cent of the initial number of Hfr bacteria. For the samples taken from the mixture, on the contrary, these plaques are replaced gradually by regular and well formed plaques which, at 60 minutes, reach about 50 per cent of the number of initial Hfr cells.

Thus, when Hfr $H(\lambda)^+$ and $F^-(\lambda)^-$ bacteria are mixed, the development of the prophage of about half the Hfr $H(\lambda)^+$ cells is induced; and this development, in all probability, occurs in the nonlysogenic recipient bacteria. This is confirmed by the following experiment.

The two crosses, Hfr $H(\lambda)^+S^s \times F^-(\lambda)^-S^r\lambda^r$ and Hfr $H(\lambda)^+S^r \times F^-(\lambda)^-S^s\lambda^r$ are carried out, and samples are plated with indicator bacteria 112 S^r in the presence and in the absence of streptomycin (Table X). On the plates without streptomycin, the results are the same in both crosses: the number of infective centers reaches, after about 1 hour, half of the initial number of Hfr bacteria. On the plates containing streptomycin, however, only the infective centers formed in the Hfr $H(\lambda)^+S^s \times F^-(\lambda)^-S^r$ cross appear. The plaques formed by samples taken from the $Hfr(\lambda)^+S^r \times F^-(\lambda)^-S^s$ cross are identical in aspect and in number to the plaques formed by a control culture of $Hfr(\lambda)$ bacteria.*

This experiment demonstrates that the *development of the prophage of the Hfr $H(\lambda)^+$ bacteria takes place, not in the Hfr cells, but in the $F^-(\lambda)^-\lambda^r$ recipient bacteria.* Inactivation of the latter by streptomycin eliminates the infective centers, whereas inactivation of the $Hfr(\lambda)^+S^s$ bacteria has no effect.

---

* When plated on indicator bacteria, Hfr $H(\lambda)+$ bacteria form more plaques than $F+(\lambda)+$ or $F-(\lambda)+$ bacteria. This difference is due to zygotic induction, the Hfr $H(\lambda)+$ cells conjugating, on the agar plate, with the bacteria of the indicator strain.

In an Hfr(λ)$^+$S^s $\times$ F$^-$(λ)$^-$S$^r\lambda^r$ cross, it is possible to follow the evolution of the number of infective centers produced by the F$^-$(λ)$^-$S$^r\lambda^r$ recipient bacteria as a function of time. The results of such an experiment are shown in Fig. 13.

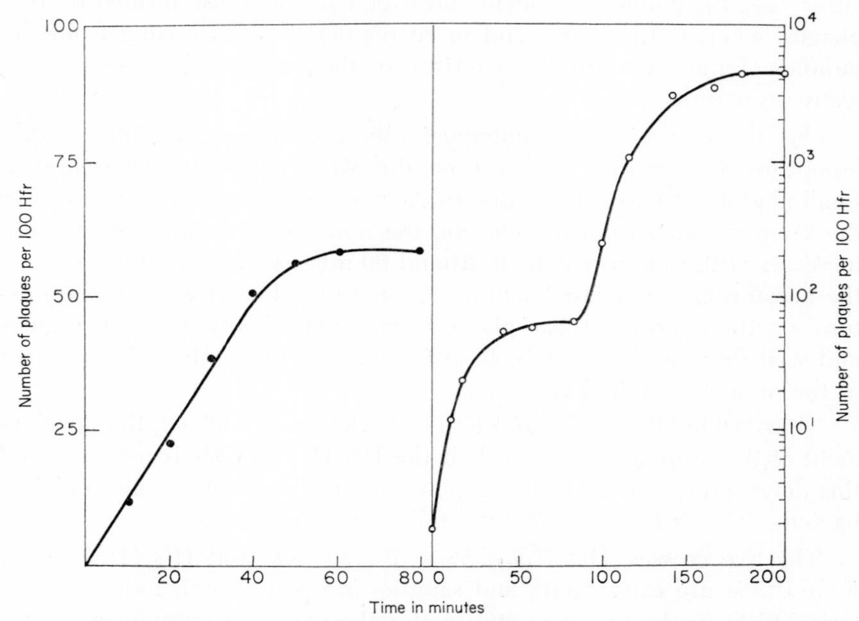

FIG. 13. Kinetics of zygotic induction of prophage λ. At time 0, suspensions of Hfr H(λ)$^+$S^s bacteria (2.10^7/ml) and F$-$ P678(λ)$^-$S^r (4.10^8/ml) are mixed. The mixture (tube 1) is shaken in a water bath at 37°C. At various time intervals, samples are taken, diluted, and plated with indicator bacteria 112 S^r onto agar medium, with or without streptomycin. At time 70 minutes after mixing, the initial tube is diluted 100 times in broth and the dilution (tube 2) is shaken at 37°C. Samples are taken at various time intervals in order to follow the production of phages λ due to zygotic induction. Abscissa: time, in minutes, after the initial mixing. Ordinate: the number of infective centers expressed in per cent of the initial number of Hfr cells; left: normal scale; right: logarithmic scale.

As can be seen, the number of infective centers increases until about the 40th minute, to reach a plateau corresponding to about 50 per cent of the initial number of Hfr bacteria. After the 80th minute, the number of infective centers increases again to reach, after 150 minutes or so, a second plateau, about 80 times higher than the first. During the first 40 minutes, a 1000 times dilution of the mating mixture in streptomycin-containing broth prevents until about the 80th minute further increase of the number of infective centers. Once the first plateau has been reached, however, dilution is without effect on the subsequent rise and the second plateau is reached under the same conditions as in a "one-step growth" experiment.

The meaning of this experiment is clear: the first part of the curve is an expression of the kinetics of conjugation; the first plateau represents the latent period, which extends from the time at which the development of the prophage is initiated to the time of lysis; the second ascending portion of the curve corresponds to the lysis of the F^- bacteria and the resulting liberation of infective particles (average burst size 80).

Another type of experiment brings further support to the conclusion that the development and maturation of the bacteriophage λ take place within the $F^-(\lambda)^-\lambda^r$ recipient bacteria and not in the $Hfr(\lambda)^+$ donor bacteria. It is known that the phage λ released by bacteria of the strain *E.coli* C forms about one-thousandth the number of plaques on *E.coli* K12 S as it does on *E.coli* C, whereas the phage λ released by K12 cells forms as many plaques on K12 as on C (Weiglé and Bertani, 1953). It is also known that *E.coli* C is F^-, and may be crossed with K12 F^+ (Lieb, Weiglé, and Kellenberger, 1955) or K12 Hfr. In the experiment reported in Table XI, $Hfr(\lambda)^+S^s$ bacteria were crossed with F^- $K12(\lambda)^-S^r\lambda^r$ bacteria in one case, and with F^- $C(\lambda)^-S^r\lambda^r$ bacteria in the other. The infective centers formed at 20 and 40 minutes and the phages released by the lysis of these infective centers were determined by plating on *E.coli* C and *E.coli* K12 respectively.

TABLE XI
HOST-INDUCED MODIFICATION OF THE PHAGES λ RELEASED IN A CROSS BETWEEN LYSOGENIC K12 Hfr H AND NONLYSOGENIC CF− BACTERIA[a]

Cross	Dilution at $t =$ minutes	Number of plaques formed per 100 initial Hfr: Plating at 40 minutes on K12	C	Plating at 200 minutes on K12	C
$Hfr\ H(\lambda)^+S^s \times F^-K12(\lambda)^-S^r\lambda^r$	20	21	23	1320	1260
	40	53	56	3070	3210
$Hfr\ H(\lambda)^+S^s \times F^-C(\lambda)^-S^r\lambda^r$	20	2.7	21	9.3	1310
	40	5.3	55	17.2	3720

[a] At time 0, $Hfr\ H(\lambda)^+S^s$ bacteria are mixed, on the one hand with $F^-K12(\lambda)^-S^r\lambda^r$, and on the other with $F^-C(\lambda)^-S^r\lambda^r$ bacteria. At various time intervals, the suspensions are diluted and samples are plated on two plates of streptomycin-agar: one with K12 S^r indicator bacteria, the other with C S^r indicator bacteria. Platings at 40 minutes indicate the number of bacterial infective centers due to zygotic induction. Platings at 200 minutes give the number of infective centers corresponding to the phages released by lysis of the F^- recipient bacteria.

In the second cross [Hfr(λ)$^{+}$S^{s} $\times$ C(λ)$^{-}$S^{r}], only one-tenth of the infective centers formed during conjugation can be detected by plating on *E.coli* K12. After lysis of these infective centers, less than one out of 200 phage particles released is capable of forming a plaque on K12. The great majority of these particles must then have multiplied in the F^{-}C recipient bacteria.

Thus, in a cross between lysogenic Hfr bacteria and nonlysogenic F^{-} bacteria, the prophage λ of more than half of the Hfr cells develops inside the F^{-} cells which undergo lysis and produce phage. The expression, *frequency of zygotic induction* (FZI), will be used to designate the number of infective centers formed by the recipient bacteria per each 100 initial cells from the minority parental type, i.e., generally speaking, per 100 initial Hfr cells.

Although the genetic effects of zygotic induction are comparable in Hfr H(λ)$^{+}$ $\times$ F^{-}(λ)$^{-}$ and F^{+}(λ)$^{+}$ $\times$ F^{-}(λ)$^{-}$ crosses, the phenomenon is less easily demonstrated in the latter case because of its rarity. It should be explicitly pointed out that the observed frequency of zygotic induction is correlated in each case with the frequency of recombinants.

Crosses between Hfr H(λ)$^{+}$ and F^{-}(λ)$^{-}$ bacteria are particularly suitable for the study of bacterial conjugation. The advantages of such crosses reside in the high frequency of zygotic induction, in the simplicity and accuracy of the methods of counting infective centers, and finally in the fact that an inducible prophage such as λ is a genetic determinant of donor bacteria the expression of which takes place in the zygote.

It is possible, for instance, to investigate by this method whether more than one Hfr bacterium may conjugate with the same F^{-} cell when an excess of Hfr H cells is mixed with F^{-} cells. Nonlysogenic F^{-} bacteria are added to a mixture of equal proportions of two strains of Hfr H bacteria, each lysogenic for a different mutant of phage λ. Single burst analysis of the individual zygotes reveals that a zygote produces either one or the other parental type of phage. There is, consequently, good reason to believe that, in most instances, only a single Hfr bacterium can conjugate effectively with one F^{-} bacterium (Jacob and Wollman, 1956b). In crosses carried out under the usual conditions, the participation of several Hfr cells in the formation of the same zygote is, in any case, excluded since the F^{-} recipient type is present in excess.

B. The Mechanism of Zygotic Induction

Zygotic induction is a particularly striking illustration of Hayes' concept of unidirectional transfer of genetic material during conjugation. In Hfr H(λ)$^{-}$ $\times$ F^{-}(λ)$^{+}$ crosses, zygotic induction does not take place

(Table XII). Nor does it occur in Hfr H(λ)$^+$ × F$^-$(λ)$^+$ crosses, as may be shown by the use of a defective lysogenic F$^-$ strain (Table XII). When the recipient bacteria carry a homologous prophage, the prophage of the Hfr donor bacteria is therefore not induced by conjugation. But, if the same recipient bacteria F$^-$(λd_1)$^+$ have been exposed to ultraviolet light before the cross, the development of the prophage transferred from the donor into the recipient by conjugation takes place (Table XII).

TABLE XII

ABSENCE OF ZYGOTIC INDUCTION IN CROSSES INVOLVING LYSOGENIC F− BACTERIA[a]

	Number of plaques per 100 bacteria of the lysogenic minority type. Dilution and plating at $t =$	
	20 minutes	40 minutes
Control Hfr(λ)+	0.27	0.41
Control F−(λ)+	1.2	2.6
Control F−(λd_1)+	< 0.01	< 0.01
Cross Hfr(λ)+ × F−(λ)−	24.8	52.1
Cross Hfr(λ)− × F−(λ)+	1.4	3.3
Cross Hfr(λ)+ × F−(λd_1)+	0.36	0.8
Cross Hfr(λ)+ × F−(λd_1)+ induced	9.1	19.2

[a] Crosses are carried out under usual conditions. In all cases the minority parent is the normal lysogenic strain (proportion 1/20):Hfr(λ)+ in crosses 1, 3, and 4, F−(λ)+ in cross 2. Platings are made on streptomycin agar with indicator bacteria 112 S^r; λ*d* refers to a defective prophage (see text, page 76).

There is good reason to believe that the genetic material of the phage carried by the donor cells is transferred into the recipient cells in the form of a prophage, located at its specific chromosomal site. In a cross between bacteria lysogenic for homologous but mutant prophages, the prophage of the donor cells is transmitted to the genetic recombinants with the same frequency as is the determinant (λ)$^-$ in an Hfr H(λ)$^-$ × F$^-$(λ)$^+$ cross, and with the same degree of linkage with the character Gal$_b$. It can also be shown that, in the vegetative state, the genetic material of a phage is not transferred from the Hfr H cells to the F$^-$ cells during conjugation. When sensitive Hfr bacteria, infected with the mutant λC, or when previously induced lysogenic Hfr bacteria are crossed with nonlysogenic F$^-$(λ)$^-$ cells, the phage material contained in the Hfr H cells is not transferred to the recipient F$^-$ bacteria. Moreover, when lysogenic Hfr H bacteria are first superinfected with a virulent mutant of the homologous phage λ and then crossed with F$^-$(λ)$^-$ cells, the prophage from the Hfr H(λ)$^+$ is transferred into the F$^-$ recipient bacteria and induced by conjugation, whereas the phage of the superinfecting type is not transferred (Jacob and Wollman, 1954a, 1956b).

The mere act of transfer of an inducible prophage such as λ during conjugation is not alone sufficient to initiate its development; as already seen, zygotic induction does not take place when the recipient bacteria are lysogenic for a homologous phage. The transfer of prophage λ may be followed by zygotic induction only when the recipient bacteria are not immune (nonlysogenic bacteria or induced lysogenic bacteria).

As for the mechanism of induction of the prophage in the recipient cell two hypotheses could be at first envisaged. Zygotic induction could be a consequence of pairing (or of the processes following it) between a chromosome (or a chromosomal segment) carrying a prophage and a chromosome carrying none. Since induction does not take place when it is the chromosome of the recipient cell that carries the prophage, additional assumptions must be made to account for the differences observed in reciprocal crosses. A more plausible hypothesis assumes that induction is the consequence of the penetration of the chromosomal segment of the donor bacterium carrying the prophage into a nonimmune cell. According to this hypothesis, the immunity of lysogenic bacteria would thus have a "cytoplasmic" expression (Jacob and Wollman, 1956b). As will be seen in Chapter XV, the available evidence favors this hypothesis.

In a cross between Hfr $H(\lambda)^+$ and $F^-(\lambda)^-$ cells, the frequency of zygotic induction is greater than 50 per cent. Assuming that all of the Hfr bacteria actually take part in conjugation, this means *that more than half the number of zygotes which could be formed are actually destroyed.* As mentioned already, and we shall come back to this point, the destruction of these zygotes although it does modify the results of the cross, does not prevent, however, the formation of some recombinants. Practically none of the recombinants formed in the cross are lysogenic. When the products of conjugation are exposed to inducing doses of ultraviolet light 70 minutes after mating (see Fig. 13), there is no increase in the number of infective centers formed by the recipient bacteria. There is good reason to believe, therefore, that practically any prophage λ, transferred from a lysogenic Hfr H cell to a nonlysogenic cell, is immediately induced under the conditions of crosses. Assuming, as it seems likely, that in most cases this induction results in the production of vegetative phage, i.e., that it manifests itself by the formation of a plaque, one is led to the conclusion that *the frequency of zygotic induction of prophage λ constitutes a measure of the frequency of its actual transfer from the Hfr H donor bacteria to the F^- recipient bacteria* (Jacob and Wollman, 1956b).

II. RELATIONS BETWEEN THE FREQUENCY OF ZYGOTIC INDUCTION AND THE GENETIC LOCATION OF THE PROPHAGES

Since the study of zygotic induction seemed to offer the possibility of measuring the frequency of transfer of an inducible prophage during conjugation, it was of obvious interest to extend these investigations to prophages other than λ. Indeed, it was for this purpose that a series of temperate phages active on *E.coli* K12 was isolated. Their characters and genetic locations have been described in the preceding chapter. We shall now examine the behavior of these different prophages in crosses between lysogenic Hfr H bacteria and nonlysogenic F− cells.

A series of Hfr H strains, each of them lysogenic for one of the temperate phages chosen, was prepared. Each of these lysogenic Hfr H strains was crossed, under identical conditions, with the same F− strain, P678, and the number of infective centers formed after 1 hour of contact was determined by plating on indicator bacteria. The results of these experiments are reported in Table XIII (Jacob and Wollman, 1956b).

TABLE XIII
INVESTIGATION OF ZYGOTIC INDUCTION IN CROSSES BETWEEN DIFFERENT LYSOGENIC Hfr H STRAINS AND NONLYSOGENIC F− P678 Sr BACTERIA[a]

Inducible prophages		Noninducible prophages	
Prophage	Number of plaques per 100 initial Hfr	Prophage	Number of plaques per 100 initial Hfr
82	65	18	<1
λ	58	370	<1
434	48	62	<1
381	25	363	<1
21	12	W	<1
424	9	299	<1
466	6	186	<1

[a] The various crosses between lysogenic Hfr H and nonlysogenic F− bacteria are carried out under usual conditions. After aeration at 37°C for 60 minutes, the suspensions are diluted and samples plated on streptomycin-agar with indicator bacteria 112 S^r.

As may be seen, only the *prophages which are inducible* by ultraviolet light are also induced during conjugation. The frequency with which these prophages are induced during conjugation varies and is characteristic of each prophage. Only with prophages 82 and 381 was the frequency of induction somewhat variable. In all likelihood, this variability is related to the high lysogenizing power of the corresponding phages.

The most important fact revealed by these experiments is that *the rate of zygotic induction of the inducible prophages* depends on their genetic location. All the inducible prophages considered in this study are located on the TL-Gal segment and beyond Gal_b. The closer to Gal_b a given prophage is located, the higher is the frequency of zygotic induction. This correlation may be exemplified by the three prophages λ, 434, and 21, all fully inducible by ultraviolet light and of low lysogenizing power under our experimental conditions. These three prophages can be arranged in the same order with respect to their frequency of zygotic induction (58, 48, and 12 per cent respectively) and with respect to their relative distance from the character Gal_b (82, 68, and 10 per cent respectively) as determined in $Hfr(ly)^- \times F^-(ly)^+$ crosses (see page 89).

The frequency of zygotic induction of a given prophage is not modified by the presence of a nonhomologous prophage in the recipient bacteria. This is shown by the results of experiments in which $Hfr(\lambda)^+$ bacteria are crossed with $F^-(82)^+$ or $F^-(434)^+$ bacteria (Table XIV). The

TABLE XIV

ZYGOTIC INDUCTION IN CROSSES BETWEEN LYSOGENIC Hfr H AND LYSOGENIC F− P678 Sr BACTERIA CARRYING DIFFERENT TYPES OF INDUCIBLE PROPHAGES[a]

Crosses	Number of plaques of Hfr type per 100 initial Hfr
$Hfr(\lambda)^+ \times F^-$ nonlysogenic	52
$Hfr(\lambda)^+ \times F^-(\lambda d_1)^+$	2
$Hfr(\lambda)^+ \times F^-(82)^+$	49
$Hfr(\lambda)^+ \times F^-(434)^+$	54
$Hfr(434)^+ \times F^-$ nonlysogenic	46
$Hfr(434)^+ \times F^-(\lambda d_1)^+$	47
$Hfr(434)^+ \times F^-(82)^+$	43

[a] Crosses are carried out under usual conditions (one Hfr for twenty F−). After 60 minutes of mating, samples are taken, diluted, and plated on streptomycin agar, with indicator bacteria sensitive to the phage produced by the Hfr cells, but resistant to the phage produced by the F− cells.

immunity of F^- bacteria lysogenic for a given phage exhibits, therefore, the same specificity whether the genetic material of this phage is introduced by conjugation or by infection. On the other hand, when Hfr H bacteria which are lysogenic for two different inducible phages, both capable of multiplying simultaneously within the same bacterium (λ and 21 for instance), are mixed with nonlysogenic F^- bacteria, the zygotic induction of each of the two prophages is found to be independent of the presence of the other prophage. Not only is the induction of a given prophage unmodified by the presence of another prophage, but each prophage is, furthermore, induced at its own characteristic rate.

The frequency with which a given prophage is zygotically induced seems to depend, therefore, on its position on the genetic linkage group transmitted with high frequency by the Hfr H bacteria. With other Hfr mutants which do not transmit with high frequency the Gal_b character (see Chapter X), zygotic induction of the prophages linked to this character is not observed (Jacob and Wollman, 1956c).

The prophages which are *not inducible* by ultraviolet light are, of course, not induced during the Hfr $H(ly)^+ \times F^-(ly)^-$ crosses, since they are not located on the linkage group transmitted with high frequency by Hfr H bacteria (Table XIII). In crosses involving other types of Hfr mutants which are capable of transmitting with high frequency such characters as maltose (Mal) or xylose (Xyl) to which some of these prophages are linked (see Chapter X), no zygotic induction of these prophages is observed. A noninducible prophage segregates among the recombinants of an $Hfr(ly)^+ \times F^-(ly)^-$ cross in the same manner as the corresponding $(ly)^-$ character segregates in the reciprocal cross, $Hfr(ly)^- \times F^-(ly)^+$. Thus, only prophages inducible by such agents as ultraviolet light can be induced also when transferred from lysogenic donor bacteria to nonlysogenic recipient bacteria (Jacob and Wollman, 1956b, 1958c).

III. THE GENETIC EFFECTS OF ZYGOTIC INDUCTION

In crosses where zygotic induction occurs, a fraction of the zygotes formed is destroyed. We shall now consider the consequences, quantitative as well as qualitative, of this phenomenon on the formation of genetic recombinants. The distortions brought about by zygotic induction of the prophage λ in the results of crosses between Hfr H and F^- bacteria will first be examined; we shall then compare them with the distortions caused by zygotic induction of other inducible prophages.

A. The Genetic Effects of Zygotic Induction of Prophage λ

In a cross between Hfr $H(\lambda)^+S^s$ and F^- $P678(\lambda)^-S^r$ bacteria, it is possible to evaluate both the number of infective centers due to zygotic induction and the number of $T^+L^+S^r$ and Gal^+S^r recombinants formed. The cross is carried out under the usual conditions already described, and the results are compared with those of a control cross, Hfr $H(\lambda)^+S^s \times P678(\lambda)^+S^r$. Only the samples taken after 60 minutes of contact, the time after which the number of infective centers and the number of recombinants formed show no further variation will be considered. The results of a cross of this type have already been mentioned (Chapter VI).

1. *Frequencies of recombinants.* Although in such a cross (Table XV), the frequency of zygotic induction reaches 57 per cent, the destruction of a number of zygotes corresponding to more than half the Hfr cells involved does not prevent the formation of some recombinants. The frequencies with which recombinants are formed differ, however, from those observed in the control cross. An important fact is that the numbers of $T^+L^+S^r$ and of Gal^+S^r recombinants are not reduced in the same

TABLE XV

EFFECTS OF ZYGOTIC INDUCTION OF PROPHAGE λ ON THE FREQUENCIES OF RECOMBINANTS OBSERVED IN CROSSES BETWEEN LYSOGENIC Hfr H AND NONLYSOGENIC F− BACTERIA

Crosses	Frequency of recombinants		Ratio $T^+L^+S^r$ / Gal^+S^r	Frequency of zygotic induction
	$T^+L^+S^r$	Gal^+S^r		
Hfr(λ)+ × P678(λ)+	16.8	3.9	4.3	—
Hfr(λ)+ × P678(λ)−	6.8	0.13	52	57
Hfr(λ)+ × Y10(λ)+	38.9	—	—	—
Hfr(λ)+ × C600(λ)−	18	—	—	54.5

proportion. Whereas the frequency of the $T^+L^+S^r$ recombinants decreases from 17 per cent in the control cross to 7 per cent in the test cross (reduction by a factor of 2.4), the frequency of the Gal^+S^r recombinants decreases from 4 to 0.13 per cent (reduction by a factor of 30). The ratio $T^+L^+S^r/Gal^+S^r$, which was 4.3 in the control cross, accordingly increases to 52.

Zygotic induction, therefore, does not affect equally the formation of the various types of recombinants. The destruction of half of all the possible zygotes decreases by half the number of the $T^+L^+S^r$ recombinants, but decreases far more the proportion of the Gal^+S^r recombinants. Since prophage λ is closely linked to the character Gal_b, it appears that the closer a given character is to the specific site of a prophage, the more zygotic induction affects the transmission of that character to a recombinant (E. L. Wollman and Jacob, 1954a, 1957).

In every cross which results in the zygotic induction of the prophage λ, the genetic effects manifest themselves in the same way (Table XV). As already discussed in Chapter V (see Table VI), the frequency of $T^+L^+S^r$ recombinants is twice as high in an Hfr(λ)$^+$ × Y10(λ)$^+$ cross as in an Hfr(λ)$^+$ × P678(λ)$^+$ cross. In the corresponding crosses Hfr(λ)$^+$ × C600(λ)$^-$ and Hfr(λ)$^+$ × P678(λ)$^-$ zygotic induction, which destroys more than 50 per cent of the possible zygotes, produces a quantitative comparable reduction in the number of the $T^+L^+S^r$ recombinants formed (Table XV).

The kinetics of formation of recombinants is also profoundly affected by zygotic induction. In the crosses, $Hfr(\lambda)^+ \times F^-(\lambda)^+$ and $Hfr(\lambda)^- \times F^-(\lambda)^-$ (see Fig. 8), the number of $T^+L^+S^r$ and Gal^+S^r recombinants increases regularly as a function of time to reach a plateau at about the 50th minute. In contrast, in an $Hfr(\lambda)^+ \times F^-(\lambda)^-$ cross, whereas the number of infective centers increases regularly (see Fig. 13), the increase in the number of the $T^+L^+S^r$ recombinants is very erratic. This also appears to be true of the Gal^+S^r recombinants, although their numbers are too few to permit an accurate kinetic analysis. The number of recombinants increases up to the 15th to 20th minute, then increases only erratically, remains constant, or even decreases. In all cases, however, a plateau is reached before the 60th minute. The meaning of these results will be discussed later (see Chapter IX).

2. *Genetic analysis of recombinants.* The distortions which zygotic induction introduces into the results of a cross are also evidenced by genetic analysis of the recombinants. The frequencies with which the various proximal characters from the Hfr H parental type appear among the $T^+L^+S^r$ recombinants are compared in Table XVI with the results in a control cross in which no zygotic induction takes place. It may be seen that the farther the unselected characters studied are located from the selector characters, T^+L^+, the lower the frequency of their transmission to the $T^+L^+S^r$ recombinants. In contrast, the genetic constitution of the rare Gal^+S^r recombinants differs only slightly from that of the Gal^+S^r recombinants formed in a control cross. The lysogenic character from the parental Hfr is practically never transmitted to recombinants. The number of cases in which the prophage λ can be found in a recombinant is of the same order of magnitude as that which can be expected from lysogenization following infection of sensitive cells with phage λ.

An interesting special case is that of crosses between defective lysogenic Hfr H bacteria and nonlysogenic F^- bacteria. A culture of defective Hfr H(λd) bacteria undergoes complete lysis when exposed to a small dose of ultraviolet light, but releases very few infective λ particles. In an Hfr $H(\lambda d)^+ \times F^-(\lambda)^-$ cross, no infective centers are formed. Genetic analysis of the recombinants reveals, nevertheless, that zygotic induction occurs exactly as in a cross between normal lysogenic Hfr H cells and nonlysogenic F^- cells (Table XVI). In this case where the transfer of the defective prophage results in the destruction of the zygote without the production of infectious phage particles, zygotic induction is manifested only by its genetic consequences.

TABLE XVI

EFFECTS OF ZYGOTIC INDUCTION ON THE GENETIC CONSTITUTION OF THE RECOMBINANTS FORMED IN VARIOUS CROSSES BETWEEN LYSOGENIC Hfr H AND NONLYSOGENIC F− BACTERIA

Crosses	Ratio $\frac{T+L+S^r}{Gal+S^r}$	Recombinants	Genetic constitution					
			T+L+	Az^s	T_1^s	Lac+	Gal_b+	(ly)+
Hfr(λ)+ × P678(λ)+	4.2	$T+L+S^r$	100	90	70	47	29	—
		$Gal+S^r$	80	78	78	82	100	—
Hfr(λ)+ × P678(λ)−	54	$T+L+S^r$	100	86	60	21	2.5	< 0.1
		$Gal+S^r$	82	79	78	74	100	< 1
Hfr(λ*d*)+ × P678(λ)−	52	$T+L+S^r$	100	84	59	24	2.2	< 0.1
Hfr(82)+ × P678(82)−	62	$T+L+S^r$	100	84	58	18	2.1	< 1
Hfr(434)+ × P678(434)−	43	$T+L+S^r$	100	90	62	26	3.2	< 1
Hfr(21)+ × P678(21)−	10	$T+L+S^r$	100	89	65	33	13.5	< 1
Hfr(424)+ × P678(424)−	6.5	$T+L+S^r$	100	88	68	36	20	< 1
Hfr(466)+ × P678(466)−	5.3	$T+L+S^r$	100	90	73	42	27	< 1

Accordingly, zygotic induction has a very uneven effect upon the transmission of genetic characters from donor Hfr cells to recombinants. The more closely a given character is linked to prophage λ, the lower is the frequency of its transmission to recombinants. In comparison with a control cross, the reduction of frequency of transmission is about 2.4-fold for the characters TL, 30-fold for Gal_b and 2400-fold for lysogeny λ.

The effects of zygotic induction on the frequency of the recombinants formed as well as on their genetic constitution further emphasize the polarity of the TL-Gal segment which had been already evident from analysis of crosses in which zygotic induction does not take place. The development of prophage λ, which destroys a significant proportion of the zygotes, has a selective action; the surviving zygotes appear to be those which have not received the prophage λ, nor, consequently, the genetic characters such as Gal_b, to which this prophage is linked (E. L. Wollman and Jacob, 1954a, 1957). The way in which these results are best interpreted will be discussed later.

B. The Genetic Effects of Zygotic Induction of Various Prophages

The frequencies of zygotic induction observed in crosses between lysogenic Hfr H and nonlysogenic F^- bacteria vary according to the type of prophage involved. It is therefore to be expected that the genetic effects of zygotic induction will vary also from one cross to another.

The results of a series of crosses between Hfr H bacteria lysogenic for various inducible temperate phages and the same nonlysogenic F^- bacterium, P678, are represented in Table XVI. In each case, the frequency of zygotic induction was measured as well as the number of $T^+L^+S^r$ and Gal^+S^r recombinants formed. The genetic constitution of the recombinants was also determined. In each cross, the ratio of the number of $T^+L^+S^r$ recombinants to the number of Gal^+S^r recombinants can be used as a measure of the effect of zygotic induction on the formation of recombinants. This ratio, which is close to 4 in a control cross where zygotic induction does not take place, reaches 50 in Hfr $H(\lambda)^+ \times F^-(\lambda)^-$ crosses. In the various Hfr $H(ly)^+ \times F^-(ly)^-$ crosses, it can be seen that the higher the frequency of zygotic induction, the greater the $T^+L^+S^r/Gal^+S^r$ ratio. The various inducible prophages can thus be arranged in the same order whatever the criterion chosen, be it the frequency of zygotic induction, the ratio $T^+L^+S^r/Gal^+S^r$ in an Hfr $H(ly)^+ \times$ P678$(ly)^-$ cross, or the linkage of Gal_b to the prophage in an Hfr $H(ly)^- \times$ P678$(ly)^+$ cross.

Analysis of the $T^+L^+S^r$ recombinants, in comparison with the same recombinants formed in a control cross, shows that the modification of their genetic constitution increases in direct proportion to the closeness of the prophage carried by the Hfr H cells to the Gal_b character (Table XVI). The genetic constitution of the Gal^+S^r recombinants, on the other hand, does not differ from that found in a control cross where there is no zygotic induction. Lastly, the lysogenic character of the parental Hfr H is practically never transmitted to the recombinants (Jacob and Wollman, 1957a, 1958b).

Consequently, the frequency of zygotic induction, the effect of this zygotic induction on the formation of recombinants, and the frequency with which the distal characters of the TL-Gal segment are found among the $T^+L^+S^r$ recombinants, all depend alike on the position that an inducible prophage occupies on the chromosome of the donor bacteria (see Chapter IX).

* * *

Zygotic induction and its genetic effects provide a particularly clear illustration of the two polarities which characterize the crosses between Hfr and F^- bacteria: sexual polarity (unidirectional transfer of genetic material) and genetic polarity (uneven transmission to recombinants of the genetic characters from the donor bacteria). An inducible prophage, carried by Hfr donor bacteria, is a genetic character of these cells which, during conjugation, is expressed as early as the zygotic stage. Zygotic induction provides, therefore, a means of distinguishing two main stages in the process of bacterial conjugation, the formation of zygotes on the one hand, and the formation of genetic recombinants on the other.

There is every reason to believe that any inducible prophage is immediately induced upon transfer from a lysogenic donor to a nonlysogenic recipient bacterium. The expression of this genetic determinant may be thus detected in every bacterium that has received the prophage as a result of conjugation. The frequency of zygotic induction is, therefore, a quantitative expression of the frequency of transfer of a given prophage (Jacob and Wollman, 1956b). The frequency of zygotic induction of different inducible prophages becomes smaller, the more distal the location of the prophage in question on the chromosomal segment transferred by Hfr H bacteria during conjugation. This fact would indicate that the frequency of their transfer, and consequently of the transfer of any genetic character linked to them, is lower when this character is situated beyond the character Gal_b, in relation to the characters TL. The genetic polarity observed in the results of crosses could well be only a secondary manifestation of a *polarity of transfer.*

CHAPTER VIII

The Successive Stages in Bacterial Conjugation

Prior to the discovery of zygotic induction, the formation of genetic recombinants was the only known expression of bacterial conjugation. It was therefore impossible, either to characterize or to analyze quantitatively the successive events which take place between the moment of contact of bacteria of opposite mating types and the moment when a clone of genetic recombinants is formed. Consequently, it was customary to lump together under the term "genetic recombination" all the observed phenomena, including those which obviously pertained to the early stages of the conjugation process. This led to a certain amount of confusion, both terminological and phenomenological. For instance, it was implicitly assumed that the frequency of recombinants was the expression of the frequency of conjugation, and consequently that a low frequency of recombination meant a low frequency of conjugation.

One can distinguish two main stages in conjugation. The first, the *formation of the zygotes*, extends from the moment when bacteria of opposite mating types meet to the time a zygote is formed by transfer of genetic material from donor bacterium to recipient bacterium. The second, the *formation of the recombinants*, takes place inside the recipient bacterium, which has become a zygote as a consequence of the transfer of genetic material, and lasts until a pure clone of bacteria of the recombinant type has been formed.

Within limits, zygotic induction allows these two steps to be differentiated since an inducible prophage carried by the donor bacteria is a genetic determinant that is immediately recognizable upon transfer to the zygotes. By comparing the results of crosses in which zygotic induction takes place with the results of crosses in which it does not, one can make a tentative evaluation of the respective roles played by the events which lead to the formation of zygotes, and by those which terminate in the formation of genetic recombinants (Jacob and Wollman, 1955a; E. L. Wollman, Jacob, and Hayes, 1956).

I. BACTERIAL CONJUGATION AND ITS MODES OF EXPRESSION

In making a quantitative analysis of conjugation, one can measure two elements: the number of recombinants formed; and (in a cross between lysogenic donor bacteria and nonlysogenic recipient bacteria) the number of infective centers resulting from zygotic induction. The *frequency of recombinants* observed in a given selection expresses the *frequency of transmission* of the genetic character (or characters) selected from the donor bacteria to the recombinants. The *frequency of zygotic induction* of an inducible prophage expresses the *frequency of transfer* of this prophage from the lysogenic donor bacteria to the nonlysogenic recipient cells.

There is every reason to believe that the different genetic characters of the donor bacteria are not transferred to the zygote with identical frequencies. Furthermore, when a genetic determinant has been transferred from the donor cells to the zygotes, it is not always inherited by a recombinant. For a given genetic determinant, it is necessary to determine both the *frequency of its transfer* from the donor cells to the zygotes, and the probability of its reappearance in a genetic recombinant. This probability will be designated as the *coefficient of integration.* The *frequency of transmission,* as determined by measurement of the *frequency of recombinants,* is a composite of these two variables.

A. The Kinetics of Conjugation

Two crosses, Hfr $H(\lambda)^+S^s$ x F^- $P678(\lambda)^+S^r$, and Hfr $H(\lambda)^+S^s$ x F^- $P678(\lambda)^-S^r$, are carried out under the usual conditions (2.10^7 Hfr and 4.10^8 F^- per milliliter, aeration at 37°C). At various intervals after mixing, the $T^+L^+S^r$ and Gal^+S^r recombinants formed in both crosses are counted, and in the second cross a count is also made of the infective centers resulting from zygotic induction. Similar experiments have been described in Chapters V and VII. In order to simplify the presentation (and because of the irregularity of the curves representing the kinetics of the appearance of recombinants in a cross where zygotic induction takes place), only the increase in the number of recombinants formed in the first cross and the increase in the number of infective centers formed in the second cross are shown in Fig. 14. The frequencies of recombinants and the frequency of zygotic induction measured after 60 minutes of contact are presented in Table XV, and the genetic constitution of the $T^+L^+S^r$ recombinants in Table XVI (see p. 104 and p. 106).

Inspection of Fig. 14 and Table XV shows how varied the expressions of conjugation can be, using the same Hfr $H(\lambda)^+$ cells as donors. Each expression taken separately, gives only a very imperfect idea of the frequency of conjugation: the frequency of Gal^+S^r recombinants, for instance, reaches only 0.13 per cent in an Hfr $H(\lambda)^+$ x $F^-(\lambda)^-$ cross, whereas, in the same cross, the frequency of zygotic induction reaches 57 per cent. It is clear, however, that the various curves in Fig. 14 are actually the expressions of the same phenomenon. As indicated previously, all these curves extrapolate to the origin, and all reach a plateau at about the same time, despite the great differences in the height of the plateau. It therefore follows that conjugation, no matter how expressed, reaches its

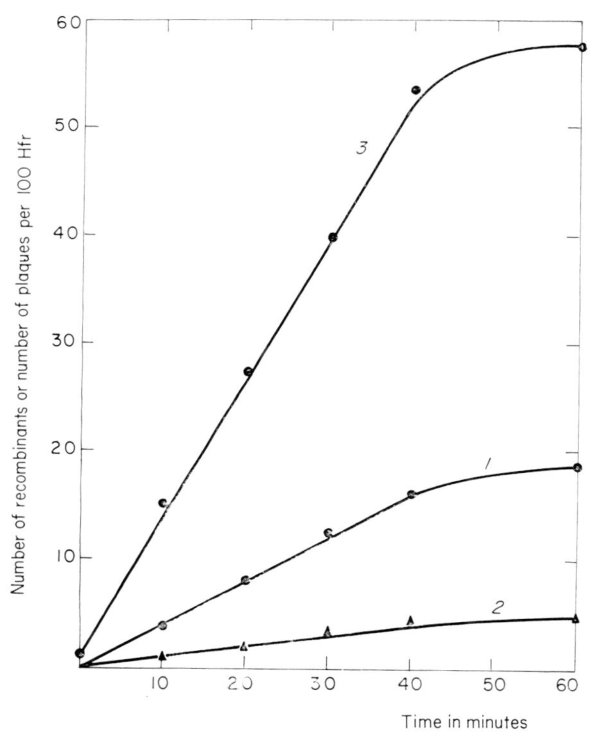

FIG. 14. The kinetics of conjugation. The crosses Hfr H(λ)+S^s × F− P678(λ)+S^r (cross 1) and Hfr H(λ)+S^s × F− P678(λ)−S^r (cross 2) are carried out under the usual conditions (Hfr: 2.10^7/ml, F−: 4.10^8/ml). Samples taken at various time intervals are plated: for cross 1, on selective media for T+L+S^r recombinants (curve 1) and for Gal+S^r recombinants (curve 2); for cross 2, on streptomycin agar medium with indicator bacteria 112 S^r for infective centers (curve 3). Abscissa: Time, in minutes, after the initial mixing. Ordinate: Number of T+L+S^r recombinants (curve 1) and Gal+S^r recombinants (curve 2) formed in cross 1; number of infective centers (curve 3) formed in cross 2. These numbers are expressed in per cent of the initial number of Hfr bacteria.

maximal value in about 50 minutes and proceeds at a rate of about 2.5 per cent per minute.

The various curves in Fig. 14 meet at the origin, which shows that the processes of dilution and plating suffice to prevent any new contact between bacteria of opposite mating types. It indicates also that the process of conjugation starts as soon as the cells are placed in contact. Accordingly, the ascending portion of the curves expresses, for the experimental conditions employed, the kinetics of *specific pairing*, or *effective contact*, between bacteria of opposite mating types. These effective contacts are strong enough to survive dilution and plating, and consequently the subsequent stages—transfer of genetic material from donor to recipient cells, and genetic recombination—can be completed on the agar medium.

B. The Frequency of Conjugation

The fact that the curves in Fig. 14 all reach a plateau at the same time indicates that after 50 minutes all the Hfr bacteria capable of transferring genetic material to the F^- cells have effectively taken part in conjugation. The frequency of zygotic induction of prophage λ shows that at least half of the total number of Hfr bacteria are involved in the process. However, the destruction of more than half the zygotes formed in an $Hfr(\lambda)^+ \times F^-(\lambda)^-$ cross reduces the number of $T^+L^+S^r$ recombinants only to about half that obtained in the control $Hfr(\lambda)^+ \times F^-(\lambda)^+$ cross. Hence one can conclude that *nearly all the Hfr H bacteria involved in the cross have effectively taken part in conjugation* and have transferred to recipient bacteria a chromosomal segment carrying the determinants of the T and L characters (Jacob and Wollman, 1955a; E. L. Wollman and Jacob, 1957).

In a given cross, one cannot infer the frequency of conjugation solely from the frequency of the recombinants obtained in a particular selection. One can therefore ask whether conjugation might not actually take place as frequently in crosses with a low frequency of recombination as in crosses with a high frequency of recombination. In fact, the difference between F^+ cells and Hfr cells might reflect properties other than the ability to establish effective contacts with recipient F^- cells and to transfer genetic material to them. This indeed seems to be the case as will be discussed in Chapter X. The efficiency of the F^+ bacteria in transmitting the "F factor" to F^- bacteria is so great that this factor has been considered to be "infectious" (Cavalli-Sforza, Lederberg, and Lederberg, 1953). The kinetics of acquisition of the F^+ character are, in fact, comparable to the kinetics represented in Fig. 14, and there is good reason to believe that transfer of the F factor takes place as a consequence of conjugation (Jacob and Wollman, 1955a).

Thus, conjugation in *E.coli* K12 is not a rare event, as was at first believed. On the contrary, it is a phenomenon of great efficiency since (at least in the case of Hfr H and F$^-$ bacteria) all the bacteria of opposite mating types participate.

C. Direct Observation of Conjugation

The high frequency of conjugation as revealed by zygotic induction of prophage λ encouraged the belief that bacterial conjugation should be directly observable. Thanks to the collaboration of T. F. Anderson, it was possible to study the morphological aspects of conjugation by electron microscopy (Anderson, Wollman, and Jacob, 1957). In order to avoid ambiguities of interpretation caused by the difficulty of recognizing morphologically the bacteria of opposite mating types, a special "labeling" technique was used. In these experiments, one of the strains used was sensitive to temperate phage λ and the other was resistant. Before the mating, the bacteria of the sensitive strain were "labeled" with phage λ inactivated by ultraviolet light. Particles of phage λ so treated adsorb normally to sensitive bacteria; they do not multiply, however, and the infected cells survive (Jacob and Wollman, 1954b). The multiplicity of infection was 50 to 100 phages per bacterium.

Equal numbers of Hfr H and F$^-$ cells were mixed and the mixture aerated at 37°C for 20 to 40 minutes. Samples were removed and prepared for observation under the electron microscope by the "critical point" method (Anderson, 1952). Photographs of conjugating bacteria are shown in Figs. 15, 16, 17, and 18.

In some experiments, crosses were carried out between Hfr H cells from strain K12 and F$^-$ cells from strain C. Cells of the C strain are ovoid in shape, and therefore easily distinguishable from the cells of strain K12 (Lieb, Weiglé, and Kellenberger, 1955), as can be seen in Fig. 17 and 18. Figure 18 illustrates conjugation between F$^+$ cells from strain K12 and F$^-$ cells from strain C.

In all cases, the images of conjugation are characteristic. The pairing is not merely a simple (and therefore possibly nonspecific) juxtaposition, but an actual fusion. In the areas of contact, which involve only a minor portion of the cell surface, the walls of the conjugating cells have disappeared. In certain favorable cases, one can see bridges which actually link the cells of opposite mating types (Figs. 16 and 17). When such a bridge is thin enough to allow penetration by electrons, its content has the same appearance as the cytoplasmic contents of the paired cells, and appears to be continuous with them. These bridges, which range in diameter from 100 to 300 mμ, are fairly strong; it is difficult to break them with a micropipette (Anderson and Mazé, 1957). No particular area of the bacterial surface is characteristically the site of conjugation.

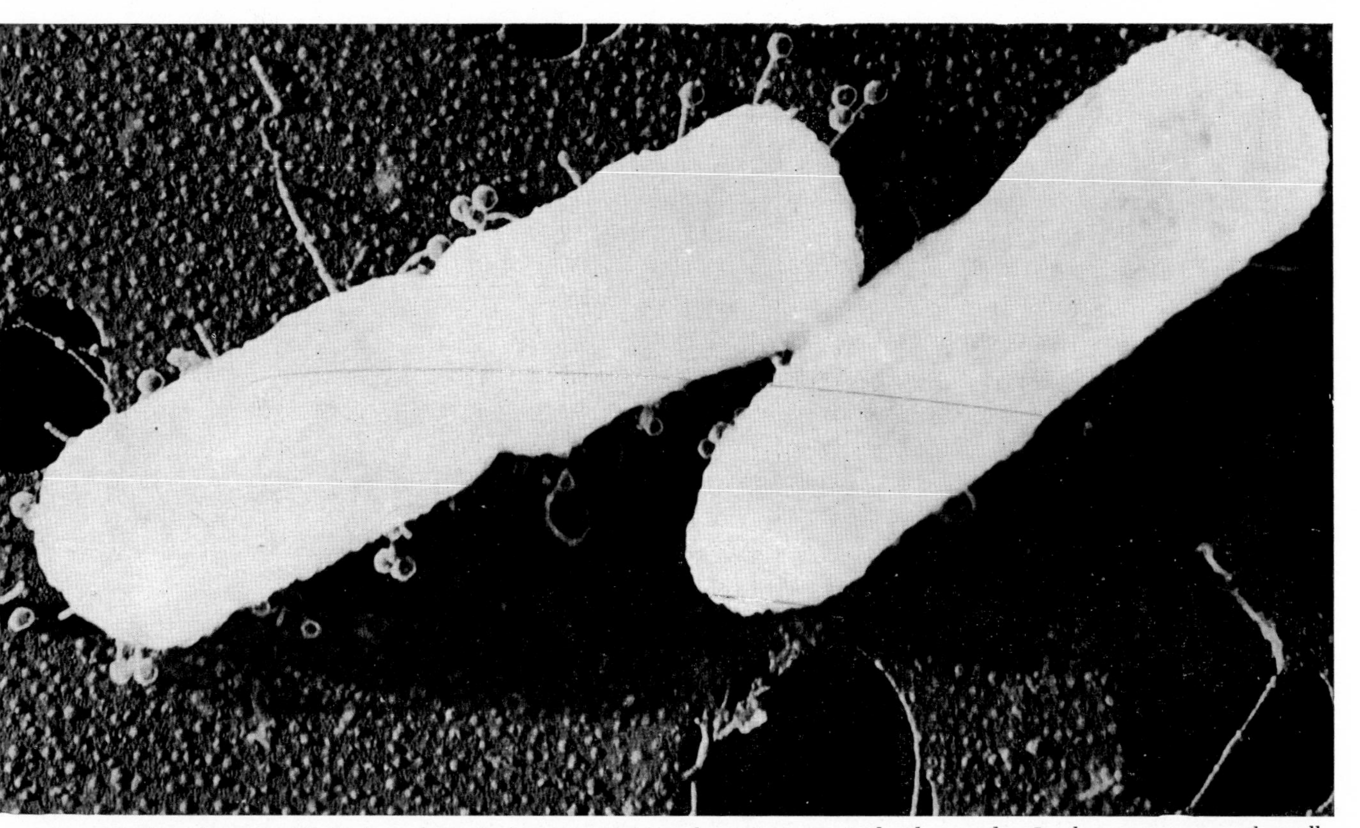

FIG. 15. Cross between Hfr H λ^r and F^- λ^s bacteria. The two bacteria are paired side to side. In the contact area, the cell walls seem to have disappeared. The F^- cell in the process of division is covered with bacteriophage λ attached by its tail and whose head is, in most cases, emptied of its DNA. (Preparation for electron microscopy and photography by T. F. Anderson.)

The formation of effective contacts very likely depends on differences in the structure and surface properties of the bacteria of opposite mating types. Differences of this kind between F^+ and F^- bacteria have been described (Maccacaro, 1955; Maccacaro and Comolli, 1956); furthermore, Hfr and F^+ bacteria appear to differ antigenically from F^- bacteria (Le Minor and Le Minor, 1956; Ørskov and Ørskov, 1960). More recently, it has also been shown that these differences in surface structure result in a difference in susceptibility to certain bacteriophages. Donor strains, whether Hfr or F^+, are sensitive to phages that are not active on the corresponding F^- recipient bacteria (Loeb, 1960). The formation of effective pairings, which depends, of course, on the frequency of the collisions, is also dependent on temperature and on the composition and pH of the medium (Hayes, 1957; Fisher, 1957a). It does not occur in the absence of a source of energy. The specific pairings are probably reversible to some extent, since at a bacterial concentration of the order of 10^9 per milliliter the rate of conjugation reaches a maximal value, which does not further increase when the concentration of bacteria is raised.

3. *The transfer of genetic material* is the essential step in the formation of zygotes. Its mechanism will be analyzed in the following chapter. Only its principal characteristics will be recalled here:

a. The transfer of genetic material is *unidirectional* from the Hfr donor bacteria to the F^- recipient bacteria. This fact is demonstrated not only by the differential effect of streptomycin but also by zygotic induction which takes place only in crosses between lysogenic donor cells and nonlysogenic recipient cells.

b. Only the *genetic material* from the donor bacteria appears to be transferred during conjugation. If there is transfer of cytoplasm, it must be in minute quantities. Streptomycin treatment of the Hfr bacteria actually has no effect on the development of the zygotes. No transfer of phages in the vegetative state (see Chapter VII) nor of enzymes, of substrates, or of inducers of enzymes has been observed to take place from donor Hfr H to F^- recipient bacteria during conjugation (Pardee, Jacob, and Monod, 1959).

c. The transfer of genetic material is probably *partial* in the sense that the great majority of the zygotes receive only a chromosomal segment from the donor bacteria. Zygotic induction furnishes the most solid evidence for this contention. The information that it provides about the nature of the contribution of the Hfr H bacteria to the constitution of zygotes will be considered below.

B. Hypotheses Concerning the Nature of the Genetic Contribution of the Donor Bacteria to the Zygotes

The essential characteristic of the crosses with a high frequency of recombination is the polarity which exists along the linkage group. This polarity, already evident from the results of crosses between nonlysogenic bacteria (see Chapter V), is shown still more clearly in crosses where zygotic induction occurs. As mentioned already, two groups of hypotheses were formulated to explain this genetic polarity. These hypotheses may be stated more precisely by means of a few simple diagrams, as shown

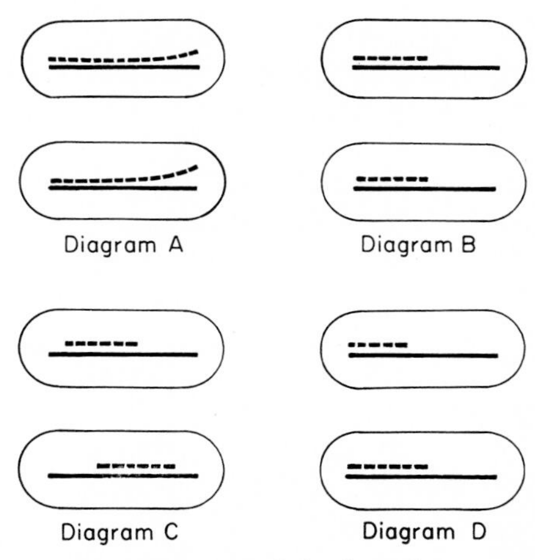

Fig. 19. Diagrammatic representation of the hypotheses concerning the formation of zygotes. For each hypothesis, two zygotes taken at random in the same cross are represented.

A: total transfer, homogeneity of the zygotes.
B: partial transfer, homogeneity of the zygotes.
C: partial transfer, heterogeneity of the zygotes, no polarity.
D: partial transfer, heterogeneity of the zygotes, polarity.

in Fig. 19. We shall consider to what extent each of these models is compatible with the facts hitherto reported.

1. *The total transfer hypothesis* (Fig. 19, diagram A). It could be assumed, as suggested by J. Lederberg (1955a) and by Cavalli-Sforza and Jinks (1956), that each zygote receives the entire chromosome of the donor bacterium. In this case, the polarity would be purely genetic; it would be a *polarity of integration*. The unequal frequency of integration of different genetic characters would be the consequence of a defect in the pairing of the chromosomes of the two parents followed by the preferential elimination of a chromosomal segment derived from the

donor bacterium. Such an hypothesis evokes in reality two distinct concepts: the polarity of pairing (or of integration), and the compulsory elimination of the unpaired chromosomal segment of the Hfr cell.

2. *The partial transfer hypothesis.* According to this hypothesis, the zygotes do not receive the entire chromosome of the donor bacterium but only a segment of it. Variants of this hypothesis must however be distinguished:

a. *Homogeneous partial transfer.* All or most of the zygotes would receive a defined linkage group (Fig. 19, diagram B). This is the hypothesis formulated originally by Hayes (1953b) to explain the difference between high and low frequency of recombination in Hfr × F^- crosses. Explanation of the polarity observed even among the characters transmitted with high frequency would necessitate the additional hypothesis of a polarity of integration.

b. *Random fragmentation* of the chromosome of the donor bacterium (Fig. 19, diagram C). This hypothesis was originally formulated by Clowes and Rowley (1954b) for crosses between F^+ and F^- bacteria. To explain the polarity observed in crosses between Hfr H and F^- bacteria, it would be necessary to assume that the fragments formed have different probabilities of transfer.

c. *Oriented unequal transfer.* According to this hypothesis, different zygotes would receive from the parental Hfr strain chromosomal segments of unequal length, but *all having an identical end or origin, O* (Fig. 19, diagram D). The probability of transfer of a given character would thus depend on its distance from the origin O: the greater its distance from O, the lower the probability of transfer. The genetic polarity would reflect, essentially, the *polarity of the transferred segment.*

Among the hypotheses just considered, there are two, that of the homogeneous transfer and that of the random fragmentation of the chromosome of the Hfr bacterium, which do not appear to be compatible with the facts. These hypotheses cannot explain, without additional assumptions, the polarity observed along the TL-Gal segment, either in the transmission of the genetic characters from the Hfr parent to the recombinants or in the rates of zygotic induction of the various inducible prophages. Consequently, the expression "partial transfer" will be reserved henceforth for the hypothesis of unequal oriented transfer (Fig. 19, diagram D).

It is necessary, in fact, to stress that the polarity of the TL-Gal segment actually extends well beyond the latter character as already indicated by the study of the inducible prophages and confirmed when further nutritional characters that can be used for the selection of recombinants became available (see Chapter IX, page 145). The distinction between characters transmitted with high frequency and characters transmitted with low frequency does not, therefore, correspond to the existence of two distinct segments. Along the linkage group of Hfr H bacteria, there is a continuous gradient in the frequencies of transmission of the genetic characters, just as there is a gradient in the rates of zygotic induction of the inducible prophages situated beyond Gal_b (Jacob and Wollman, 1958b).

The distinction between the hypothesis of a total transfer with polarity of pairing (Fig. 15, diagram A) and that of the partial and oriented transfer (diagram D) rests, in fact, on the interpretation given to the phenomenon of zygotic induction. As already indicated, all the available evidence is in favor of the hypothesis that zygotic induction results from the transfer of an inducible prophage into the cytoplasm of a nonimmune recipient bacterium. The information provided by zygotic induction on the nature of the segments transferred to the zygotes during conjugation will be considered on the basis of this interpretation.

C. The Heterogeneity of the Zygotes Formed in a Cross between Hfr H and F^- Bacteria

According to the hypothesis of a partial and oriented transfer, different zygotes receive chromosomal segments of unequal lengths from the parental Hfr H type. In a cross between Hfr H and F^- bacteria, an attempt can be made to estimate what proportion of the zygotes have received characters such as TL on the one hand, and Gal_b on the other from the Hfr donor cells.

Let us compare again the results of Hfr $H(\lambda)^+ \times F^-$ $P678(\lambda)^+$ and Hfr $H(\lambda)^+ \times F^-$ $P678(\lambda)^-$ crosses (Table XV). In the latter cross, the destruction of more than half the zygotes also reduces by slightly more than half the number of $T^+L^+S^r$ recombinants. More than half the zygotes have therefore received a TL-Gal-λ segment and have been destroyed. Slightly less than half the zygotes have received a shorter segment and have survived (E. L. Wollman and Jacob, 1957). It is thus possible to distinguish two distinct, although heterogeneous, classes of zygotes: more than 55 per cent of them have received a segment longer than TL-Gal-λ and less than 45 per cent have received a shorter segment (less than 2 per cent of the latter group receive a TL-Gal segment without λ). By comparing the $T^+L^+S^r$ recombinants formed by this second class of zygotes in the Hfr $H(\lambda)^+ \times F^-$ $P678(\lambda)^-$ cross with all of the $T^+L^+S^r$ recombinants formed in the control Hfr $H(\lambda)^+ \times F^-$ $P678(\lambda)^+$ cross, where no zygotic induction occurs, it is possible to determine (in

TABLE XVII
HETEROGENEITY OF THE ZYGOTES

Crosses	Classes of recombinants	Approximate percentage of corresponding zygotes	Genetic constitution of the various classes of recombinants in per cent				
			T+L+	Az^s	T_1^s	Lac+	Gal_b+
Hfr(λ)+ × P678(λ)−	T+L+S^r	42	100	86	60	21	2.5
	Gal+ S^r	2	82	79	78	74	100
Hfr(λ)+ × P678(λ)+	T+L+S^r	100	100	90	70	47	29
		among 42	100	86	60	21	2.5
		which 58	100	96	83	72	54
	Gal+ S^r	60	80	78	78	82	100

terms of per cent of the class of zygotes considered) the genetic constitution of the $T^+L^+S^r$ recombinants formed by each category of zygotes (Table XVII). As can be seen, the genetic constitution of these two classes of recombinants is very different: the $T^+L^+S^r$ recombinants formed by the zygotes that have received the whole TL-Gal-λ segment in the control cross inherit the characters Az, T_1, Lac, Gal from the Hfr parental type in 96, 83, 72, and 54 per cent of the cases, respectively, whereas those descended from zygotes that have received a segment shorter than TL-Gal-λ inherit these characters only in 86, 60, 21, and 2.5 per cent of the cases respectively.

On the contrary, the Gal^+S^r recombinants, all arising from zygotes that have received at least the TL-Gal segment, have the same genetic constitution, whether they are formed by 60 per cent of the zygotes, as in a cross in which no zygotic induction takes place, or by only 2 per cent of the zygotes, as in a cross in which zygotic induction occurs (Table XVII).

One can thus conclude that the genetic polarity of the TL-Gal segment, as revealed, for example, by analysis of the recombinants formed in an Hfr H(ly)$^-$ × F$^-$(ly)$^-$ cross (Chapter V) expresses primarily a heterogeneity of the zygotes, itself the consequence of the polarity of the chromosomal segments transferred by the donor bacteria Hfr H.

Similar conclusions can be drawn from analysis of the crosses between Hfr H bacteria lysogenic for different inducible prophages and nonlysogenic F$^-$ bacteria (see Table XVI, p. 106). The further a given prophage is located from TL on the bacterial chromosome, the lower is the proportion of zygotes that receive this prophage (and consequently the characters linked to it). Furthermore, the number of recombinants that inherit a character such as Gal situated far from TL becomes greater, the further the prophage is located beyond Gal; i.e., the greater the number of zygotes that receive a TL-Gal segment not carrying the prophage.

* * *

Zygotic induction and its genetic effects are best interpreted by the hypothesis of a partial, oriented transfer. By revealing the heterogeneity of the zygotes formed in a cross, zygotic induction makes it possible to analyze quantitatively the process of genetic recombination. When characters linked to inducible prophages are available, it is indeed possible to determine for each its frequency of transfer, and in addition its genetic linkage to other characters, in considering only those zygotes which have received simultaneously the characters whose linkage is to be determined (see Chapters IX and XIII).

III. THE FORMATION OF GENETIC RECOMBINANTS

Following the transfer of genetic material from a donor to a recipient bacterium, a zygote is formed which consists essentially of the recipient bacterium. In all likelihood, each zygote contains only a segment, variable in length, of the chromosome of the donor cell. It is therefore an incomplete zygote or *merozygote*. In it there take place the phenomena of recombination which will lead to the formation of individuals possessing hereditary characters derived from each of the parental types.

A. The Successive Steps Leading to the Formation of Genetic Recombinants

In this second phase, properly speaking genetic, of bacterial conjugation, two main steps may be distinguished.

1. *Genetic integration.* This term encompasses all the events leading to the formation of a recombinant chromosome. It was chosen in preference to the term "genetic recombination," partly because it does not imply any particular mechanism, and partly to underline the asymmetry of the phenomenon. What one in fact studies is the eventual integration of genetic determinants originating from the donor parental type.

2. *Segregation of the recombinants.* Since bacteria usually contain several nuclei, a genetic recombinant is a haploid bacterium in which all the nuclei are of the recombinant type. Such a bacterium will arise when, as a result of chromosomal replications and bacterial divisions, segregation has taken place between the chromosome of recombinant type and the other nuclear elements contained in the merozygote. The moment when this segregation is completed may be determined by following, as a function of time, the development of the number of recombinants formed in a cross (see Fig. 8, page 69).

More precise information can be derived from studies on the segregation of zygotes plated on nonselective complete medium (Skaar and Garen, 1956; Hayes, 1957; Tomizawa, 1960) or from micromanipulation experiments on individual zygotes (Anderson and Mazé, 1957; J. Lederberg, 1957). Such experiments, which will be described later (see Chapter XIII), make it possible to examine all the progeny of the zygotes. It can thus be verified that part of this progeny consists of bacteria which have the genotype of the recipient bacteria and that bacteria with the genotype of the donor bacterium never appear. As a general rule, recombinants which have inherited characters transmitted with low frequency by the parental Hfr type do not occur.

B. The Coefficient of Integration of the Genetic Characters Transferred to the Zygotes

Genetic determinants from the donor Hfr bacteria which have been transferred to the zygotes may thereafter become integrated in genetic recombinants. By measuring the frequency of transmission of a given genetic character and the frequency of its transfer, it becomes possible to determine its coefficient of integration.

1. *The efficiency of integration.* When a genetic determinant of the donor has been transferred to a zygote, it is inherited by a recombinant in only a fraction of the cases. One of the first questions which may be raised is that of the factors which affect the efficiency of integration.

One of these factors is the very nature of the strains used in a cross. Inspection of Table VI (see p. 71) shows that in a series of crosses between Hfr H and F^- bacteria, the frequency of $T^+L^+S^r$ recombinants varies from one cross to another. Although the frequency of transfer of the T^+L^+ determinants is close to 100 per cent in all cases, these markers are inherited in one cross in about 10 per cent of the cases and in another cross in about 40 per cent of the cases. The coefficient of integration of the T^+L^+ markers therefore varies from 0.1 to 0.4 in different crosses.

Other factors which affect the probability of integration are the environmental conditions to which the zygotes are submitted. These factors have not yet been carefully analyzed. It is known, however, that starvation of the zygotes decreases the frequency of integration. Integration is also reduced when zygotes are plated on carefully washed MA medium, whereas it is increased when platings are made on MA medium supplemented with enough broth to allow a limited residual growth of the recipient bacteria.

2. *Integration of different genetic determinants.* Another important question is that of the relative efficiency with which different genetic characters of the donor bacteria are integrated. From the results reported in Table VI, the impression could be gained that the Gal_b marker, which is transferred to more than half the zygotes, is integrated with an efficiency which is only half that of the TL markers. This could be interpreted, and was indeed at first interpreted, as indicating the existence of a polarity of integration along the TL-Gal segment. It will be seen in the next chapter that such a polarity of integration does not exist. The decreasing frequencies of zygotic induction of a series of inducible prophages located distally to Gal on the TL-Gal segment already establishes the existence of a gradient of transfer along the Hfr chromosome. By comparing the frequencies of transfer of these prophages and the frequencies of transmission of genetic markers to which such prophages

are linked, it has indeed been possible to demonstrate (see p. 152) that no gradient of integration exists along the linkage group of bacteria Hfr H.

The preceding discussion has been given only as an illustration of the concepts of transfer and of integration as they were defined at the beginning of the present chapter. It shows the kind of information that can be obtained by comparing crosses in which zygotic induction takes place with those in which it does not.

The problems concerning recombinational analysis in bacteria and those pertaining to the mechanism of genetic recombination will be considered in Chapter XIII.

* * *

Thanks to zygotic induction, the sequence of events which take place when bacteria of opposite mating types are mixed together can be studied at two different levels: the level of the zygotes and that of the genetic recombinants. It thereby becomes possible to define and, in some cases, to determine experimentally three principal parameters of bacterial conjugation: the frequency of conjugation, the frequency of transfer of genetic characters, and the coefficient of genetic integration.

It can be thus demonstrated that, in a cross with a high frequency of recombination and probably also in a cross with a low frequency of recombination, all the bacteria of opposite mating types mate in a comparatively short time. A transfer of genetic material takes place from the donor to the recipient cell, which consequently becomes a zygote. There is a polarity along the chromosome of a given type of donor bacterium Hfr H, of such a nature that the chance of transfer of a genetic character diminishes the further it is situated from one of the extremities—or origin—of the chromosome of the bacterium. The zygotes formed during conjugation are therefore heterogeneous and differ from one another with regard to the genetic contribution from the donor cell. They are incomplete zygotes or *merozygotes.* In these merozygotes, genetic recombination may take place between the chromosomal segment from the donor cell and the chromosome of the recipient cell. In this way a recombinant chromosome is formed, the segregation of which leads to the formation of a bacterium of recombinant type.

Bacterial conjugation thus differs from the sexual processes of other organisms since the zygotes formed do not, in general, contain all the genome from one of the parental types. This peculiarity, which is the essential cause of the anomalies observed in the results of bacterial crosses, is the consequence, as we shall now see, of the very process through which the transfer of genetic material is achieved in the course of conjugation.

CHAPTER IX

The Process of Genetic Transfer During Conjugation

Conjugation between Hfr H and F^- bacteria is characterized by the unidirectional transfer of genetic material and by the unequal frequency with which the different genetic characters of the donor bacteria are transmitted to recombinants. In comparing the numbers of genetic recombinants or of infective centers formed in various types of crosses, we have seen that deductions can be made about the nature of the genetic contribution from the Hfr parental type. The conclusion has thus been reached that the genetic polarity characteristic of crosses with high frequency reflects the incomplete nature of the genetic segments transferred from the Hfr H bacteria to the zygotes. In the preceding chapter, we have discussed the properties of these genetic segments and given the arguments in favor of the hypothesis that they are unequal in length and oriented. We shall now show that the fragmentation of the chromosome of the donor bacterium, which according to Lederberg and Cavalli-Sforza, was supposed to take place *after* the transfer, while according to Hayes, it existed *before* the transfer, actually occurs *during* the transfer.

I. THE KINETICS OF GENETIC TRANSFER

In the process which results in the formation of the zygotes, we have been led to distinguish *a priori* three successive stages: the collisions, the specific pairings, and the genetic transfer itself. Whereas dilution of a mating mixture makes it possible to distinguish collisions from effective contacts that have already taken place, we have not yet been able to distinguish the effective contacts from the genetic transfer itself.

The kinetic study of conjugation shows that effective contacts between bacteria of opposite mating types begin as soon as these bacteria are mixed together (see Fig. 14). One can ask whether the transfer of a given genetic determinant is completed immediately following the specific pairing or whether there may not be some delay between the moment when the contact becomes effective and the time when the genetic determinant is transferred to the zygote. It is known that, once the genetic transfer is effected, the successive events which will lead to the formation either of a genetic recombinant or of an infective center take place inside the zygote. The donor bacterium is no longer necessary and may therefore be eliminated.

A. Kinetic Studies on the Formation of the Zygotes

Hayes was the first to study the kinetics of zygote formation by destroying the Hfr H donor bacteria with a virulent bacteriophage (Hayes, 1955, 1957). In an Hfr $T^+L^+M^-T_6{}^s \times F^-T^-L^-M^+T_6{}^r$ cross, samples were taken at various intervals during conjugation, and these samples were either immediately diluted and plated on minimal medium or treated with bacteriophage T_6 and then diluted and plated. In samples *treated* with phage, $T^+L^+M^+$ recombinants were formed only when the samples had been taken at least 10 minutes after mixing. The number of recombinants, thereafter, increased essentially in the same manner as on the curve represented in Fig. 14 ($T^+L^+S^r$ recombinants). This experiment seemed to indicate that about 10 minutes had elapsed between the moment when the parental bacteria had been mixed and the time when the T^+L^+ determinants had been transferred to the zygotes. In the *untreated* samples, however, the kinetics of formation of $T^+L^+M^+$ recombinants was not very different, and it seemed that a definite period of time elapsed also between the moment when the cells were mixed and the moment when recombinants began to appear.

A simpler method of distinguishing the actual formation of zygotes from the specific pairings might consist in attempting a mechanical separation of mating pairs during the process of conjugation. Such a separation may be achieved by subjecting the conjugating bacteria to violent agitation in a mixer. It is known that bacteria, and more particularly *E. coli*, survive such treatment (Anderson, 1949). It is also known that bacteria infected with a bacteriophage can also resist such treatment and remain capable of producing phage. By the use of this technique, Hershey and Chase (1952) were able to demonstrate that, after infection of *E. coli* with bacteriophage T_2, the deoxyribonucleic acid of the bacteriophage was injected into the bacterium whereas the protein shell remained outside and could be separated by mechanical agitation.

Experiments with different strains of *E. coli* K12 showed that treatments lasting from 1 to 8 minutes, in a Waring blendor, operating at high speed and kept at a temperature of 4°C, did not decrease the number of bacteria capable of giving rise to a colony (see Table XIX, page 142). Such treatments do not reduce the number of plaques of bacteriophage λ, whether formed by infected sensitive bacteria or by induced lysogenic bacteria. In actual practice, treatment in the blendor for 2 minutes is sufficient to separate bacteria undergoing the process of conjugation. It is possible in this way to follow the variation in the number of zygotes formed during conjugation, whether the final expression of the formation of the zygote is the production of genetic recombinants or of infective centers due to zygotic induction.

In an Hfr $H(\lambda)^- \times F^-(\lambda)^-$ or Hfr $H(\lambda)^+ \times F^-(\lambda)^+$ cross, one can follow, as a function of time, the transfer to the zygotes of the characters T^+L^+ and $Gal_b{}^+$. In an Hfr $H(\lambda)^+ \times F^-(\lambda)^-$ cross, it is also possible to follow the transfer of prophage λ. The experiments are carried out under the usual conditions of crosses (see Chapters V and VI). Samples are taken at various time intervals after the mixing of the cells. They are diluted in buffer and then plated onto appropriate media, either directly or after treatment in the mixer. After each operation, the metal container in which the mechanical agitation was carried out is carefully rinsed with sterile chilled buffer. The object of dilution is to prevent pairing, while the treatment in the mixer is intended to dissociate the pairings already completed.

The results of such experiments are given in Fig. 20. For the untreated samples, the curves representing the variation in the number of infective centers or of recombinants are identical to those of Fig. 14: all of them extrapolate to the origin of the coordinates and form a plateau after about 50 minutes. Very different on the contrary are the curves for the mixer-treated samples. Neither of them extrapolates to the origin. But while the first $T^+L^+S^r$ recombinants begin to appear in the samples taken after 10 minutes of contact, one can detect no Gal^+S^r recombinants in an Hfr $H(\lambda)^+ \times F^-$ P678$(\lambda)^+$ cross, and no infective centers in an Hfr $H(\lambda)^+ \times F^-$ P678$(\lambda)^-$ cross, in samples taken after contact for less than 25 minutes.

Once the infective centers or the recombinants begin to appear, their number increases regularly until a maximum value is reached which is identical to that of the plateau in the curve for the untreated samples. It should be noted that the first recombinants which have acquired the characters T^+L^+ from the Hfr H bacteria begin to appear at the same time, whether conjugation is interrupted by mechanical agitation or whether the Hfr H bacteria are destroyed by a virulent bacteriophage (Hayes, 1957).

The curves expressing the kinetics of the transfer of various genetic determinants thus differ considerably, depending on the character of the donor bacteria under investigation. The moment when a given genetic determinant begins to be detectable in the zygotes depends not upon the expression of this determinant but upon its situation on the TL-Gal chromosomal segment. Determinants such as TL and Gal_b, the expression of which requires the whole sequence of events culminating in the formation of genetic recombinants, but which are located far

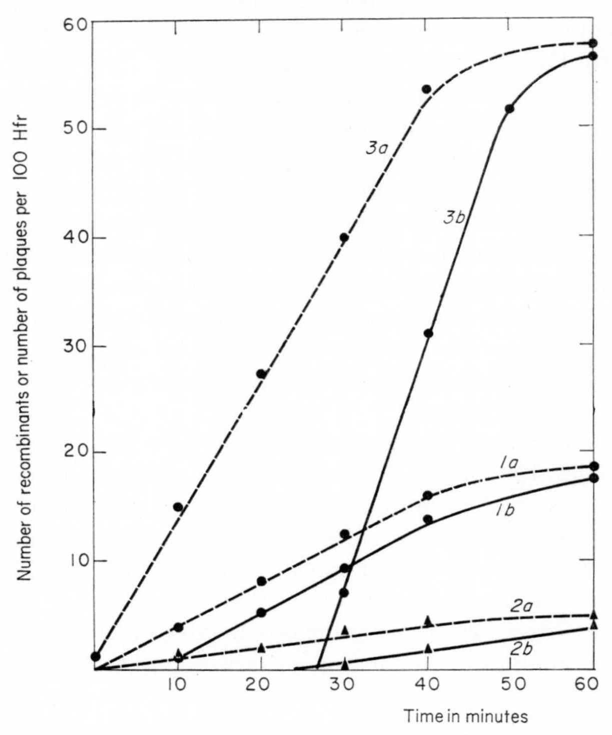

FIG. 20. The kinetics of genetic transfer. The crosses are the same as those illustrated in Fig. 14.

Cross 1: Hfr H(λ)+S^s × F− P678(λ)+S^r

Cross 2: Hfr H(λ)+S^s × F− P678(λ)−S^r

Samples taken at various time intervals are, either plated directly on selective media (dotted lines), or treated for 2 minutes in a Waring blendor before plating (solid lines). Abscissa: Time, in minutes, after the initial mixing. Ordinate: Number of T+L+S^r recombinants (curves 1a and 1b), and of Gal+S^r recombinants (curves 2a and 2b) in cross 1; number of infective centers (curves 3a and 3b) in cross 2. These numbers are expressed as percent of the initial number of Hfr bacteria.

apart on the TL-Gal segment, seem to be transferred to the zygotes at very different time intervals. In contrast, determinants such as Gal_b, and the prophage λ, the modes of expression of which are different, but which are located near one another on the chromosome of the donor bacteria, appear to be transferred to the zygotes at very close time intervals. There is a close relationship, therefore, between the time when a given genetic determinant is transferred from an Hfr bacterium to an F^- bacterium and the location of this determinant on the chromosome of the Hfr cell. The transfer occurs earlier for the determinants located on the proximal portion of the TL-Gal segment than for those located on the distal portion of the segment. By taking the intersection with the abscissa (Fig. 20) of the curves which express the kinetics of transfer of the various genetic determinants studied, one may assess the time when these determinants begin to enter the recipient bacteria. For the characters TL, Gal_b and λ, these time intervals are respectively 9, 24, and 26 minutes after the onset of conjugation. From this it can be concluded that *the genetic characters of the Hfr H bacteria enter the F^- bacteria in the order of their location along the TL-Gal segment.* The polarity of the chromosomal segments transferred from the Hfr H bacteria to the zygotes appears therefore to be the expression of a polarity of the process of transfer (E. L. Wollman and Jacob, 1955, 1958b).

B. The Polarity of Transfer

If these conclusions are correct, it may be expected that in an Hfr $H(\lambda)^+ \times F^-$ $P678(\lambda)^+$ cross, the genetic constitution of the $T^+L^+S^r$ recombinants formed will vary with the length of time that has elapsed between the mixing of the bacteria and the removal and treatment of the sample in the blendor. In particular, the first $T^+L^+S^r$ recombinants formed should not have received from the Hfr parental type genetic characters located on the distal portion of the TL-Gal chromosomal segment. On the contrary, the $T^+L^+S^r$ recombinants formed from samples removed at the same time, but untreated, should have the same genetic constitution, regardless of the time of sampling, since in this case the whole sequence of events which extends from effective contact to the constitution of genetic recombinants can proceed without interruption.

This prediction is confirmed by genetic analysis of the $T^+L^+S^r$ recombinants, as may be seen in Table XVIII. Whereas the genetic constitution of the recombinants obtained from the untreated samples is relatively independent of the time of sampling, that of the recombinants formed after mechanical treatment varies widely. The later the time of sampling, the more frequently a genetic character located on the TL-Gal segment of the Hfr H bacterium is present among the $T^+L^+S^r$ recombinants.

For each of the genetic characters studied, the kinetics of the appearance among the $T^+L^+S^r$ recombinants can thus be determined. This

TABLE XVIII

ORIENTATION OF THE TRANSFER OF GENETIC CHARACTERS IN A CROSS BETWEEN Hfr H S^s AND F− P678 Sr BACTERIA[a]

Time of sampling (in minutes)	Genetic constitution of the $T^+L^+S^r$ recombinants: Untreated samples					Treated samples				
	T^+L^+	Az^s	T_1^s	Lac^+	Gal_b^+	T^+L^+	Az^s	T_1^s	Lac^+	Gal_b^+
5	100	90	73	34	17	—	—	—	—	—
10	100	89	74	38	18	100	12	3	0	0
15	100	90	75	32	19	100	70	31	0	0
20	100	91	74	34	18	100	88	71	12	0
25	100	94	81	39	18	100	92	80	28	0.6
30	100	90	78	39	22	100	90	75	36	5
40	100	90	80	42	19	100	90	75	38	20
50	100	91	78	44	21	100	91	78	42	27
60	100	90	77	41	19	100	91	78	42	27

[a] The cross is carried out under usual conditions. At various time intervals, samples are taken and diluted; they are plated on selective medium either immediately, or after a 2 minutes treatment in a Waring blendor. For each time of sampling, 200 $T^+L^+S^r$ recombinants were analyzed.

analysis is illustrated in Fig. 21 where the distribution of the various genetic characters from the Hfr H parental type per 100 $T^+L^+S^r$ recombinants formed is plotted against the time of sampling and exposure to mechanical agitation. It can be seen that each of the characters under study begins to appear among the $T^+L^+S^r$ recombinants at a definite time. A correlation exists between the time of appearance of a given

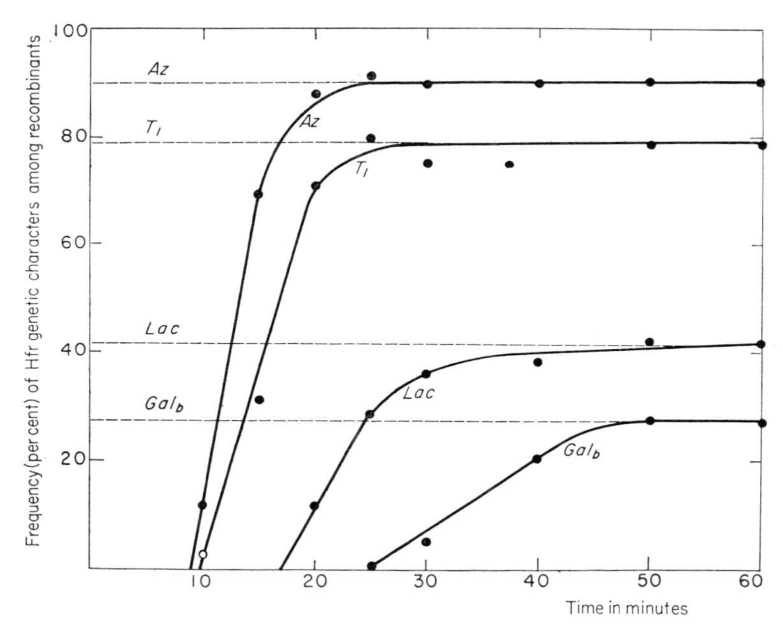

FIG. 21. The order of penetration of the genetic characters of Hfr H bacteria during conjugation. In a cross between Hfr H(λ)+S^s and F− P678(λ)+S^r bacteria, the $T^+L^+S^r$ recombinants formed at various times, either after direct plating (curve 1a in Fig. 20), or after treatment in a blendor (curve 1b in Fig. 20) are analyzed as to their genetic constitution (see Table XVIII). Abscissa: Time of sampling. Ordinate: The frequency, per hundred $T^+L^+S^r$ recombinants, of various genetic characters from the Hfr bacteria. Dotted lines: the genetic constitution of the $T^+L^+S^r$ recombinants from the untreated samples (curve 1a, Fig. 20); solid line: the genetic constitution of the same recombinants from the treated samples (curve 1b, Fig. 20).

genetic determinant among the $T^+L^+S^r$ recombinants and its linkage to the selected T^+L^+ characters as observed by usual genetic methods: the closer the linkage, the sooner the appearance among the $T^+L^+S^r$ recombinants. From the intersection with the time coordinate of the different curves represented in Fig. 21, it is possible to determine the moment when any given genetic character begins to appear among the $T^+L^+S^r$ recombinants. For instance, the character Az begins to appear at about

9 minutes, T_1 at 10 minutes, Lac at 18 minutes, and Gal_b at about 25 minutes. Once a particular character has appeared, the frequency with which it may be found among the $T^+L^+S^r$ recombinants rises rapidly with time, and reaches asymptotically the characteristic frequency with which this particular character is found among the $T^+L^+S^r$ recombinants formed in the untreated samples. About 50 minutes after the initial mixing of the bacteria, the various markers scored are found among the $T^+L^+S^r$ recombinants with their usual frequency.

It seems clear, therefore, that the various genetic characters from the Hfr H parental type begin to appear in the zygote in a definite order. *It is as if the penetration of the chromosome from the donor bacteria into the recipient bacteria were an oriented process.* This penetration appears always to start with the same extremity O (or origin) of the chromosome, followed in order by the characters TL, Az, T_1, Lac, and Gal_b (E. L. Wollman and Jacob, 1955).

As indicated previously, the genetic characters of the Hfr H bacteria are transmitted to recombinants with ever decreasing frequencies as their linkage to the characters TL diminishes; or in other words, as their distance from the origin O of the chromosome of the Hfr H donor bacteria increases. Similarly, the farther an inducible prophage is located from O, the less frequently it is transferred to the zygotes. It can also be shown that the farther the determinants of these characters are located from the proximal extremity of the Hfr H chromosome, the later they enter the recipient bacteria (E. L. Wollman and Jacob, 1958b).

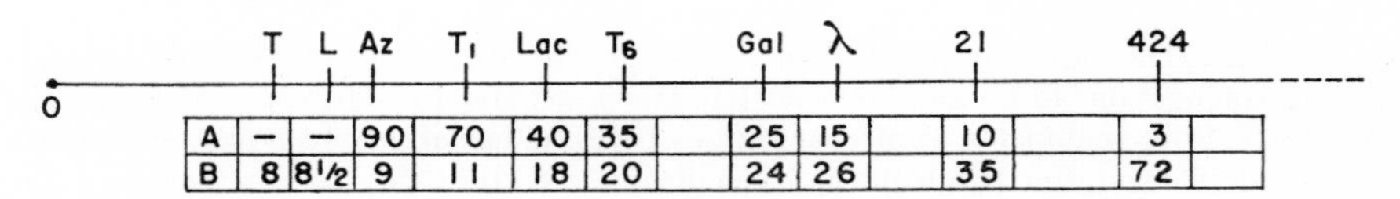

	T	L	Az	T_1	Lac	T_6	Gal	λ	21	424
A	—	—	90	70	40	35	25	15	10	3
B	8	8½	9	11	18	20	24	26	35	72

FIG. 22. The proximal segment of the chromosome of Hfr H bacteria. A. The frequencies with which various characters of Hfr H bacteria are found per hundred $T^+L^+S^r$ recombinants formed in crosses Hfr H × F^- P678. B. The times at which the genetic determinants of these characters begin entering the recipient bacteria in experiments of interrupted matings. O is the origin of the chromosome, i.e., the end which enters first the F^- cell.

Figure 22 indicates the relative frequencies of transmission to the $T^+L^+S^r$ recombinants and the times of penetration into the F^- bacteria of the various genetic characters carried by the O-TL-Gal_b segment, and of some of the inducible prophages located beyond Gal_b.

C. Specific Pairings and Genetic Transfer

From inspection of Fig. 20, it appears that the curves which express the kinetics of formation of the zygotes (curves 1*b*, 2*b*, and 3*b*) are not parallel to the curves which, in the same experiment, express the kinetics of formation of effective contacts (curves 1*a*, 2*a*, and 3*a*). As it seems

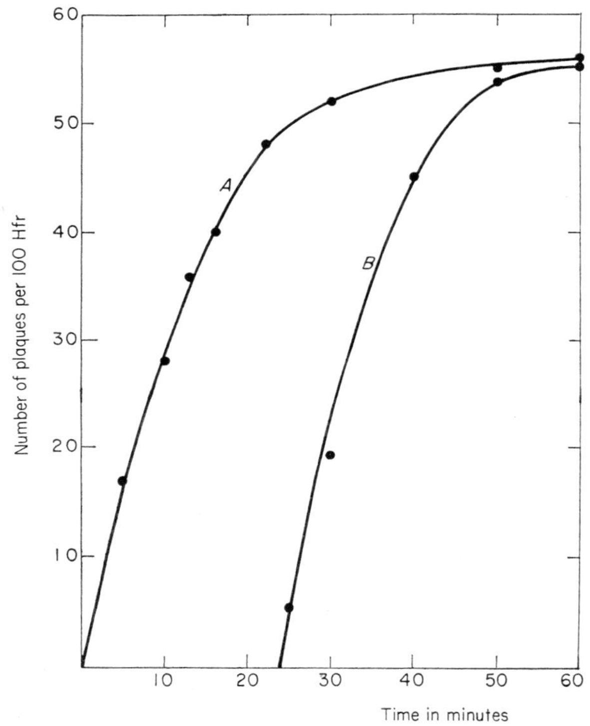

Fig. 23. The kinetics of specific pairings. Hfr H(λ)+S^s and F− P678(λ)−S^r bacteria are mixed under usual conditions (Hfr: 2.10^7/ml, F−: 4.10^8/ml) and the mixture is gently shaken in a water bath at 37°C. Samples taken at various time intervals are, either carefully diluted 1000-fold in 1/10th strength broth, or treated in a blendor. The treated samples are immediately plated with 112 S^r bacteria onto streptomycin-CA medium (curve *B*). The untreated samples, diluted 1000-fold and kept in a water bath at 37°C without agitation, are plated 60 minutes after the beginning of the experiment (curve *A*).

unlikely that the average rate of progression of the chromosomal O-TL-Gal segment will vary according to the moment when effective contacts are established, it has to be assumed that the method hitherto used to follow the kinetics of formation of effective contacts is not satisfactory. The curves which express the kinetics of specific pairings should actually start from the origin of the coordinates and continue parallel to the curves which express the kinetics of formation of the zygotes. There is good reason to believe that the dilution of the samples, and, even more, their immediate plating onto streptomycin-agar result actually in the destruction of a certain proportion of the pairings already effected, or sometimes even in the rupture of the chromosomal segments as they are being transferred. In fact, if the samples taken at various time intervals in an Hfr $H(\lambda)^+ \times F^-$ $P678(\lambda)^-$ cross are not plated immediately, but are diluted in broth with great care, kept at 37°C, and plated only 60 minutes after the beginning of the experiment, the number of infective centers resulting from zygotic induction of the prophage λ is found to increase more rapidly than when the platings are carried out immediately after sampling. The initial slope of the curve thus obtained is essentially the same as that of the curve obtained after interruption of the conjugation process by treatment in the blendor (Fig. 23). It can thus be concluded that all of the bacteria able to mate have paired in less than 30 minutes (E. L. Wollman and Jacob, 1958b).

The experiments just reported allow a clear distinction to be made between specific pairing and the transfer of genetic material which follows it. At the present time, we do not know of any conditions which would allow the formation of specific pairings, while preventing the subsequent occurrence of genetic transfer. In particular, we do not know how to obtain populations of bacteria in which all the specific pairings are completed without the transfer itself having started.

II. THE MECHANISM OF GENETIC TRANSFER

The kinetic analysis of genetic transfer, as described in the preceding section, shows that the different genetic determinants from the Hfr H bacteria enter the recipient bacteria at different times. For a given genetic determinant, this time is characteristic and, under given experimental conditions, depends only on its position on the chromosome of the donor bacterium. It is thus possible to draw a genetic map of the chromosomal segments of the Hfr H bacterium in time units (Fig. 22).

A. Genetic Transfer as an Oriented Process

The simplest interpretation of these findings is that, as soon as specific pairing is effected, the chromosome of the donor bacterium begins to enter the recipient cell. Since this penetration always begins with the same extremity, O, of the Hfr H chromosome, the genetic determinants located on this chromosome also enter the bacterium according to a fixed and predetermined order. The mechanical agitation, which separates the cells in the process of conjugation, results in the rupture of the bridge which connects them and in the breakage of the Hfr chromosome passing through that bridge. The progression of the chromosome is slow enough so that during its passage it may be broken at will at any point of its length. If it is assumed that the passage of the chromosome of the Hfr H bacterium takes place at a constant speed when the experimental conditions are themselves constant, it follows that the time which elapses between the moment of penetration of two given genetic determinants is proportional to the physical distance which separates these two determinants (E. L. Wollman and Jacob, 1958b).

The penetration of the O-TL-Gal segment takes about 25 minutes and there is good reason to believe that this segment represents between one-fifth and one-quarter of the total length of the chromosome. The quantitative study of the transfer provides, therefore, a means, both convenient and accurate, of determining the order and the relative distance of the bacterial genetic determinants. It is conceivable that spontaneous ruptures may occur during the slow passage of the chromosome of the donor cell. In such an event, the more distant the location of a genetic character from the origin of the chromosome, the smaller will be the probability of its transfer during conjugation. This would explain the rarity with which the entire chromosome of the Hfr H bacterium is transferred during conjugation and, consequently, the low frequency of transmission of characters located far from TL to recombinants. It also explains the fact that the zygotic induction of a prophage such as λ and the interruption of conjugation immediately before the time of penetration of such a prophage both have the same effect on the genetic constitution of the $T^+L^+S^r$ recombinants formed. As can be seen from a comparison of the data in Tables XVII and XVIII, the different genetic characters of the O-TL-Gal segment appear with essentially the same frequency among the $T^+L^+S^r$ recombinants formed in an Hfr $H(\lambda)^+ \times F^- P678(\lambda)^-$ cross, and in an Hfr $H(\lambda)^+ \times F^- P678(\lambda)^+$ cross in which conjugation is interrupted at 25 minutes.

The results obtained in the kinetic studies of genetic transfer have been confirmed by the investigations of Hayes and Fisher as well as by those of Skaar and Garen.

As shown by Hayes (1955), conjugation can be interrupted by destroying the Hfr H cells through the action of a virulent phage. If this treatment is applied at various times after mixing the bacteria, and the genetic constitution of the recombinants that have received the characters T^+L^+ from the Hfr H parental type is then determined, it is found that the other genetic characters of the Hfr H parent show the same pattern of appearance among the recombinants as that demonstrated when conjugation is interrupted by mechanical agitation (Hayes, 1957). In order for the genetic transfer to take place, the donor bacteria must be provided with a source of energy. It is possible therefore to arrest genetic transfer either by lowering the temperature sufficiently or by adding an inhibitor of metabolism such as 2,4-dinitrophenol (Fisher, 1957b). When the temperature is lowered from 37° to 32°C, the speed of genetic transfer is reduced by half; the penetration of the characters TL occurs at 18 minutes instead of 8 minutes, and that of Lac at 38 minutes instead of 17 (Hayes, 1957).

Such dissimilar techniques as the mechanical interruption of conjugation and the destruction of the donor bacteria produce results which are completely comparable. It seems reasonable to conclude therefore that genetic transfer is actually accomplished by the mechanism described above (E. L. Wollman, Jacob, and Hayes, 1956).

The experiments of Skaar and Garen (1956) were carried out with Cavalli-Sforza's Hfr C strain rather than with Hayes' Hfr H strain. These authors used the same technique as Hayes; at various times during conjugation, the Hfr C bacteria were destroyed by the virulent phage T_6. Instead of selecting for recombinants, however, Skaar and Garen plated the treated samples onto a complete nutritive medium containing lactose and a color indicator. On this medium, zygotes which can give rise to Lac^+ recombinants form mixed colonies, which contain both cells with the Lac^- genotype of the recipient bacteria and Lac^+ recombinants. The genetic constitution of these recombinants varies with the time of sampling, but the order in which the genetic characters from the Hfr C bacteria enter the zygotes (Lac T_1L) is the reverse of that observed with Hfr H bacteria.

B. The Process of Genetic Transfer and Its Interruption

The interpretation of the mechanism of genetic transfer during conjugation which has been outlined above seems the simplest one that can satisfactorily explain the kinetics of zygote formation; furthermore, it explains most of the anomalous facts about bacterial genetic recombination which have been described in earlier chapters. Nevertheless, when it was originally put forward, this interpretation aroused certain objections, which principally concerned the technique of interrupting conjugation by mechanical means. On the one hand, it was argued that the mechanism by which such artificially interrupted conjugation produces its genetic effects was by no means clear; on the other hand, it was argued that the conclusions drawn from such experiments could not justifiably be extended to the normal process of transfer. We shall now briefly examine these criticisms.

We have already mentioned several times Lederberg's view that the chromosome of the donor bacteria is transferred in its entirety, the elimination of chromosomal segments being only a secondary event. According to J. Lederberg (1955b), mechanical agitation could cause anomalies in the pairing of the chromosomes from the two parental types. Such a mechanism seems very unlikely; furthermore, it could hardly apply to cases where conjugation is interrupted by a virulent bacteriophage which affects only the Hfr donor bacteria. The contention that the conclusions drawn from interrupted mating experiments can not be validly extended to noninterrupted crosses likewise appears unjustifiable.

According to Skaar and Garen (1956), the fragmentation of the chromosome of the Hfr cell might precede its transfer. The interruption of conjugation might result, not in the breaking of the chromosome of the donor bacterium, but rather in effecting a selection among the recombinants. The hypothesis of a fragmentation of the Hfr chromosome preceding its transfer has already been considered at the beginning of the present chapter; it must now be presented more precisely as a basis for the following discussion.

The nature of the chromosomal contribution of the donor Hfr H bacteria to the zygotes has been discussed in Chapter VIII. It has been seen that this contribution must be partial, one extremity of the chromosomal segments transferred being always the same, while the length of the chromosomal segments contributed to different zygotes is variable. If fragmentation occurred in the donor bacterium before transfer, it would have to take place through a rather peculiar mechanism. As to the mechanism of transfer of such genetic segments, it could not be very different from that proposed above for the transfer of the entire chromosome, if one is to explain the order of penetration of the various genetic markers of the donor Hfr bacteria. Were every chromosomal segment transferred at once, no polarity of transfer would be observed. Such an hypothesis is not very different, therefore, from the more general one we have proposed, but the difficulties it raises are far greater.

Let us suppose, however, that this hypothesis is correct. The transfer of the various segments would take place in a progressive, orderly way. A short segment would be transferred more rapidly than a long one. The role of mechanical agitation (or treatment by a phage) would be to select those zygotes which had already received the entire chromosomal fragment from the Hfr parental type, the other zygotes being destroyed by the treatment. As a function of time, the number of viable zygotes would increase as would also the length of the chromosomal fragments which had been completely transferred.

It can be demonstrated that such an hypothesis is not compatible with the facts. Let us consider the Hfr HS^s x F^- P678 S^r cross, in which the Hfr H cells are in excess of the recipient cells (ratio Hfr/F^- = 20/1). It is known that 25 minutes after mixing the cells, almost all specific pairings are completed (see Fig. 23) and that about half of the zygotes capable of giving rise to $T^+L^+S^r$ recombinants are formed (Fig. 20). According to the hypothesis of chromosomal fragmentation preceding conjugation, these zygotes should have received segments shorter than O-TL-Gal. The other half of the zygotes, which would receive a segment at least equal to TL-Gal if conjugation were not interrupted, would then be destroyed by treatment in the blendor. During the process of conjugation, samples of the mating mixture are plated at variable times onto streptomycin-CA medium. On this medium, only the F^- cells or the zygotes multiply. If the above-mentioned hypothesis were correct, there should be a considerable decrease in the number of colonies formed when mechanical agitation is applied at 25—30 minutes. At 60 minutes, on the

TABLE XIX
FATE OF THE PARENTAL BACTERIA IN CROSSES BETWEEN Hfr(λ)+ AND P678(λ)+ BACTERIA[a]

Time of sampling (in minutes)	Number of colony-formers per ml of the mating mixture (× 10^5): On MA glucose medium in a cross 1 Hfr H × 20 F^- — Without mechanical stirring	After mechanical stirring	On CA-streptomycin medium in a cross 1 F^- × 20 Hfr H — Without mechanical stirring	After mechanical stirring
0	146	132	120	133
10	151	141	136	122
20	151	163	112	105
30	167	159	110	112
40	159	147	122	117
50	162	158	128	121
60	166	163	132	130

[a] Crosses are carried out under usual conditions. The minority parent is, in one case, the Hfr type and, in the other, the F^- type. At various time intervals, samples are diluted and plated in triplicate on MA medium (Hfr bacteria) or on CA medium + streptomycin (P678 bacteria and zygotes). The figures represent the average number of colonies formed.

contrary, the transfer of all the characters located on the TL-Gal segment being completed, this number should be very much larger. The results of such an experiment, reported in Table XIX, show that the number of recipient bacteria capable of forming a colony remains essentially constant during the whole process of conjugation, regardless of whether or not conjugation was interrupted by mechanical agitation. The results of a similar cross, in which the minority parent is the Hfr H type, are also presented in Table XIX. As may be seen, the number of Hfr cells remains essentially constant during conjugation and is not affected by treatment in the blendor. Thus neither conjugation nor the rupture of the bridge which connects the bacteria during conjugation has any effect on the viability of the parental cells.

The hypothesis that mechanical treatment has a direct action on the transfer is strengthened even further by the following experiment. It is known that, in an Hfr $H(\lambda)^+ \times F^-$ $P678(\lambda)^-$ cross, zygotic induction, which destroys more than half the zygotes, reduces in the same proportion the number of $T^+L^+S^r$ recombinants formed as compared with a control Hfr $H(\lambda)^+$ x F^- $P678(\lambda)^+$ cross in which zygotic induction does not take place. If the effect of the mechanical treatment is to interrupt the transfer of the chromosome from the donor cells, it can be predicted that the kinetics of formation of the zygotes capable of giving rise to $T^+L^+S^r$ recombinants will be identical in both crosses provided that conjugation is interrupted before 25 minutes, the time at which the character Gal_b and the prophage λ linked to it begin to enter the recipient bacteria. The results reported in Table XX show that this is exactly what happens.

In the control cross, the kinetics of formation of $T^+L^+S^r$ recombinants proceeds in the same manner as in the experiment illustrated by Fig. 20: the recombinants formed by the treated samples begin to appear after about 10 minutes, and their number increases regularly thereafter.

In the cross in which zygotic induction occurs, the number of recombinants formed by the untreated samples increases erratically, as indicated previously (Chapter VII): a maximum is reached at 15 minutes, then the number of recombinants decreases slightly. In the treated samples, the kinetics of formation of recombinants for the first 20–25 minutes after mixing approximates closely that in the control cross. At 25 minutes, *this number is even higher than that found in the untreated samples.* After 25 minutes, however, the number of recombinants decreases until about the 50th minute.

The interpretation of these results is the following. In the cross where zygotic induction occurs, the number of recombinants formed by the treated samples increases normally until the moment when the prophage λ enters the zygotes: in fact, some zygotes are rescued which would have been destroyed by the development of prophage λ, had the progression of the chromosome not been interrupted before the prophage had the opportunity to enter the recipient. After 25 minutes, on the contrary, an increasingly larger proportion of zygotes receives the prophage λ and is destroyed. The situation is even more complex in the case of untreated samples, for the effect of plating at an early stage of conjugation is likely to interrupt the transfer of prophage λ to a certain fraction of the zygotes (see Figs. 20 and 22).

TABLE XX

KINETICS OF THE FORMATION OF $T^+L^+S^r$ RECOMBINANTS IN CROSSES BETWEEN LYSOGENIC Hfr H BACTERIA AND F− P678 BACTERIA EITHER LYSOGENIC OR NONLYSOGENIC[a]

Time of sampling (in minutes)	Frequencies of $T^+L^+S^r$ recombinants			
	Cross Hfr(λ)+ × F−(λ)+		Cross Hfr(λ)+ × F−(λ)−	
	Untreated samples	Treated samples	Untreated samples	Treated samples
5	2.5	0	2.3	0
10	5.3	0.49	5.8	0.3
15	8.6	5.3	8.3	3.9
20	11.7	10.6	7.5	10
25	12.9	11.3	7.2	9.6
30	13.8	13.5	6.5	8.4
40	15.6	14.2	6.2	7.3
50	16.7	14.8	6.7	6.5
60	17.4	16.8	6.8	6.7

[a] Crosses are carried out under usual conditions. At various time intervals, samples are plated on selective medium ($T^+L^+S^r$ recombinants), immediately after dilution and after a 2 minutes treatment in a Waring blendor.

There is little doubt, therefore, that the hypothesis of an oriented and progressive transfer of the chromosome of the donor Hfr bacteria is the only one which explains all the known facts pertaining to crosses between bacteria Hfr and F^-. This interpretation has in fact been gradually accepted by all workers in the field (see J. Lederberg, 1959; Cavalli-Sforza, 1959).

III. THE GRADIENT OF TRANSFER ALONG THE WHOLE Hfr CHROMOSOME

In crosses between Hfr H donor and F^- recipient bacteria, a distinction had been made at first between characters that are transmitted with high frequency to recombinants, and characters that are transmitted only with a low frequency (Hayes, 1953b). Even for those characters which are transmitted with high frequency, however—the characters located on the TL-Gal segment—a polarity exists: the closer a genetic determinant is to the proximal end of the Hfr chromosome, its origin O, the higher the frequency of transmission of the corresponding character to recombinants. The mechanism of genetic transfer as analyzed in the preceding section indicates that the unequal frequencies of transmission of different genetic characters must be the direct consequence of the unequal frequencies of their transfer. When the frequencies of transmission of a variety of genetic characters are analyzed, a continuous gradient must therefore be found, which renders meaningless the original distinction between characters transmitted with high frequency and characters transmitted with low frequency.

A. The Gradient of Transmission of Genetic Characters

In order to demonstrate the existence of a gradient of transmission of genetic characters, it was necessary to have available a variety of genetic characters which marked out the entire bacterial chromosome, and which could be used for selecting genetic recombinants. For this purpose, a series of nutritional mutants were isolated after ultraviolet irradiation of the F^- strain P678. In individual crosses between each of these mutants and strain Hfr H, the frequency of transmission to recombinants of the corresponding wild allele of Hfr H bacteria was determined, as well as its linkage relationships to the other genetic characters which distinguish the P678 and Hfr H strains. Some of the polyauxotrophic F^- mutants were used in a second step to select new nutritional mutants, and the same procedure was applied again to isolate highly marked recipient strains. The results obtained with strain PA209, which requires tryptophan (Tr) and histidine (H), and with strain PA260, which requires histidine and serine or glycine (SG), will be given as examples (Jacob and Wollman, 1958c).

The crosses were performed under standard conditions. In some crosses, a streptomycin-sensitive Hfr H strain (S^s) and a resistant recipient F^- were used, the recombinants being selected in the presence of streptomycin. In other crosses, the Hfr H strain used was $M^-T_6{}^sS^r$ (methionine requiring and sensitive to bacteriophage T_6) the recipient bacteria having the opposite properties (Hayes, 1953b); in this case, selection against the Hfr H bacteria can thus be achieved either by selecting the recombinants on a medium devoid of methionine, or by treatment with virulent bacteriophage T_6 (Hayes, 1957). In each of these crosses, several classes of recombinants can be selected; in particular, in the last cross mentioned, one can select recombinants that have acquired streptomycin-resistance from the donor bacteria.

The results of two crosses are presented in Table XXI. It can be seen that, in each cross, the different classes of recombinants are formed with different frequencies. The characters of Hfr H bacteria used for the selection of recombinants can be thus ordered according to the decreasing frequencies of their transmission to recombinants. From the results of the

TABLE XXI
THE GRADIENT OF TRANSMISSION OF GENETIC CHARACTERS IN CROSSES BETWEEN Hfr H AND F− BACTERIA[a]

Crosses	Selected recombinants	Frequency (per cent of initial Hfr)	Relative frequency
Hfr H $S^sTr^+H^+$ × F− PA209 $S^rTr^-H^-$	$T^+L^+S^r$	18.2	1
	Gal^+S^r	5.1	0.28
	Tr^+S^r	3.7	0.20
	H^+S^r	2	0.11
Hfr H $S^rM^-T_6{}^sH^+SG^+$ × F− PA260 $S^sM^+T_6{}^rH^-SG^-$	$T^+L^+M^+$	16.1	1
	Gal^+M^+	4.2	0.26
	H^+M^+	1.5	0.093
	SG^+M^+	0.3	0.018
	S^rM^+	0.04	0.0025
	$T^+L^+T_6{}^r$	9.1	1
	$Gal^+T_6{}^r$	1.9	0.21
	$H^+T_6{}^r$	0.84	0.092
	$SG^+T_6{}^r$	0.14	0.015
	$S^rT_6{}^r$	0.024	0.0026

[a] Crosses are performed under usual conditions (2.10^7 Hfr/ml and 4.10^8 F−/ml). Samples are plated at 90 minutes. In the first cross, Hfr H bacteria are eliminated by streptomycin. In the second cross, the recombinants having inherited from the Hfr parent the characters T^+L^+, Gal^+, H^+, SG^+, and S^r respectively are selected, in the absence of methionine on the one hand, after addition of phage T_6 to the mixture on the other. The frequency of recombinants corresponds to the ratio "number of recombinants of a given type/number of initial Hfr bacteria," the relative frequency corresponds to the ratio "number of recombinants of a given type/number of $T^+L^+S^r$ recombinants."

first cross, the following sequence of characters can be established: TL Gal Tr H. The second cross makes it possible to place the characters SG and Sm beyond H. It must be stressed that in such studies the nature of the characters used for selecting against the Hfr bacteria is of great importance. This fact is illustrated by the results reported in Table XXI, where in one particular cross, counterselection of Hfr H bacteria is achieved either by the distal character M or by the proximal character $T_6{}^s$, the determinant of which is located between Lac and Gal (see Fig.

6, page 53). It can be seen that counterselection for a proximal marker reduces by about half the number of recombinants, in particular of recombinants that inherit proximal characters such as TL. Analysis of the genetic recombinants formed with low frequency makes it possible to localize other genetic characters that differentiate the two parental strains and that cannot be used for the selection of recombinants. As shown in Table XXII, it is thus possible to place in order, beyond Sm on the distal

TABLE XXII
LOCALIZATION OF DISTAL CHARACTERS OF Hfr H BACTERIA[a]

Characters of the Hfr H parent	Frequency (per cent) among recombinants	
	S^rM+	$S^rT_6{}^r$
T+L+	60	23
Lac+	62	8
$T_6{}^s$	58	—
Gal+	57	34
H+	72	48
SG+	81	67
S^r	100	100
Mal+	74	74
Xyl+	21	42
Mtl+	5	31
M−	—	9

[a] In a cross Hfr H $T_6{}^sM-S^r \times F-$ PA 260 $T_6{}^rM+S^s$ bacteria, the recombinants S^rM+ and $S^rT_6{}^r$ were selected. The genetic constitution of these recombinants is analyzed as to the unselected characters T+L+, Lac+, Gal+, H+, SG+, Mal+, Xyl+, Mtl+ and $T_6{}^s$ or M− respectively. Notice the effect on the genetic constitution of recombinants of the characters used for contraselection of the Hfr H bacteria according to whether a proximal character ($T_6{}^s$) or a distal character (M−) is used.

part of the linkage group of Hfr H bacteria, the following characters: Mal (maltose), Xyl (xylose), Mtl (mannitol), and M (methionine). The linkage group of Hfr H bacteria, as deduced from these results, is shown in Fig. 24 (Jacob and Wollman, 1958c).

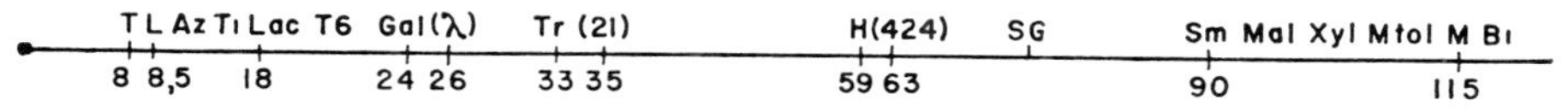

FIG. 24. The linkage group of Hfr H bacteria.

By using a variety of polyauxotrophic recipient strains marked with the most diverse nutritional markers, it is thus possible to determine the frequency of transmission to recombinants of each character studied, and to localize the corresponding genetic determinant on the linkage group of Hfr H bacteria. Such experiments show that each genetic character of Hfr H bacteria is transmitted to recombinants with a characteristic frequency, and that there is a continuous gradient between those characters which are transmitted with the highest frequencies and those which are transmitted with the lowest frequencies.

B. Gradient of Transmission and Gradient of Transfer

The availability of genetic characters which are located beyond Gal_b on the chromosome of Hfr H bacteria and which can be used for the selection of recombinants has made it possible to localize with more precision the inducible prophages described in Chapter VI. It can be seen in Table XXIII that prophage 21 is located close to and beyond Tr, and that prophage 424 is located close to and beyond H. By interrupted mating experiments, one can determine the time of entry into the zygotes of each genetic character and each inducible prophage. As also shown in Fig. 24, the order in which different genetic characters had been arranged by their decreasing frequencies of transmission to recombinants, or in which different inducible prophages had been placed according to the decreasing frequencies of zygotic induction, corresponds to the order of their transfer in the course of conjugation. Thus, as seen in Fig. 24 the Tr, H, Sm, and M characters start entering the zygotes approximately 33, 59, 90, and 115 minutes, respectively, after the onset of conjugation (E. L. Wollman and Jacob, 1958b).

It may be concluded therefore that the oriented transfer of the Hfr chromosome during conjugation is actually the cause of the gradient of transmission of genetic characters and of the gradient of zygotic induction observed with a series of inducible prophages. Under the usual experimental conditions, the transfer of the entire chromosome would take about 2 hours, which explains why this transfer is rarely complete. Spontaneous ruptures do occur, with the result that the majority of the zygotes formed receive only a segment, of variable length, of the chromosome of the donor bacterium. The proportion of zygotes that have received such distal markers as Sm or M is extremely small. As a first approximation, it can be supposed that the probability of spontaneous breakage of the Hfr chromosome is constant per unit length. The probabilities for any genetic determinant of Hfr H bacteria to be transferred during conjugation would therefore decrease exponentially as a function of the distance x which separates this determinant from the origin O of the Hfr chromosome, according to the expression:

$$p = e^{-kx}$$

TABLE XXIII
LOCALIZATION OF PROPHAGES 21 AND 424

Cross[a]	Recombinants	Relative frequency	Genetic constitution						
			T+L+	T_1^s	Lac+	Gal+	Tr+	H+	(ly)−
Hfr H(ly)− × F− PA209(ly)−	T+L+S^r	1	—	71	44	26	17	7	—
	Gal+S^r	0.28	69	71	72	—	45	13	—
	Tr+S^r	0.20	56	57	59	64	—	20	—
	H+S^r	0.11	46	47	45	47	49	—	—
Hfr H(ly)− × F− PA209(21)+	T+L+S^r	1	—	72	46	25	19	7	10
	Gal+S^r	0.31	83	80	80	—	32	10	25
	Tr+S^r	0.24	56	57	59	64	—	20	88
	H+S^r	0.12	46	47	45	47	49	—	44
Hfr H(ly)− × F− PA209(424)+	T+L+S^r	1	—	73	45	26	18	8	2
	Gal+S^r	0.27	76	74	78	—	39	11	6
	Tr+S^r	0.22	57	59	59	63	—	19	13
	H+S^r	0.10	44	46	47	51	52	—	72

[a] From each cross, T+L+S^r, Gal+S^r, Tr+S^r, and H+S^r recombinants are selected. The relative frequencies, i.e., the ratio "number of recombinants of each type/number of recombinants T+L+S^r formed in the same cross" are reported as well as the genetic constitution of these recombinants.

where k is a constant. Assuming that the migration of the chromosome proceeds at a velocity which is approximately constant for most of its length, the units of length x may be replaced by units of time t. If one accepts the proposition established below, that the gradient of transmission reflects essentially the gradient of transfer, i.e., is directly proportional to it, then the value k characteristic of the gradient of transfer in any given experiment can be calculated. For instance, in the second cross reported in Table XXI, the value of this transfer coefficient k is 0.06 min^{-1}.

It becomes evident that the results of any given cross, and consequently the value of k, depend in large part on the experimental conditions of the cross. The results obtained are remarkably reproducible when the conditions of crosses are kept constant (see Chapter V); however, possibly important variations are observed when the experimental conditions are changed, particularly when genetic analysis bears on distal characters of the linkage group of Hfr H bacteria. If shaking is too vigorous, if dilution is too rough, if plating is too early, a far from negligible fraction of the matings are interrupted. The gradient of transfer of genetic characters and consequently their gradient of transmission, can thus be substantially modified. On the contrary, none of these factors will change the time at which a given genetic determinant starts to enter the zygotes.

It is thus advisable, especially when studying the transmission of characters located on the distal part of the linkage group of Hfr H bacteria, to modify the conditions of the crosses so as to avoid interruptions of mating (Jacob and Wollman, 1958c; E. L. Wollman and Jacob, 1958b). When such precautions are taken, one observes an increase in the frequencies of recombinants and a reduction in the gradient of transfer of genetic characters (see Tables XXIV and XXV). Nevertheless, this gradient always exists. The transmission to recombinants of distal characters is always very rare, and can be observed only when appropriate selections are made.

These considerations explain why curves prepared on the basis of samples plated directly and on the basis of samples treated before plating in the Waring blendor have different slopes (Fig. 20). They make it possible also to obtain better information on some of the problems discussed in the preceding chapter. This is the case for the genetic effects of zygotic induction. Since the transfer of an inducible prophage to a nonimmune bacterium generally results in the destruction of the corresponding zygote, it is to be expected that zygotic induction will have more pronounced effects on the transmission of distal markers than on the transmission of proximal ones. The results of a series of crosses between Hfr

TABLE XXIV

GENETIC EFFECTS OF ZYGOTIC INDUCTION OF PROPHAGES λ, 21, AND 424

Cross[a]	Recombinants: Relative frequency, Gal+S^r / T+L+S^r	Tr+S^r / T+L+S^r	H+S^r / T+L+S^r		Genetic constitution: T+L+	Lac+	Gal+	Tr+	H+	(ly)+
Hfr H(ly)− × F− PA209(ly)−	0.59	0.38	0.13	T+L+S^r	—	58	45	35	14	—
				Gal+S^r	62	63	—	52	19	—
Hfr H(λ)+ × F− PA209(ly)−	0.05	0.13	0.035	T+L+S^r	—	26	3	6	3	1
				Gal+S^r	61	45	—	25	9	2
Hfr H(21)+ × F− PA209(ly)−	0.25	0.04	0.02	T+L+S^r	—	60	28	3	2	1
				Gal+S^r	70	80	—	5	2	1
Hfr H(424)+ × F− PA209(ly)−	0.45	0.30	0.033	T+L+S^r	—	72	46	42	2	2
				Gal+S^r	82	87	—	35	2	1

[a] From each cross, $T+L+S^r$, $Gal+S^r$, $Tr+S^r$, and $H+S^r$ recombinants are selected. The relative frequencies, i.e., the ratio "number of recombinants of each type/number of recombinants $T+L+S^r$ formed in the same cross" are reported as well as the genetic constitution of these recombinants. This series of crosses was performed under particularly cautious conditions of aeration and sampling, so that the relative frequencies of transmission of distal characters to recombinants are high. Note the effect of zygotic induction of the different prophages on the transmission of the distal characters of Hfr H to the recombinants.

H bacteria, lysogenic for prophages λ, 21, or 424 (which are closely linked, respectively, to the Gal, Tr, and H characters), and the same, nonlysogenic, F− bacteria are shown in Table XXIV. It can be seen that the transmission of markers distal to the prophage is always greatly reduced; the transmission of characters proximal to the prophage is the more reduced, the closer the marker to the prophage. The fact that distal characters are nevertheless transmitted to recombinants, although with greatly reduced frequencies, indicates that zygotic induction is not effective in 100 per cent of the cases. The data in Table XXIV show that survival of the zygotes, which occurs in about 10 per cent of the cases, is not due to the failure of induction, since lysogeny is only rarely inherited by the recombinants. It can more probably be ascribed to early abortion of prophage development (Jacob and Wollman, 1958c).

The localization of three inducible prophages in the immediate vicinity of three reasonably distant genetic markers, makes it possible to compare experimentally the frequency of transmission of genetic markers and the frequency of transfer of the corresponding genetic determinants. In a series of parallel crosses, conducted with all precautions to prevent interrupted matings, the frequencies of transfer of prophage λ, 21, and 424, as measured by zygotic induction, were compared with the frequencies of transmission, in a cross in which zygotic induction does not occur, of the Gal, Tr, and H characters. The results of these experiments are summarized in Table XXV. It may be seen that along the O-H segment, which covers about half the length of the Hfr H chromosome, there is a strict

TABLE XXV
GRADIENT OF TRANSFER AND GRADIENT OF TRANSMISSION

Crosses[a]	Frequency of zygotic induction	Cross Hfr H(ly)− × F− PA209(ly)−		
		Selected recombinants	Frequency	Relative frequency
		T+L+Sr	45.5	1
Hfr H(λ)+ × F− PA209(ly)−	70	Gal+Sr	30	0.66
Hfr H(21)+ × F− PA209(ly)−	45	Tr+Sr	18.2	0.40
Hfr H(424)+ × F− PA209(ly)−	18	H+Sr	6.4	0.14

[a] In the cross Hfr H T+L+Gal+Tr+H+Ss(ly)− × F− PA209 T−L−Gal−Tr−H−Sr(ly)−, the recombinants T+L+Sr, Gal+Sr, Tr+Sr, and H+Sr are selected (right). In a series of crosses between lysogenic Hfr H and nonlysogenic F− PA209 Sr bacteria, the frequencies of zygotic induction of the three prophages λ, 21, and 424, linked to Gal_b, Tr, and H respectively, are measured (left). All these crosses have been performed using great precautions for not interrupting mating. Platings are made at 70 minutes.

parallelism between the gradient of transfer and the gradient of transmission of genetic characters. The three characters investigated have about the same probability, when transferred, of being subsequently transmitted to recombinants. In the experiments reported this probability is about 0.5. It may be concluded, therefore, that along the O-H segment there is no gradient of integration (Jacob and Wollman, 1958c).*

* * *

The analysis of crosses with a high frequency of recombination has thus led to a coherent picture of the process of conjugation in bacteria (see Fig. 25). When Hfr and F^- bacteria are mixed together, specific pairings are very rapidly established between bacteria of opposite mating types. A conjugation tube is formed, through which one chromosome of the donor bacterium starts penetrating, always the same end, O, first. The migration of the chromosome takes place at a constant, slow rate. In the course of conjugation, spontaneous ruptures of the chromosome may take place. The probability of transfer of any given genetic character of the donor bacterium becomes smaller, the farther it is located from the origin of the chromosome. For markers located far from the origin, the probability that a rupture will occur before their transfer becomes so great that they will only exceptionally be found in recombinants. The zygotes formed are thus incomplete, and differ from one another in the contribution from the donor parent. There is, therefore, a continuous gradient of transmission of genetic characters along the chromosome of Hfr H bacteria; this gradient reflects the gradient of transfer of the corresponding determinants.

The mechanism by which genetic transfer is accomplished in bacterial conjugation permits the use of a new and exact method for mapping genetic characters. By measuring the relative time of transfer of different genetic characters, one obtains not only a direct demonstration of their linear arrangement on the chromosome, but also a measure of the relative distances which separate the corresponding determinants. These

* The results reported in Tables XXIV and XXV differ markedly from those obtained in earlier experiments which had been performed before the mechanism of genetic transfer had been clarified. This seems to be due mainly to modifications of the techniques of the crosses, particularly the late plating of the zygotes. In earlier crosses, the recovery of the recombinants Gal+S^r was low when compared to the observed frequency of zygotic induction of prophage λ. This could have given the impression that a gradient of integration existed along the O-Gal segment. It seems likely however that too early platings on galactose synthetic medium (selection of the Gal+S^r recombinants) caused the interruption of a larger fraction of the matings than similar platings on complete medium (formation of infectious centers).

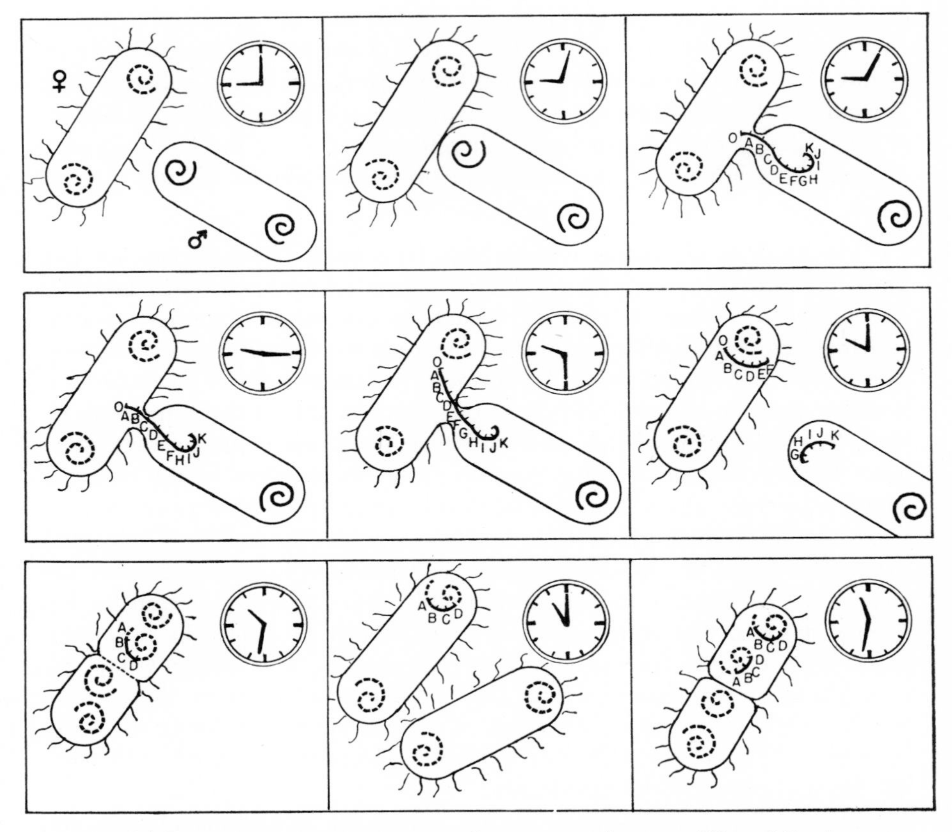

FIG. 25. Diagrammatic representation of conjugation between Hfr and F− bacteria. The F− recipient in this diagram is represented with bristles. Conjugation begins shortly (at upper right) after the two cultures are mixed, soon followed by transfer of genetic material. The letters represent the location of various markers along the donor chromosome.

circumstances, as will be seen in Chapter XII, are particularly favorable for relating genetic to physical measurements, i.e., for studying the relationships between the genetic determinants of bacteria and the structure on which they are carried, the bacterial chromosome.

CHAPTER X

The Analysis of F^+ x F^- Crosses and the Organization of the Genetic Material in *Escherichia coli* K12

The genetic analysis of bacterial crosses between F^- recipient and Hfr H donor bacteria has led to the definition of three main steps in the process of bacterial conjugation: conjugation proper, which involves a specific pairing between donor and recipient bacteria, chromosomal transfer from the donor to the recipient; and, finally, integration of the transferred genetic material, a process which results in the formation of genetic recombinants. We shall now consider the extent to which this scheme may be generalized and, in particular, how it applies to crosses between F^+ and F^- bacteria.

I. THE MECHANISM OF THE LOW FREQUENCY OF RECOMBINATION IN F^+ x F^- CROSSES

In crosses between Hfr H and F^- bacteria, in which the observed frequency of recombination varies according to the characters used for selection, it has been demonstrated that the unequal frequency of transmission of different genetic characters reflects the unequal frequency of transfer of the corresponding genetic determinants. In $F^+ \times F^-$ crosses, a low frequency of recombination is the rule whatever the characters chosen for selection. The question therefore arises, whether this low frequency of recombination results from a low frequency of conjugation, a low frequency of transfer or a low frequency of integration.

A. Conjugation, Transfer, and Integration

It was thought at first that the low frequency of recombination characteristic of $F^+ \times F^-$ crosses was the expression of a low frequency of conjugation. It has been seen already that this cannot be the case. On the one hand, the sex factor F is transmitted with a high frequency from F^+ to F^- bacteria, and its transfer, so far as we know, is a consequence of bacterial conjugation. On the other hand, as mentioned in Chapter VIII, when mixtures of F^+ and F^- bacteria are examined in the light or in the electron microscope, conjugation figures are apparently as numerous and as characteristic as those found in crosses between Hfr and F^- bacteria.

It seems unlikely also that the low frequency of recombination could be a consequence of a low frequency of integration. In crosses between nonlysogenic F^- bacteria and F^+ bacteria which are lysogenic for any one of the inducible prophages described previously (see Chapter VII), zygotic induction always occurs at low frequency and is evidenced only by its genetic effects. Neither these prophages nor the genetic determinants to which they are linked appear, therefore, to be transferred at high frequency in such crosses. Consequently it can be concluded that the linkage group of F^+ bacteria, or segments of this linkage group, are transferred only exceptionally upon conjugation and that the low frequency of recombination is due to a low frequency of transfer. Certain hereditary properties of F^+ bacteria are, however, transmitted with high frequency to F^- bacteria, notably the sex factor F. It is also the case for the determinants which control the production of antibiotic substances called *colicins,* (see Chapter XVI). When colicinogenic bacteria (col^+) are mixed with noncolicinogenic bacteria (col^-), the colicinogenic character is transmitted from the col^+ to the col^- bacteria, as shown by Frédéricq (1954b). This transfer appears to be a consequence of conjugation: when bacteria of known mating types are mixed, the character is transmitted only from F^+ to F^- bacteria.

Only the case of a colicin originally produced by strain K30 of *E. coli,* which has been studied extensively by Frédéricq, will be mentioned here. The corresponding colicinogenic factor, like the F factor, is transferred at high frequency, and no linkage appears to exist between this factor and the other genetic characters of the F^+ bacteria. In both cases transfer occurs soon after the onset of conjugation, as can be demonstrated by the interruption of mating at various times in a Waring blendor. It starts less than 5 minutes after the time at which the two strains have been mixed (Jacob and Wollman, 1955a; E. L. Wollman, Jacob, and Hayes, 1956).

In $F^+ \times F^-$ crosses, as in Hfr H $\times$ F^- crosses, certain hereditary properties are transmitted, therefore, with high frequency, whereas others are transmitted only with low frequency. There exists, however, a fundamental difference between the two systems. In Hfr H $\times$ F^- crosses, there is a continuous gradient in the frequencies with which different genetic determinants are transferred during conjugation. In $F^+ \times F^-$ crosses, on the contrary, all the determinants which can be mapped appear to be transferred at low frequency, and the recombinants formed generally inherit but a limited number of characters from the donor bacteria. Only certain peculiar genetic structures, such as the sex factor and some colicinogenic factors, are transferred at high frequency. One is led to assume, therefore, that they are not located on the same structure as the other genetic determinants of bacteria. The genetic nature of these factors will be discussed later (see Chapter XVI).

B. The Origin of the Recombinants Formed at Low Frequency

The origin of the genetic recombinants formed at low frequency in crosses between F^+ and F^- bacteria must now be considered. It could be supposed that, when F^+ and F^- bacteria mate, there is only a low probability for each F^+ bacterium to transfer a segment of its genetic material to the recipient bacterium. Alternatively, it could be supposed that F^+ bacteria, as such, are unable to transfer any of their genetic material upon conjugation but that, in any F^+ population, there is a small fraction of individuals which can do so at high frequency. According to the former hypothesis, the population of F^+ bacteria would be *homogeneous* in its ability to give rise to genetic recombinants. According to the latter hypothesis, on the contrary, the population of F^+ bacteria would be *heterogeneous*, and would contain a small proportion of Hfr mutants. It should be recalled in this context that the two Hfr strains first isolated, that of Cavalli and that of Hayes, arose from the same strain of F^+ bacteria.

The problem thus raised does not differ from that of the appearance of Lac^+ individuals in a population of Lac^- bacteria, or of phage-resistant individuals in a population of phage sensitive bacteria (see Chapter I); and it can be investigated by similar methods.

1. *Fluctuation test.* This method was introduced by Luria and Delbrück (1943) to demonstrate the spontaneous nature of bacterial mutations (see p. 11). Let us consider its application to the present problem. When a sample from a culture of F^+ bacteria is mixed with a fixed quantity of F^- bacteria and, after an hour of contact, the mixture is plated on a selective medium, a certain number of recombinants are obtained. If, instead of withdrawing only one sample, several identical samples are withdrawn from the same culture of F^+ bacteria and each of them is mixed with a single quantity of F^- bacteria, the number of recombinants formed in each of these identical crosses is almost identical. The variance, that is the expression $(X - M)^2/N$ (where X is the number of recombinants on each plate, M the mean number of recombinants per plate, and N the number of plates) will be very close to the mean. On the contrary, when a series of crosses is made using equal samples from independent F^+ cultures, all grown from small inocula, it is found that the

number of recombinants formed varies from cross to cross and that the variance, in this case, is much greater than the mean. The results of such an experiment are reported in Table XXVI (Jacob and Wollman, 1956c).

TABLE XXVI

FLUCTUATION TEST OF THE NUMBER OF RECOMBINANTS FORMED BY INDEPENDENT CULTURES OF F+ BACTERIA[a]

	Samples from independent cultures		Samples from a single culture
	Number of F+ bacteria per tube (x 4.8 × 10^6)	Number of $T^+L^+S^r$ recombinants per 0.15 ml of each tube	Number of $T^+L^+S^r$ recombinants per 0.15 ml
Minimum number	55	1	10
Maximum number	82	116	23
Mean	67.90	15.30	16.33
Variance	45.77	351.54	13
χ^2	33.3	1105	12
p	> 0.1	$\leqslant 0.01$	0.6

[a] Bacteria $F^+ M^- S^s$ are inoculated (250 bacteria/ml) in a synthetic medium containing a limiting concentration of methionine (0.2 μg/ml). Half of this suspension is distributed among 50 tubes (1.2 ml/tube); the other half is kept in a single flask. The tubes and the flask are incubated at 37° until arrest of growth. Crosses are made by mixing 0.15 ml samples from the tubes or from the flask with an excess (10^8) of $F^- T^- L^- S^r$ bacteria. After 1 hour at 37°, the mating mixtures are plated on selective MA medium and the number of $T^+L^+S^r$ recombinants formed in each cross is determined.

The results are those predicted by the hypothesis that the recombinants formed in an $F^+ \times F^-$ cross are due to rare Hfr mutants which have arisen in the F^+ population prior to the cross. In the experiment summarized in Table XXVI, the different independent cultures were each inoculated with a small number of F^+ bacteria. During the growth of these cultures, mutations occurred at random. The moment at which such a mutation occurs will vary considerably from one culture to another. Once it has appeared, an Hfr mutant forms a clone. The growth of all the cultures having been stopped at the same level of development by lack of methionine before too many mutations appeared, those cultures in which a mutation arose early contain the greatest number of Hfr mutants, and consequently form the greatest number of recombinants.

This type of experiment indicates, therefore, that every bacterium of an F^+ culture does not have an equal, although low, probability of forming recombinants, but rather that this ability is possessed by a few individuals of the population which, once they have acquired it, thereafter transmit it to their progeny. Now it is known that all the genetic characters of F^+ bacteria studied can be transmitted at low frequency to recombinants but that any given type of recombinant inherits only a limited number of the genetic characters of the F^+ donor bacteria. It can be expected, therefore, that the recombinants obtained in different selections should be produced by different types of Hfr mutants which have arisen in the same population of F^+ bacteria. It can also be expected that, in a fluctuation test such as that presented in Table XXVI, the Hfr mutants produced by independent cultures, although they are all capable of transmitting the selected T^+L^+ characters, nevertheless differ in their properties. These expectations are confirmed when the recombinants formed in such an experiment are analyzed with regard to their genetic constitution. Whereas the recombinants formed by different samples of the same F^+ culture tend to be homogeneous with respect to the proportions in which the unselected markers of the F^+ bacteria are found, the recombinants formed by independent F^+ cultures differ widely in their genetic constitution (Jacob and Wollman, 1956c). In the experiment summarized in Table XXVI, for instance, when four independent F^+ cultures served as donors, the percentage of the $T^+L^+S^r$ recombinants which inherited the markers Lac^+, Gal^+, and Xyl^+ of the Hfr parent were 30, 0, 5; 60, 30, 5; 27, 48, 0 and 20, 15, 0 respectively.

2. *Isolation of Hfr mutants.* If the recombinants formed at low frequency in an $F^+ \times F^-$ cross are indeed due to Hfr mutants, it should be possible to isolate such mutants. Isolation may be achieved in practice by making use of the method of indirect selection evolved by J. and E. M. Lederberg (1952). Adapted to the present case, this method consists in replicating, with a velvet pad, onto a solid selective medium covered with F^- recipient bacteria, a culture of F^+ bacteria grown on a complete solid medium. When recombinants have appeared, the corresponding area on the original master plate is ascertained and the bacteria in this area are replated and tested. By successive enrichments of this sort, it is possible to isolate in four or five steps the mutant clone which is capable of transferring to F^- bacteria the characters chosen for the selection of recombinants. When technical conditions are favorable, one may isolate in this fashion, with a high probability of success, the Hfr mutant which is responsible for the formation of a recombinant colony. It seems very likely, therefore, that the formation of genetic recombinants in $F^+ \times F^-$ crosses is accounted for mainly by the presence of Hfr mutants in the population of F^+ bacteria (Jacob and Wollman, 1956c). The isolation of Hfr mutants is particularly easy if one starts

with the cultures that, in fluctuation tests, yield the largest number of recombinants.

When a given character is used for selection, different Hfr types may be isolated, all of which transmit efficiently the characters used for selecting recombinants. By varying the means of selection, Hfr strains of various types may be isolated which differ with respect to the characters that they transmit with high frequency. The properties of these different Hfr types will be described in the next section. It may be mentioned here that they differ in the order in which their genetic characters are transferred during conjugation. It should be noted, however, that in a certain fraction of the cases, the isolation of the Hfr mutant presumed to be responsible for the formation of a recombinant clone fails. Such recombinants could be due to transient or unstable Hfr types; however, some failures to obtain the Hfr mutant may simply reflect the limitations of the method used for the isolation of these types.

It is known that, although the recombination frequencies observed in $F^+ \times F^-$ crosses are always low, they can vary with the characters used for selection. It seems probable, therefore, that, in a given F^+ strain, certain types of Hfr mutants arise more frequently than others. Quantitative data on this point are lacking, but it can be anticipated that different F^+ strains may have different patterns of mutability to Hfr types.

In the light of these observations, the difficulties encountered in the early attempts at genetic analysis of crosses between F^+ and F^- bacteria (see Chapters III and IV) can now be largely understood. A population of F^+ bacteria actually contains a majority of bacteria which are themselves incapable of forming genetic recombinants, together with a much smaller number of different Hfr mutants. These mutants not only belong to a variety of types but are present also in different proportions. The zygotes formed are even more heterogeneous than this description might suggest, since each Hfr type can give rise to a whole spectrum of zygotes. The results obtained in a cross with an F^+ strain depend, therefore, on the properties of the different Hfr mutants present in the culture of F^+ bacteria and also on the relative proportions of these mutants. When crosses involving different F^+ strains are compared, even greater variability is to be expected because it seems likely that different F^+ strains will vary in their pattern of Hfr mutability.

II. THE PROPERTIES OF DIFFERENT Hfr TYPES

From cultures of F^+ bacteria, a variety of Hfr types may be isolated. Their genetic behavior can be investigated by the methods which have been evolved in the study of strain Hfr H. It is of particular interest to determine the nature of the linkage group in each of a number of Hfr types.

A. The Chromosomal Organization of Hfr Bacteria

Analysis of the process of conjugation between donor Hfr H and recipient F^- bacteria has led to a visualization of the linkage group of Hfr H bacteria as a linear, discontinuous structure which is defined by its two extremities: one proximal (the origin), the other distal. The origin is that portion of the linkage group which first enters the F^- cell during conjugation. The methods used to arrive at this representation may be applied to any type of Hfr bacteria and will be briefly summarized.

1. *Determination of a gradient of transmission.* Different genetic characters of an Hfr strain are transmitted to recombinants with different and characteristic frequencies. The genetic characters of the Hfr strain under study may thus be ordered according to the decreasing frequency of their transmission (see Chapters V and IX).

2. *Genetic analysis of recombinants.* By using a small number of appropriate selections, linkage relationships may be established between the unselected characters of the Hfr strain and those genetic characters which have been chosen for the selection of recombinants. This method allows, in particular, the mapping of those genetic characters which are distal to the selected characters (see Chapters V and IX).

3. *Determination of the order of transfer.* In experiments in which mating is interrupted at different times, the relative time at which different genetic determinants start to enter the zygotes can be established and these determinants can be ordered accordingly (see Chapter IX).

In the case of Hfr H bacteria, the results obtained by these three methods agree. They also give concordant results with all other Hfr strains so far examined. The combined results obtained by the three methods allow the determination of the linkage group of any particular Hfr strain. Linkage maps for a few Hfr strains are represented in Fig. 26 (Jacob and Wollman, 1957b).

It may be seen that each Hfr type is characterized by the nature of the characters that it transmits with high frequency, and by the order in which these genetic characters are transmitted. The linkage group of any

Types of Hfr	Order of Transfer of Genetic Characters																		
Hfr H	O	T	L	Az	T_1	Pro	Lac	Ad	Gal	Try	H	S-G	Sm	Mal	Xyl	Mtl	Isol	M	B_1
1	O	L	T	B_1	M	Isol	Mtl	Xyl	Mal	Sm	S-G	H	Try	Gal	Ad	Lac	Pro	T_1	Az
2	O	Pro	T_1	Az	L	T	B_1	M	Isol	Mtl	Xyl	Mal	Sm	S-G	H	Try	Gal	Ad	Lac
3	O	Ad	Lac	Pro	T_1	Az	L	T	B_1	M	Isol	Mtl	Xyl	Mal	Sm	S-G	H	Try	Gal
4	O	B_1	M	Isol	Mtl	Xyl	Mal	Sm	S-G	H	Try	Gal	Ad	Lac	Pro	T_1	Az	L	T
5	O	M	B_1	T	L	Az	T_1	Pro	Lac	Ad	Gal	Try	H	S-G	Sm	Mal	Xyl	Mtl	Isol
6	O	Isol	M	B_1	T	L	Az	T_1	Pro	Lac	Ad	Gal	Try	H	S-G	Sm	Mal	Xyl	Mtl
7	O	T_1	Az	L	T	B_1	M	Isol	Mtl	Xyl	Mal	Sm	S-G	H	Try	Gal	Ad	Lac	Pro
AB 311	O	H	Try	Gal	Ad	Lac	Pro	T_1	Az	L	T	B_1	M	Isol	Mtl	Xyl	Mal	Sm	S-G
AB 312	O	Sm	Mal	Xyl	Mtl	Isol	M	B_1	T	L	Az	T_1	Pro	Lac	Ad	Gal	Try	H	S-G
AB 313	O	Mtl	Xyl	Mal	Sm	S-G	H	Try	Gal	Ad	Lac	Pro	T_1	Az	L	T	B_1	M	Isol

Fig. 26. The linkage groups of different Hfr types. The last three Hfr strains were isolated by Taylor and Adelberg (1961). Strain 3 is similar to that originally isolated by Cavalli (1950) and analyzed by Skaar and Garen (1956).

particular Hfr strain may be represented, therefore, as an oriented linear structure with a proximal extremity (origin) and a distal extremity. For each of these Hfr strains, the order in which the genetic characters can be arranged is the same, whether determined by the relative frequency of their transmission to recombinants or by their relative time of entry in the zygotes. This fact is, in itself, remarkable. As different Hfr strains transmit with high frequency different genetic characters, these differences could have been the consequence of chromosomal rearrangements such as transpositions or inversions. If this had been the case, discrepancies could have been found between the order deduced from the frequencies of transmission of characters to recombinants and the order indicated by the time of entry of different Hfr determinants in interrupted mating experiments. The fact that such discrepancies are not observed points to the existence of a basic genetic order which relates the diverse Hfr types to one another. It points also, as will be seen in the next chapter, to a fundamental homology between the chromosomal structure of any Hfr type and that of the F^- recipient bacterium.

When the linkage groups represented in Fig. 26 are compared, it is apparent that, in all Hfr types, the linkage relationships between characters are constant and uniform, except for those characters which, in a given Hfr type, happen to be linked either to the proximal extremity (O region) or to the distal one of the Hfr chromosome. In types 2, 3, and 5, for example, the characters T L are linked on one side to Az and T_1, and, on the other side to B_1 and M. In type Hfr H, the characters TL remain linked to Az and T_1 on one side; but, on the other side, they are linked to O and no longer to B_1 and M. In Hfr type I, on the contrary, the characters T L which are linked to B_1 and M on one side are linked to O on the other side and not to Az and T_1, which have become terminal. Whichever characters are transferred first upon conjugation, and whatever the order of transfer of these characters from an Hfr to an F^- recipient, there exists, therefore, an unequivocal *order in which the different genetic characters of E. coli K12 can be arranged* (Jacob and Wollman, 1957b, 1958a).

B. The Linkage Group of *Escherichia coli* K12

In order to draw a genetic map of *E. coli* K12, all the information gained from the study of the different Hfr types has to be taken into account. Although the linkage group of each specific Hfr type must be represented as a linear structure defined by its proximal extremity O, there is no reason to choose the specific linear structure of any one strain as the basis for constructing a general chromosomal map of *E. coli* K12.

One is led, therefore, to place all the known genetic characters on a closed curve, a circle for example (see Fig. 27). From this representation, the linkage group of any particular Hfr type may be easily deduced by opening the closed curve at a defined point and inserting the origin O at one of the two extremities thus formed. This process establishes unequivocally both the nature of the genetic segment transferred with high frequency, and the order of transfer of the genetic characters located on this segment.

The availability of a series of Hfr strains which transfer with high frequency different segments of the linkage group of *E. coli* K12 greatly facilitates, as will be discussed in the next section, the location on this linkage group of hitherto unmapped genetic characters. It also makes possible the measurement, with greater precision, of the relative distances between genetic markers. When a single Hfr strain is used, the exact time of entry of distal characters into the zygotes is rather difficult to determine: such a determination is much easier when the markers are proximal. By the use of a selected group of Hfr strains, the relative distances between markers can be assessed, and it can be shown that these distances do not vary appreciably whether the markers are proximal to or relatively distant from the origin. The assumption that the rate of progression of the chromosome during its transfer is approximately constant, at least for the first half of its length, therefore appears justified.

The general picture of the bacterial chromosome as it results from the study of a variety of Hfr types is further supported by the recent isolation of new Hfr types, from a particular F^+ strain of *E. coli* K12 (A. L. Taylor and Adelberg, 1960). These strains called Vhf (for very high frequency) possess the remarkable property of transferring their entire chromosome to F^- recipients with a frequency much higher than that normally characteristic of Hfr strains. This property, which appears to be genetically controlled, indicates a smaller probability of spontaneous breaks interrupting the migration of the chromosome during conjugation. Such strains provide a useful tool for mapping and linkage analysis.

As pointed out in the previous section, no discrepancies in the order of the transferred markers have been observed among Hfr strains isolated from F^+ bacteria, a result which excludes the hypothesis that the differences between Hfr strains result from chromosomal rearrangements. This finding, however, does not mean that chromosomal rearrangements cannot occur in *E. coli.* Such rearrangements have been found after treatment of cultures with agents such as nitrogen mustard or X-rays, known to produce chromosomal breaks in higher organisms. The recognition of

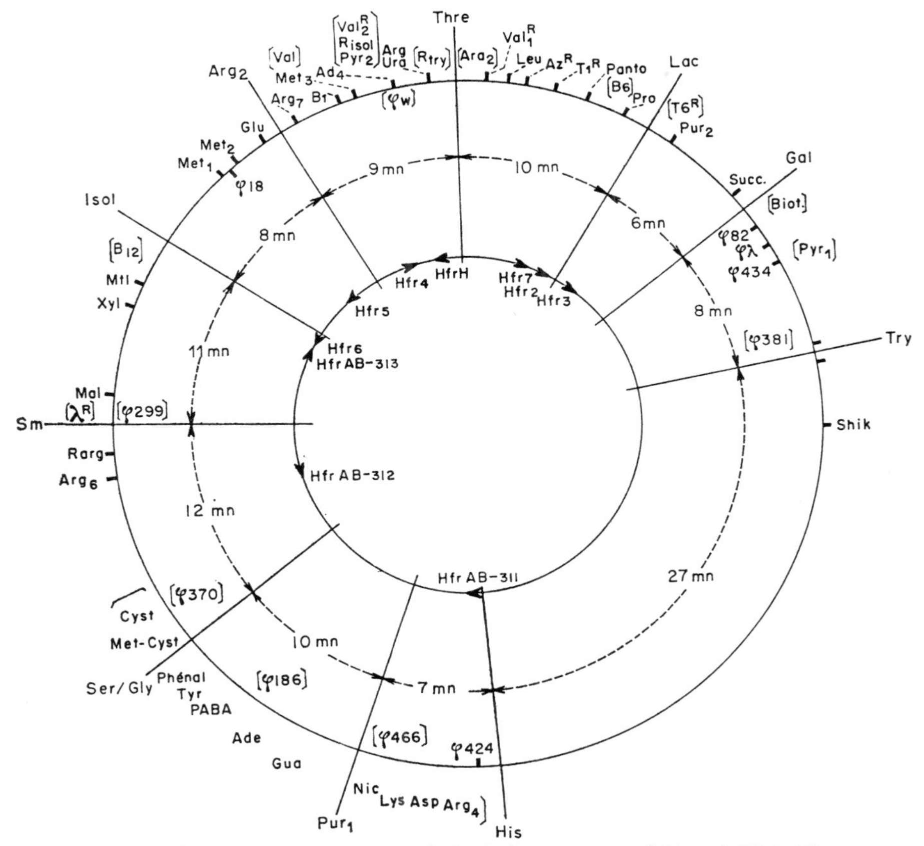

FIG. 27. Schematic representation of the linkage group of *E. coli* K12. The outer line represents the order of the characters (not their absolute distances). The dotted lines represent the time intervals of penetration between pairs of markers corresponding to the radial lines. The inner line represents the order of transfer of different Hfr types described in Fig. 26. Each arrow corresponds to the origin of the corresponding Hfr strain.

Symbols correspond to synthesis of threonine (Thre), leucine (Leu), pantothenate (Panto), proline (Pro), purines (Pur), biotine (Biot), pyrimidines (Pyr), tryptophan (Try), shikimic acid (Shik), histidine (His), arginine (Arg), lysine (Lys), nicotinamide (Nic), guanine (Gua), adenine (Ade), para-aminobenzoic acid (PABA), tyrosine (Tyr), phenylalanine (Phenal), glycine (Gly), serine (Ser), cystein (Cyst), methionine (Met), vitamin B_{12} (B_{12}), isoleucine (Isol), thiamine (B_1), valine (Val); to fermentation of arabinose (Ara), lactose (Lac), galactose (Gal), maltose (Mal), xylose (Xyl), mannitol (Mtl); requirement for succinate (Succ), aspartate (Asp), glutamate (Glu); resistance to valine (Val^r), to sodium azide (Az^r), to phages T1 ($T1^r$), T6 ($T6^r$), λ (λ^r); repression for arginine (R_{arg}), isoleucine (R_{isol}), tryptophan (R_{try}), location of inducible prophages 82, λ, 434, 381, 21, 424, 466, and of noninducible prophages 186, 370, 299, 18 and W. Symbols in brackets indicate that the location of the marker with respect to neighboring markers has not been exactly determined.

The figures given for the time intervals between two markers correspond to the average of several experiments of interrupted mating, using Hfr strains which inject early the region involved.

TABLE XXVII

CHROMOSOMAL REARRANGEMENTS OBSERVED AFTER TREATMENT OF Hfr H BACTERIA WITH NITROGEN MUSTARD

Strain																				
Hfr H	O	T	L	Az	T_1	Pro	Lac	Ad	Gal	H	S-G	Sm	Mal	Xyl	Mtl	Isol	M	Arg	B_1	
Hfr H CR1	O	T	L	Az	T_1	Pro	[Xyl	Mtl	Isol	M	Arg]	Ad	Gal	H	S-G	Sm	Mal	B_1		
Hfr H CR2	O	Lac	Ad	Gal	H	S-G	[T	L	Az	T_1	Pro]	Sm	Mal	Xyl	Mtl	Isol	M	Arg	B_1	

a rearrangement is particularly easy when it occurs in an Hfr strain, because the change in the order of transfer of markers can be accurately determined by interrupted mating experiments.

From Hfr H bacteria treated with nitrogen mustard, two strains have been isolated in which the sequence of markers has been radically altered as shown in Table XXVII. In Hfr H CR1, a break has occurred in the Lac region which is entirely deleted; the segment Xyl-Mtl-Isol-M-Arg has been transposed into the place of the Lac region, between Pro and Ad. In Hfr H CR2, the TL-Az-T_1-Pro segment has been transposed into the Sm region. It must be emphasized once again that such transpositions are rare and have not been found as a result of $F^+ \rightarrow$ Hfr mutations, but only after treatment with chromosome-breaking agents. In bacterial populations treated in this way, large deletions have also been found; one covers the whole Pro-Lac segment, which comprises about 1 per cent of the total chromosome of *E. coli* K12.

III. MAPPING OF GENETIC CHARACTERS IN *Escherichia coli* K12

Mapping of genetic characters in *E. coli* K12 involves the use of strains of opposite mating type, Hfr and F^-, which differ not only in the characters under investigation but also in a variety of other genetic characters already located. As we have emphasized throughout this monograph, some of these characters are used to prevent the growth of the Hfr parental type or even to destroy it, others serve for the selection of recombinants, whereas still others distributed throughout the linkage group play the role of markers. The use of highly marked recipient strains and of a small number of appropriate Hfr types greatly facilitates the mapping.

In order to obtain a satisfactory representation of the linkage group of *E. coli* K12, a series of nutritional mutants were selected after ultraviolet treatment of the F^- strain P678. With the help of Dr. E. A. Adelberg, whose experience was particularly valuable, some of these mutants were used in turn for isolating a wide variety of new polyauxotrophic mutants. This process was repeated thereafter several times.

In certain cases, it is useful to mark the Hfr donors, rather than the F^- recipient bacteria. In particular, this procedure permits one to perform reciprocal crosses, since it is easier to introduce an Hfr marker into an F^- recombinant than to make an Hfr strain from an F^- recipient.

The methods used for locating genetic characters in Hfr $\times$ F^- crosses have been reviewed in the preceding section (see page 161). The choice of method varies according to the nature of the character (nutritional, fermentative, prophage, etc.) and, for a given character, also depends on whether or not its wild allele can be used as a selective marker. The results of such mapping are summarized in Fig. 27. A few examples will be given to illustrate the methods employed.

A. Mapping of Selective Characters

When the Hfr strain carries a character which can be used for the selection of recombinants (the ability to synthesize a growth factor, for instance) and the F^- strain carries the mutant allele of this character, the frequency of transmission of the Hfr character to recombinants depends on the location of its genetic determinant on the Hfr linkage group. The greater the distance of this determinant from the origin of the Hfr, the lower the frequency of its transmission to recombinants. By measuring the frequency of recombinants formed in selections for this character, and by comparing it with the frequencies of recombination obtained in selections for other known characters, the region of the Hfr chromosome on which this character is located may be determined. Such a determination is valid only when the character under investigation is not too closely linked to the character used for selecting against the Hfr parent. More precision can be obtained by the use of several Hfr strains, which differ in the location of their point of origin. An example of such mapping is given in Table XXVIII.

An F^- strain, unable to synthesize threonine (T^-), leucine (L^-), histidine (H^-), methionine (M^-), vitamin B_1 (B_1^-), unable to ferment lactose, galactose, maltose, mannitol, and xylose, and resistant to streptomycin (S^r), was irradiated with ultraviolet light, and a clone which requires arginine (Arg^-) in addition to the characters mentioned previously was isolated. All the other markers having already been located on the bacterial linkage group, the problem was to localize the Arg^- marker. This F^- strain was crossed with three different Hfr strains, all prototrophic and S^s. From each cross, the $T^+L^+S^r$, H^+S^r, and Arg^+S^r recombinants were selected and counted. From the results given in Table XXVIII, it is apparent that, irrespective of the Hfr strain used, the numbers of M^+S^r and Arg^+S^r recombinants are very similar. The Arg marker is therefore located close to the M marker.

This conclusion was strengthened by analyzing the genetic constitution of the recombinants formed in such crosses (Table XXIX). It can be seen that about 90 per cent of the M^+S^r recombinants also inherited the Arg^+ character of the Hfr parent, and vice versa for the Arg^+S^r

TABLE XXVIII

LOCALIZATION OF AN ARG MARKER BY DETERMINATION OF THE FREQUENCY OF TRANSMISSION[a]

Hfr type	Selection						
	$T+L+S^r$	$H+S^r$	$M+S^r$	$Arg+S^r$	$T+L+Arg+S^r$	$H+Arg+S^r$	$M+Arg+S^r$
Hfr H	1.5×10^6	2×10^5	1.1×10^3	1.4×10^3	$< 10^3$	$< 10^3$	1×10^3
Hfr type 2	1.9×10^6	2.3×10^3	2.7×10^5	2.6×10^5	1.4×10^5	$< 10^3$	2.3×10^5
Hfr type 4	$< 10^3$	9×10^4	2.3×10^6	2.2×10^6	$< 10^3$	1.5×10^4	2.1×10^6

[a] An F^- $T^- L^- M_1^- Arg_7^- H^- S^r$ strain is crossed with three different prototroph Hfr S^s strains under standard conditions (2.10^7 Hfr and 4.10^8 F^- bacteria per ml). Various types of recombinants are selected. The figures represent the numbers of recombinants per milliliter of the mating mixture after 60 minutes. For the order of transfer of genetic markers by the three Hfr strains, see Fig. 26.

recombinants. It can be concluded, therefore, that the two markers are closely linked. The relative order of the two markers was investigated by interrupted mating experiments in crosses between the same F^- strain and an Hfr strain of type 4 (see Fig. 26), which is known to inject its chromosome in the order O B_1 M Mtl Xyl. . . . .S^s. . . . . . .H. . . . . . . .LT. At different times after the two cultures had been mixed, samples were

TABLE XXIX
LOCALIZATION OF AN ARG MARKER BY ANALYSIS OF THE GENETIC CONSTITUTION OF RECOMBINANTS[a]

Unselected characters	Per cent of unselected markers among recombinants	
	M^+S^r	Arg^+S^r
TL	<1	<1
M	—	92
H	2	1
Arg	93	—
Lac	<1	<1
Gal	<1	<1
Mtol	37	31
Xyl	35	29
Mal	8	6

[a] In a cross Hfr type 4 (see Fig. 26) prototroph S^s × F^- $T^-L^-M^-Arg_7^-H^-Lac_1^-Gal_b^-Mtl^-Xyl^-Mal^-S^r$, M^+S^r, and Arg^+S^r recombinants are selected and their genetic constitution analyzed. The figures represent the per cent of recombinants which have inherited the unselected markers from the Hfr parent.

withdrawn, treated in the Waring blendor and plated on selective media for M^+S^r and Arg^+S^r recombinants. The results reported in Table XXX show that the Arg^+S^r recombinants started appearing about 1 minute before the M^+S^r recombinants. A large proportion of the first Arg^+S^r recombinants, moreover, were M^-, whereas the majority of the first M^+S^r recombinants recovered were Arg^+. The next known marker, Mtl, started appearing only several minutes later. The sequence of genetic characters is thus B_1 Arg M Mtl, with Arg located close to M.

When two characters are found to be closely linked, it is useful to determine whether they can be incorporated into, and transmitted simultaneously by a transducing bacteriophage. Such a cotransduction by phage 363 can be achieved in the case of the M and Arg markers. As shown in Table XXXI, a strong association, 30 per cent or more, is found in all selections, although the degree of this association varies in a significant and reproducible way depending on the selection.

TABLE XXX
LOCALIZATION OF AN Arg MARKER BY INTERRUPTED MATINGS[a]

Time of interruption (minutes)	Number of recombinants		Per cent of unselected Hfr markers among recombinants			
			$Arg+S^r$		$M+S^r$	
	$Arg+S^r$	$M+S^r$	M+	Mtl+	Arg+	Mtl+
0	0	0	—	—	—	—
6	0	0	—	—	—	—
8	3	0	0	0	—	—
10	19	4	12	0	75	0
11.5	56	28	39	0	92	0
13	126	62	57	0	87	0
14.5	217	183	82	1	94	3

[a] In a cross Hfr type 4 (see Fig. 26) prototroph S^s × F− Arg_7 $-M_1-$Mtl$-S_r$, samples are taken at various times and treated in a Waring blendor. After treatment, samples are plated on selective media, and the number of $Arg+S^r$ and $M+S^r$ recombinants is measured (left). The genetic constitution of these recombinants is determined and expressed as per cent of these recombinants which have inherited the unselected markers Mtl+, Arg+, or M+ from the Hfr parent (right).

TABLE XXXI

LOCALIZATION OF AN ARG MARKER AND OF PROPHAGE 18 BY TRANSDUCTION[a]

1. Number of transduced bacteria/ml

Selection	Number of colonies/ml
M+	10.8×10^3
Arg+	8.07×10^3
M+Arg+	2.92×10^3

2. Genetic constitution of recombinants

M+	Exp. 1	Exp. 2	Arg+	Exp. 1	Exp. 2
Arg+(18)+	26	32	M+(18)+	45	51
Arg+(18)−	3	7	M+(18)−	14	14
Arg−(18)+	65	50	M−(18)+	5	7
Arg−(18)−	6	11	M−(18)−	36	28
Total Arg+	29	39	Total M+	59	65
Total (18)+	91	82	Total (18)+	50	58

[a] $M_1^-Arg_7^-(18)^-$ bacteria are infected with the transducing phage 363 grown on M+Arg+(18)+ bacteria. Bacteria transduced for M+ and for Arg+ are scored on MA selective media. For each class of transduced cells, the figures represent the per cent of unselected markers from the donor bacteria.

B. Mapping of Unselected Characters

When the characters under study cannot be used for selecting genetic recombinants, the frequency of their transmission cannot be measured directly. The methods of mapping are restricted, therefore, to the genetic analysis of recombinants selected for other known markers. This situation obtains for mutations involving nutritional requirements or the inability to utilize a carbon source, which, although carried by the F^- recipient, cannot be used in selecting recombinants because of the presence of impurities in the selective medium, of an incomplete block in the reaction involved, or of a high reversion rate. It is also the case for those characters of the recipient which determine resistance to agents such as drugs, antibiotics, bacteriophages, etc. Finally, it is the case for most mutations when borne by an Hfr strain.

Of particular interest among the genetic characters which have been studied in bacteria is the location of the prophages which have been described in Chapters VI and VII. It has been seen that among a series of temperate bacteriophages active on *E. coli* K12, all the ultraviolet inducible prophages are located on a segment of the chromosome of Hfr H which extends from Gal to a region beyond His. All the ultraviolet noninducible prophages, on the contrary, appear to be located more distally on the chromosome of Hfr H bacteria. Additional information on the location of these prophages and on their behavior in reciprocal crosses has been gained by the use of Hfr strains which differ in the location of their point of origin.

When bacteria lysogenic for an inducible prophage are crossed with nonlysogenic F^- recipients, zygotic induction takes place, its frequency depending on the distance between the location of the inducible prophage on the Hfr chromosome and the origin of this chromosome. That the extent of zygotic induction is actually an expression of the distance of a prophage from the origin of the Hfr chromosome, and, therefore, of the frequency of its transfer, is confirmed by experiments in which different Hfr strains, lysogenic for the same inducible phage, are crossed with a nonlysogenic F^- recipient. The results of such crosses involving two Hfr strains, Hfr H and an Hfr strain of type 4 (see Fig. 26), and two inducible prophages, λ and 424, are given in Table XXXII. In Hfr H, the Gal and H characters are relatively proximal and transferred in the order Gal — H, whereas in Hfr type 4, these characters are relatively distal and transferred in the reverse order H — Gal. It is seen that the frequency of zygotic induction of prophage λ is much lower in an Hfr type $4(\lambda)^+ \times F^-(\lambda)^-$ cross than in an Hfr H $(\lambda)^+ \times F^-$ $(\lambda)^-$ cross.

Moreover the frequency of zygotic induction of prophage 424 is higher than that of prophage λ in crosses involving Hfr type 4, contrary to what is observed in the corresponding crosses involving Hfr H. This result could be predicted from the fact that, on the chromosome of Hfr type 4, prophage 424 is proximal to prophage λ, whereas the opposite is true in the case of Hfr H.

TABLE XXXII
ZYGOTIC INDUCTION OF TWO INDUCIBLE PROPHAGES IN CROSSES INVOLVING TWO DIFFERENT Hfr TYPES

Crosses[a]	Frequency of zygotic induction
1. Hfr type 4(λ)+ × F−(λ)−	3.2
2. Hfr type 4(424)+ × F−(424)−	14.3
3. Hfr H(λ)+ × F−(λ)−	68
4. Hfr H(424)+ × F−(424)−	15.4

[a] Crosses are performed under usual conditions (ratio Hfr/F− = 1/20, mild shaking). Times of plating vary according to the cross: 120 minutes for cross 1, 90 minutes for crosses 2 and 4, 70 minutes for cross 3. The frequencies of zygotic induction correspond to the number of infective centers formed per 100 initial Hfr bacteria. For the order of transfer of genetic characters by the two Hfr strains, see Fig. 26.

The use of Hfr types other than Hfr H has permitted also the location of the noninducible prophages described in Chapter VI (Jacob, Ionesco, and Wollman, 1961). When an F− strain, lysogenic for a noninducible prophage, is crossed with a nonlysogenic Hfr strain, the genetic analysis of the recombinants formed in different selections indicates the linkage relationships between the corresponding ly− character and the other genetic characters of the Hfr bacteria. Comparable results are obtained in the reciprocal cross between nonlysogenic F− and lysogenic Hfr strains. In such crosses, zygotic induction does not occur. The lysogenic character of the Hfr parent is accordingly transmitted to certain classes of recombinants and can thus be mapped on the Hfr chromosome. An example of the mapping of a noninducible prophage, prophage 18, is given in Table XXXIII.

It may be seen that, in the reciprocal crosses, Hfr type 2 (18)+ × F− (18)− and Hfr type 2 (18)− × F− (18)+, lysogeny segregates, prophage 18 being strongly linked to the Arg marker. More precise information on the location of prophage 18, recorded in table XXXI, is obtained by transduction experiments which not only confirm the linkage of prophage 18 to Arg, but also show that this prophage is even more closely linked to M than to Arg (Jacob, Ionesco, and Wollman, 1961).

TABLE XXXIII
LOCALIZATION OF PROPHAGE 18 BY RECIPROCAL CROSSES

Unselected markers	Genetic constitution of recombinants in crosses[a]					
	Hfr(18)+ × F−(18)− Recombinants			Hfr(18)− × F−(18)+ Recombinants		
	T+L+S^r	Arg+S^r	H+S^r	T+L+S^r	Arg+S^r	H+S^r
TL	—	67	41	—	64	34
Arg	21	—	46	16	—	38
(18)	17	92	33	14	84	31
Mtl	12	33	16	12	38	18
Xyl	11	30	12	10	34	14
Mal	4	18	2	4	21	8
H	< 0.5	2	—	< 0.5	4	—
Gal	< 0.5	< 0.5	4	< 0.5	< 0.5	2
Lac	< 0.5	< 0.5	0.5	< 0.5	< 0.5	< 0.5

[a] In the two reciprocal crosses Hfr type 4 prototroph S^s(18)+ × F− T−L−Arg_7−H−Mtl−Xyl−Mal−Gal−Lac−S^r(18)− and Hfr type 4 S^s(18)− × F− T−L−Arg_7−H−Mtl−Xyl−Mal−Gal−Lac−S^r(18)+, T+L+S^r, Arg+S^r, and H+S^r recombinants are selected and their genetic constitution analyzed. The figures represent the per cent of recombinants which have inherited the unselected characters from the Hfr parent.

Of the six noninducible prophages which have been investigated, five have been localized on the bacterial chromosome. These are prophages W, 18, 299, 370, and 186. Each of them occupies a specific site, and these sites are distributed over about half of the linkage group of *E. coli* K12, on a segment which extends from serine-glycine (S-G) to threonine (T) (see Fig. 27). No overlapping has yet been observed between the region where the noninducible prophages are located and the region where the inducible ones are located.

For one of the noninducible prophages, prophage 363, no chromosomal location has been found. In a series of reciprocal crosses involving different Hfr strains, neither the ly^+ nor the ly^- character of the Hfr parent was transmitted to recombinants, whatever the characters used for selection. This observation is of particular interest in view of the fact that, of all the temperate phages investigated, phage 363 is the only one capable of generalized, nonspecific transduction. A plausible hypothesis is that prophage 363 does not occupy a permanent specific site on the bacterial chromosome, but can rather undergo transient fixation at any of numerous positions on this chromosome. Its ability to transduce any of the bacterial characters of *E. coli* K12 would be an expression of this lack of specific chromosomal localization.

* * *

The analysis of crosses between Hfr H and F^- bacteria has led to a coherent picture of the process of bacterial conjugation with its three main steps: conjugation proper, genetic transfer and genetic integration. Extension of this analysis to $F^+ \times F^-$ crosses leads to the conclusion that the difference between the two systems is a difference not in degree but in nature. In both cases, the efficiency of conjugation, that is, of specific pairing, appears to be the same. The distinction lies in the process of genetic transfer. In an Hfr $\times$ F^- cross, almost every Hfr cell is capable of transferring its chromosome in an orderly, oriented way. The unequal frequency of transfer of different genetic characters is a direct consequence of the mechanism of transfer of the bacterial chromosome. The characters of an Hfr bacterium which are transmitted with low frequency are those that are located on the distal part of the chromosome. In an $F^+ \times F^-$ cross, the transfer of chromosomal markers from donor to recipient bacteria is not the rule, but the exception. An F^+ bacterium, as such, appears to be incapable of transferring its chromosome, or segments of it, after conjugation. Transfer of chromosomal markers is accomplished by F^+ cells which have mutated to other donor types; i.e., by cells which are no longer F^+.

The recombinants which are formed in $F^+ \times F^-$ crosses result mainly from Hfr mutants (stable or unstable) which have appeared in the population of F^+ bacteria. These Hfr mutants may be of a variety of types, each type being characterized by a linear, oriented linkage group. Notwithstanding their apparent diversity, all Hfr types are only particular representations of a unique underlying pattern, the continuous, uninterrupted linkage group which can best describe their common features. Because all Hfr types arise by mutation from F^+ bacteria, the conclusion appears inescapable that this continuous linkage group is that of F^+ bacteria. One is led, therefore, to propose the hypothesis that the chromosome of an F^+ bacterium and that of an Hfr cell differ in configuration, and that the mutation from F^+ to Hfr results in a change in the structure of the chromosome. As to those hereditary properties of F^+ bacteria which are transmitted to F^- bacteria during conjugation, such as the sex factor F and colicinogeny, it may be supposed that they are under the control of determinants the relation of which to the bacterial chromosome, if such a relation exists, differs from that of the other genetic determinants of F^+ bacteria. This problem will be discussed later (see Chapters XI and XVI).

There is some indication that conjugation between F^+ and F^- bacteria might differ from that between Hfr and F^- bacteria with respect to transfer of cytoplasmic constituents. In Hfr $\times$ F^- crosses, elements as diverse as enzymes, substrates, inducers or repressors of enzyme synthesis (Pardee, Jacob, and Monod, 1959), or bacteriophages in the vegetative state (Jacob and Wollman, 1956b), which may all be considered to be located in the cytoplasm, are not found to be transferred during conjugation (see Chapter VIII). In contrast, a product formed after U.V. irradiation of F^+ lysogenic bacteria is transferred, upon conjugation, to lysogenic F^- cells, in a fraction of which it duplicates the effects of U.V. induction. Such effect is not observed in crosses involving Hfr lysogenic donors (Borek and Ryan, 1960). Similarly the cytoplasmic factor, or repressor, which determines the immunity of lysogenic bacteria (see Chapter XV, page 302) appears to be transferred from lysogenic donors to nonlysogenic recipients during conjugation between F^+ and F^- bacteria, but not between Hfr and F^- bacteria (Fisher, 1961). It seems likely, therefore, that the transfer of cytoplasmic constituents through the conjugation bridge may occur only when chromosomal transfer does not take place.

The existence of different Hfr types which transfer different segments of the chromosome of *E. coli* K12 at high frequency greatly facilitates the location of genetic characters on this chromosome. In consequence, and considering how recent is the introduction of bacteria into genetics, *E. coli* appears already as an organism the genetic map of which is among the best known.

CHAPTER XI

The Genetic Basis of Sexual Differentiation

In *E. coli* K12, conjugation takes place between bacteria of opposite mating types which, for convenience, have been called *donors* and *recipients.* In view of the different roles played by each type during conjugation, donor bacteria may be considered analogous to males and recipient bacteria to females.

I. THE SEXUAL TYPES OF *Escherichia coli*

Before examining the factors which are at play in the determination of these sexual types, their distinctive properties will be summarized briefly.

A. Differences between Donor and Recipient Bacteria

The sexual types of *E. coli* K12 may be best defined by enumerating those properties of donor bacteria which distinguish them from recipients (E. L. Wollman, Jacob, and Hayes, 1956). Although they may belong to types which are as distinct as F^+ and Hfr, donor bacteria all have certain common properties, which differentiate them from recipient bacteria.

1. *Surface properties which allow donor bacteria to pair specifically with F^- recipients.* The nature of the surface structures which are responsible for specific pairing is still unknown; but in a given strain, such as *E. coli* K12, these structures appear to be identical in F^+ bacteria and in the different Hfr strains, since all donor strains can mate with F^- bacteria with comparable efficiency. As already seen in Chapter VIII, the difference in surface structure between donor and recipient bacteria is also revealed by other properties, such as antigenicity and susceptibility to certain bacteriophages (see p. 119).

2. *The ability to transfer genetic material to recipient bacteria.* All donor types possess the actual or potential ability to transfer genetic determinants upon conjugation, although the nature and the extent of such transfer varies from one donor type to another. F^+ and Hfr donors in particular differ widely in this respect.

3. *The ability to mutate from one donor type to another and from the*

donor to the recipient type. Mutation from the F^- to the F^+ or Hfr types has never been described. On the contrary, mutation from F^+ to F^- is often observed, and mutations from F^+ to Hfr have been found whenever they have been looked for. It seems, moreover, that the recombinants formed at low frequency in $F^+ \times F^-$ crosses are due mainly to Hfr mutants present in the population of F^+ bacteria. Some of these Hfr mutants may be unstable and transient, since mutations from Hfr to F^+ are known also to occur. As for the Hfr $\rightarrow$ F^- or $Hfr_1 \rightarrow Hfr_2$ mutations, it is probable that they can occur only in two steps, the first of which involves mutation to the F^+ state.

B. Differences among Donor Types

Although they have some common properties, donor bacteria may belong to different types such as F^+ and Hfr. It should be observed that the original distinction between F^+ and Hfr bacteria in terms of a difference in fertility between these two types of strains can no longer be maintained, since F^+ and Hfr bacteria both conjugate with F^- bacteria with a similar, high efficiency. However, the distinction between them deserves to be kept because of the difference in the genetic determinants which are transferred by the different types of Hfr bacteria on one hand and by F^+ bacteria on the other (see Chapter XVI). The properties by which Hfr and F^+ bacteria differ will be now summarized.

1. During conjugation, Hfr bacteria are able to transfer their chromosome progressively in a specifically oriented way. F^+ bacteria, on the contrary, appear to be unable to transfer the genetic determinants which are an integral part of their chromosomal structure. Only when F^+ bacteria have mutated to one of many possible Hfr types can the transfer of such chromosomal determinants be accomplished.

2. By contact, F^+ donors are able to transfer the sex factor F with high frequency to F^- bacteria. The F^- bacteria which have been thus converted to the F^+ type can subsequently transmit the F^+ character to other F^- strains. Hfr bacteria do not possess this property. They do not transmit with high frequency either the F^+ or the Hfr character. When placed in contact with F^+ bacteria, they acquire neither the F^+ character, nor the ability to transmit this character to F^- bacteria.

3. The recombinants formed in $F^+ \times F^-$ crosses are in general F^+; but the F^+ character cannot be mapped on the linkage group derived from the analysis of $F^+ \times F^-$ crosses (see Chapter IV). In an Hfr $\times$ F^- cross, on the contrary, the great majority of the recombinants formed are F^-. It is only among the recombinants formed with the lowest frequency that some Hfr strains may be found (Hayes, 1953b; Cavalli-

Sforza and Jinks, 1956); and these recombinants are of the same Hfr type as the Hfr parent.

There are, accordingly, two distinct categories of donors, which differ by a number of properties: Hfr bacteria, whatever the type to which they belong, and F^+ bacteria. It must be pointed out, however, that these types are readily interconvertible by what appears to be a single event, the "mutation" $F^+ \rightleftarrows$ Hfr; this "mutation" affects simultaneously all the properties which have been listed above.

In addition to the two extreme types, F^+ and Hfr, other donor types have been found. Some of these donor types, which arise from Hfr bacteria, may be called "intermediate" (see page 192). They can transfer their chromosome in a specifically oriented order, although with a much lower frequency than a typical Hfr; they can also transfer the sex factor, F, in a specifically modified form, with high frequency.

As will be seen below, the donor character of a strain is determined by a genetic structure, the sex factor. The donor character is, however, not always expressed phenotypically. F^+ or Hfr cultures in the stationary phase of growth may lose their "fertility." Bacteria from such cultures behave phenotypically as recipients, although genotypically they remain donors. This ability of donor bacteria to behave phenotypically as recipient phenocopies is very useful in certain crosses.

II. THE GENETIC DETERMINATION OF SEXUAL TYPES

Sexual differentiation in bacteria is under genetic control. This section will be devoted to the analysis of the factors which operate in the determination of sexual types.

A. Sex Factor and Sexual Type

The sexual type of a bacterial strain depends upon a specific genetic structure, the sex factor, the presence or absence of which conditions the donor (male) or recipient (female) character of a strain. The type to which a donor strain belongs seems to depend, as will be seen below, on the *state* and the *position* in the cell of this particular genetic entity.

1. *In F^- recipient bacteria,* the sex factor appears to be absent. The mutation of the recipient F^- type to any of the donor types has never been observed. When F^+ bacteria lose their donor character, this loss appears to be irreversible. It is only by contact with donor bacteria that F^- recipients can acquire the donor character. This acquisition is due to the transfer of the determinant from the donor type during conjugation.

2. *In F^+ donor bacteria,* the genetic determinant of sex is present, but it appears to behave independently of the rest of the genome. During conjugation with F^- bacteria, F^+ donors transmit the F^+ character with extraordinary efficiency. When mixed with an excess of F^+ bacteria, the majority of F^- recipients are converted to the F^+ state in less than 1 hour (J. Lederberg, Cavalli, and Lederberg, 1952; Cavalli-Sforza, Lederberg, and Lederberg, 1953; Hayes, 1953a). In such matings, the transfer of the sex factor occurs very early; it begins less than 5 minutes after mixing of the parental strains (Jacob and Wollman, 1955a). Accordingly, in F^+ bacteria, transfer of the sex factor occurs independently of the transfer of other genetic determinants, which takes place only with low frequency. It seems likely, therefore, that the F factor is not an integral part of the chromosomal structure which bears the hereditary determinants of F^+ bacteria. This conclusion does not necessarily imply a total absence of relation of the sex factor with the bacterial chromosome.

When a minority of F^+ bacteria are mixed with an excess of F^- bacteria, the F^+ character rapidly spreads in the F^- population, but the original F^+ bacteria do not lose their F^+ character. This finding indicates that F^+ bacteria contain several units of the sex factor, and that this factor is able to "reproduce" at a faster rate than the rest of the bacterial genome (J. Lederberg, Cavalli, and Lederberg, 1952; Cavalli-Sforza, Lederberg, and Lederberg, 1953). This conclusion is reinforced by the analysis of individual zygotes formed in $F^+ \times F^-$ crosses. No segregation of sexual types is found in the progeny of such zygotes isolated with the micromanipulator. Whenever a zygote gives rise to F^+ individuals, all the progeny of this zygote are composed of F^+ bacteria (J. Lederberg, 1958; E. L. Wollman and Jacob, 1958a).

Although it seems likely that each F^+ bacterium contains several units of the sex factor per nucleus, the number of such units is probably not very high. F^- variants can be indeed isolated from F^+ strains; in certain cases, they may even be selected. When F^+ bacteria are seeded on a semisolid medium (soft agar) in order to isolate motile strains, a large fraction of these motile bacteria is found to be F^- (Skaar, Richter, and Lederberg, 1957). Furthermore, the conversion of F^+ to F^- bacteria can be induced by treating F^+ bacteria with salts of heavy metals (cobalt or nickel) or, even more effectively, with acridine dyes (Hirota, 1956; Hirota and Iijima, 1957). In the course of such treatment, strains may arise which have a lower fertility than that of the original F^+ culture. Hirota has interpreted these results to mean that such bacteria contain fewer F particles than untreated F^+ bacteria. When the conditions of the treatment are well controlled, a high proportion of the F^+ bacteria are converted to F^- in a rather short time; this result substantiates the interpretation that acridine dyes do not select preexisting F^- variants, but actually convert F^+ bacteria to the F^- type (Hirota, 1960). The inference that the number of F particles present in an F^+ cell is probably small—of the order of 3 or 4 per chromosome—is also supported by the study of variant sex factors which have incorporated chromosomal segments. This will be discussed in a later section of this chapter (see page 195).

From all these facts, it can be concluded that in F^+ bacteria the sex factor F is a structure which is not integrated into the bacterial chromosome; the number of F units is small, but larger than the number of nuclei; and the F units are able to replicate independently and more rapidly than the bacterial genome. Because of the small number of copies present in the cell, it seems likely, however, that the sex factor is not an element randomly distributed in the cytoplasm, but rather that it occupies specific positions which allow its efficient transfer during conjugation.

3. *In the Hfr donor bacteria,* the genetic determinant of the donor type is also present, but its properties are completely different from those of the determinant in the F^+ bacterium. Hfr bacteria are unable to transmit the donor character at high frequency. The Hfr character can be found only among those recombinants which are formed at the lowest frequency (Hayes, 1953b; Cavalli-Sforza and Jinks, 1956). The genetic determinant of the Hfr character appears, therefore, to be located on the distal part of the Hfr chromosome, and to be linked to those genetic determinants which are transferred last during conjugation. This linkage has been confirmed experimentally. When various Hfr types, in which the distal extremity of the linkage group is known to bear identifiable genetic characters, are crossed with appropriate F^- recipients, the Hfr locus is found to be linked to the most distal character of the Hfr linkage group, and can be mapped in this fashion at the distal extremity of the Hfr chromosome (Jacob and Wollman, 1957b; E. L. Wollman and Jacob, 1958b).

In contrast to its extrachromosomal location in F^+ bacteria, the donor character of any particular Hfr type (i.e., the Hfr determinant of this type) is a chromosomal structure with a specific location which differs in the different Hfr types. As will be seen in the next section, the most reasonable hypothesis is that this chromosomal structure is the sex factor itself, now integrated into the bacterial chromosome. In Hfr bacteria, therefore, the sex factor has the properties of a chromosomal structure, which replicates in synchrony with the rest of the bacterial genome, and whose position determines the particular type of the Hfr strain under consideration.

B. The Mechanism of the $F^+ \rightleftharpoons$ Hfr Mutation

As established in the preceding chapter, the linkage group of any particular Hfr strain may be represented unambiguously as a linear, specifically oriented structure, which may be thought to correspond to the chromosome of this particular Hfr strain. At the distal end of this chromosome is located the integrated sex factor. All the linear linkage groups characteristic of the individual Hfr types are, however, only special cases of a more general structure. This more general structure, the idealized continuous linkage group of *E. coli* K12, can be deduced from the information gained by the analysis of the several Hfr types (see Fig. 27). Since all Hfr types were originally isolated as mutants of F^+ bacteria, it seems reasonable to suppose that the continuous linkage group is that of the F^+ bacteria from which the Hfr types originate.

A mutation from F^+ to any one of the possible Hfr types must be considered as a single event. However, such a single event has multiple consequences:

(1) It converts a probably continuous chromosomal structure which is not transferable during conjugation into a linear, oriented, and transferable structure, characteristic of a particular Hfr type.

(2) It suppresses the ability of the sex factor F to be transmitted freely during conjugation.

(3) It modifies not only the expression of the donor character, but also the location of its determinant in the cell, since this determinant becomes mappable thereafter on the bacterial chromosome at a location which is specific for the Hfr type considered.

The mutational event which brings about all these changes can be formally envisaged as the attachment of the sex factor at a given point of the continuous linkage group which is supposedly that of F^+ bacteria, with a concomitant opening of this structure. One extremity of the linear linkage group thus formed would carry the integrated sex factor and become the distal end of the Hfr chromosome, the other extremity becoming the origin of this chromosome (Fig. 28).

This interpretation of the $F^+ \rightarrow$ Hfr mutation accounts for all the distinctive features of F^+ and Hfr bacteria described above. Although it provides a gross explanation of this rather peculiar mutational process, the detailed sequence of events is still obscure. It is not known, in particular, whether the fixation of the sex factor induces the interruption of the continuous linkage group of F^+ bacteria, or whether an interruption of this linkage group precedes the fixation of the sex factor. The fixation of the sex factor could be thought to occur at random at any point of the bacterial chromosome; alternatively, a preliminary change (mutation) which took place at a particular site on this chromosome could determine the subsequent fixation of the sex factor. Irrespective of the detailed mechanism of the $F^+ \rightarrow$ Hfr mutation, it appears from the preceding analysis that the sexual type of a bacterial strain does not

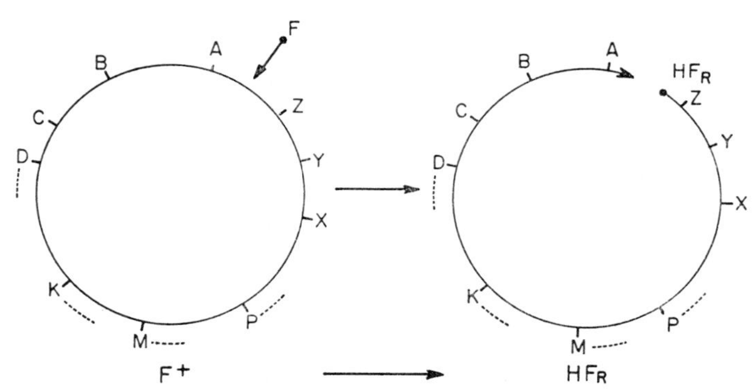

FIG. 28. Diagrammatic representation of the variation $F^+ \rightarrow$ Hfr.

depend simply on the presence or absence of the sex factor. Sexual type is also governed by the integrated versus autonomous state of this factor, by its location, and by the structure of the bacterial chromosome. This aspect of the problem will be now considered briefly.

C. SEXUAL TYPE AND CHROMOSOME STRUCTURE

The analysis of Hfr $\times$ F^- crosses led to the assignment of a specifically oriented, linear linkage group to each particular Hfr type. The chromosomal structure of F^+ donor bacteria and of F^- recipients, on the contrary, cannot be investigated directly, although some indirect information concerning it can be gained from the comparative study of different Hfr strains. As noted above, the continuous linkage group derived from the analysis of linkage relationships in a variety of Hfr strains can be thought to correspond to the chromosomal structure of F^+ bacteria.

The particular properties of any given Hfr type are due both to the integration of the sex factor and to the linear orientation of its chromosome. These two properties are correlated: it is the position occupied by the integrated sex factor which determines the particular order of transfer of the Hfr chromosome.

Let us consider an Hfr strain having the characters A^+ B^+...G^+... P^+.......Y^+ Z^+ (Fig. 28). A^+ and B^+ are proximal characters, and one of them, A^+, is located close to the origin O. Characters Y^+ and Z^+ are distal and one of them, Z^+, is located close to the distal end of the Hfr chromosome. In a cross with F^- bacteria having the opposite characters A^-B^-...G^-...P^-....Y^- Z^-, one can select the recombinants formed *with high frequency* which have received from the Hfr parental type the proximal characters A^+ and/or B^+, as well as the recombinants formed *with low frequency* that have inherited the distal characters Y^+ and/or Z^+. The genetic constitution of these recombinants and their behavior in subsequent crosses can then be determined.

As stated previously, the recombinants formed with a high frequency are F^-. The Hfr character is found only among recombinants formed with a low frequency. These Hfr recombinants are of a type identical to that of the parental Hfr strain, and include only those cells which have inherited the most distal character, Z^+ (on the condition, needless to say, that Z^+ is very close to the distal extremity of the Hfr linkage group). Recombinants which are Y^+ Z^- are never Hfr. Not all Y^+ Z^+ recombinants, however, are Hfr. Although the acquisition by a recombinant of the distal end of the Hfr linkage group is a necessary condition for this recombinant to be Hfr, it is not a sufficient one (E. L. Wollman and Jacob, 1958a).

From the genetic analysis of the recombinants formed with low frequency, indications may be obtained of the linkage relationships which exist, in such recombinants, between the distal and the other genetic characters of Hfr bacteria. It is found that a large proportion of the recombinants which have inherited the Z^+ distal character have inherited also proximal characters such as A^+ and B^+. Among Z^+ recombinants, there is a closer linkage between the distal character, Z^+, and the proximal character, A^+, than between Z^+ and another distal character such as P^+ (Fig. 28). If the parental Hfr strain is one in which the most distal character, Z^+, is equidistant from Y^+ and A^+ on the continuous linkage group of Fig. 28, the same linkage relationship between these three characters is found by analysis of the Z^+ recombinants. It seems accordingly that pairing between the Hfr and F^- chromosomes reestablishes the linkage relationships between the Z^+ and the A^+ characters which had been disrupted by the $F^+ \rightarrow$ Hfr mutation. This observation lends support to the hypothesis that, like an F^+ chromosome, the F^- chromosome is a closed, continuous structure (E. L. Wollman and Jacob, 1958a).

The sexual behavior of the recombinants which have inherited the most distal character, Z^+, of Hfr bacteria, can be better understood in the light of these observations. The A^+ Z^+ recombinants, which have inherited both the most distal and the most proximal characters of Hfr bacteria, are in general Hfr. On the contrary, most of the A^- Z^+ recombinants are not Hfr. Many of these recombinants have peculiar properties. They are donor bacteria, since they form recombinants when crossed with F^- recipients, but at much lower frequency than the original Hfr type. When such recombinants, A^- B^- Z^+, are used as recipient bacteria in a back cross to the parental Hfr type, most of the A^+ B^+ Z^+ recombinants formed with high frequency are Hfr, and of the same type as the original Hfr. Such Hfr strains have been formed therefore in two

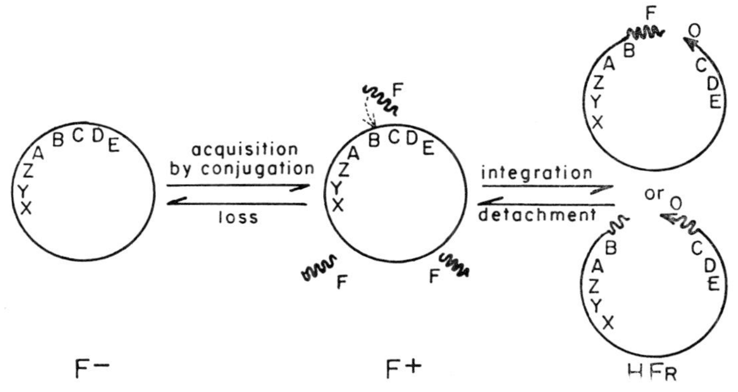

FIG. 29. Diagrammatic representation of sexual types in *E. coli*. An F− recipient has a closed chromosome but no sex factor. An F+ donor has a closed chromosome and contains several nonintegrated sex factors per chromosome. An Hfr has a linear chromosome with an integrated sex factor. The F+ → Hfr variation may be visualized as the attachment of the sex factor at any given point of the bacterial chromosome.

steps. In a first step, they have acquired the distal extremity of the Hfr linkage group with the integrated sex factor. In a second step, they have acquired the proximal extremity of the Hfr linkage group. It is not possible at present to decide whether the sex factor, when attaching to the chromosome, actually splits into two parts, one proximal and one distal, or whether the sex factor is attached at the terminal end, the proximal extremity determining only the linear, discontinuous character of the recombinant chromosome.

One is thus led to a representation of the different sexual types of *E. coli* K12 which takes into account the presence or absence of the sex factor, its properties and position in the cell, and the structure of the chromosome (see Fig. 29).

1. *F^- bacteria,* according to this representation, would be devoid of

the sex factor, and the chromosome of such bacteria would be (actually or virtually) continuous. The hypothesis that the chromosome of F^- bacteria is continuous is based on two lines of evidence, one of which has just been given. The second one comes from the analysis of different Hfr types. The fact that, in all cases analyzed so far, the gradient of transmission of genetic characters is the same as their order of penetration during transfer suggests that the F^- chromosome is not a discontinuous structure.

2. *F^+ bacteria* would carry the sex factor as an autonomous genetic structure not integrated into the bacterial chromosome, this chromosome being (actually or virtually) also a continuous structure.

3. *Hfr bacteria* would have a chromosome that is (actually or virtually) linear, with the sex factor integrated into it and located at the distal end of the chromosome. These two conditions, integration of the sex factor and discontinuity of the chromosome, would both be necessary for the expression of the Hfr character. According to this view, the $A^- B^- Z^+$ recombinants described above could be thought of as having an integrated sex factor but a continuous chromosome, the actual Hfr character being expressed only in a small fraction of the population.

In addition to the classic sexual types, F^-, F^+, and Hfr, it can be anticipated that other sexual types may exist in *E. coli.* A given phenotype, F^-, for example, may even correspond to different genotypes, according to whether its chromosome is continuous or linear, or whether it carries certain mutations which could affect the expression of the sex factor, when present. An example is found in the case of certain recombinants formed with low frequency in a cross between F^- bacteria and an Hfr strain studied by Richter (1957). When mixed with F^+ bacteria, these F^- recombinants become Hfr, and of a type identical to that of the original Hfr strain from which they were derived. According to Richter, such recombinants would carry a specific locus having a special affinity for the sex factor. The nature of this affinity locus will be discussed in the next section.

Finally, the sexual types of *E. coli* may be affected by the genetic constitution of the bacteria and by the intrinsic genetic properties of the sex factor itself. The differences which are observed in the sexual behavior of different strains of *E. coli* may be due to one or the other of these causes. Several examples of such differences have been described although the underlying mechanism has not been analyzed as yet. Different F^+ or F^- strains of *E. coli* K12 appear to differ, for instance, in their ability to transmit or to acquire the F factor (Hayes, 1953a, b). The strain *E. coli* B which behaves as an F^- recipient in crosses with *E. coli*

K12 F^+ or Hfr, is extremely difficult to convert to the F^+ state when mixed with K12 F^+ bacteria (Haan, 1954a; Calef and Cavalli-Sforza, 1955).

The sexual behavior of several different wild strains of *E. coli* has been investigated by Furness and Rowley (1957), and by Bernstein (1958). They studied the ability of these strains to form recombinants when mixed with either F^+ or F^- *E. coli* K12, and also their ability to transmit a sex factor to K12 F^- or to acquire the sex factor from K12 F^+. These studies have shown that other strains of *E. coli* differ from *E. coli* K12 in their sexual properties. In particular, certain "donor" strains are incapable of transmitting their sex factor to K12 F^- bacteria and certain "recipient" strains are incapable of acquiring the sex factor from *E. coli* K12 F^+. Finally, the sex factor of certain donor strains differs from that of *E. coli* K12, as shown by experiments in which K12 F^- bacteria were rendered F^+ either with the sex factor of K12 F^+ bacteria, or with the sex factor of another strain of *E. coli*. These two kinds of derived F^+ strains differ in such properties as the frequencies of recombination found in $F^+ \times F^-$ crosses, the genetic constitution of the recombinants formed, and the efficiency of transmission of the F^+ character to the same F^- recipient. The sexual behavior of a donor strain can therefore depend not only on the diverse factors which have been mentioned already, but also on the very nature of the sex factor itself.

III. THE SEX FACTOR AS A GENETIC ELEMENT

By virtue of its inheritance, stability, and transmissibility in crosses, the sex factor of bacteria has all the distinctive traits of a structure endowed with genetic continuity. In addition, it is a mutable structure since defective mutant sex factors can be isolated as will be discussed in a later section of this chapter (see page 196). This genetic structure, however, differs markedly from the other genetic determinants of bacteria which are constituent parts of their chromosomal structure. There is indeed every reason to believe that the sex factor, present in donor bacteria, is absent from recipient bacteria. Unlike the other characters of a strain, the donor or recipient state appears to correspond, therefore, to the presence or absence of a specific genetic structure and not to the existence of a specific determinant in one of two or more alternative allelic states.

Furthermore, when present in a bacterium, the sex factor may be either independent of the bacterial chromosome, as in F^+ bacteria, or attached to this chromosome at any one of a number of sites, as in the different Hfr types. It even appears that these two states, autonomous and integrated, are to a certain extent mutually exclusive, since integration of the sex factor prevents the continued replication of the same factor in the autonomous state.

In all these respects, the sex factor differs from the normal genetic units of the bacterial chromosome, but resembles the genetic material of temperate bacteriophages. Both the sex factor of bacteria and the genetic material of temperate bacteriophages are genetic structures which are nonessential to bacteria and which may be, therefore, either present or absent. When absent, they can be acquired only from an external source: by conjugation or by transduction (Arber, 1960) in the case of the sex factor; by infection, by conjugation, or by transduction in the case of the bacteriophage. When present, both can exist in alternative states, autonomous or integrated; and, in this latter state, they occupy definite positions on the bacterial chromosome. To elements having these properties, the name of *episomes* has been given (Jacob and Wollman, 1958b). The properties of episomes will be discussed in Chapter XVI.

The similarities which exist between the genetic material of temperate phages and the sex factor are exemplified further by the genetic interactions which can take place between these elements and the bacterial chromosome. Before examining the interactions which have been discovered in the case of the sex factor, it seems appropriate first to summarize the properties of transducing bacteriophages λ. This example of interaction between the genetic material of a temperate phage and a segment of the bacterial chromosome was discovered earlier and is better known; its analysis will, therefore, help in understanding the more recent findings involving the sex factor.

A. The Properties of Transducing Bacteriophages λ

Among the known mechanisms of genetic transfer in bacteria which were briefly described in Chapter II, that which has been called *phage mediated transduction,* or more simply transduction, consists in the transfer of genetic characters from a donor to a recipient strain by means of a temperate bacteriophage. As mentioned already, two main types of transduction may be distinguished: the type first discovered by Zinder and Lederberg (1952) in *Salmonella typhimurium* may be called *generalized, nonspecific transduction;* the second type, discovered by Morse (1954) with bacteriophage λ of *E. coli* K12, may be called *limited, specific transduction.*

As already mentioned, prophage λ is closely linked to a series of loci which control the fermentation of the galactose. When K12 $Gal^{+}(\lambda)^{+}$

bacteria are induced by ultraviolet light, a small proportion of the bacteriophages produced (about 10^{-6}) are able to transfer the Gal+ character to Gal− recipient bacteria (low frequency of transduction: Lft). The Gal+ transduced bacteria have acquired simultaneously the Gal+ character and prophage λ. They are not, however, true genetic recombinants, since the Gal+ strains obtained in this fashion are unstable and segregate stable Gal− offspring. They are *heterogenotes*: i.e., partial diploids that possess both the Gal− allele of the recipient and the Gal+ allele originating from the donor (Morse, Lederberg, and Lederberg, 1956a, b).

When such heterogenotes are in turn induced, a high proportion of the phages λ released are now able to transduce the Gal+ character (high frequency of transduction: Hft). The association which had been established between the original transducing phage λ and the Gal+ locus has therefore maintained itself during the lysogenic cycle, as well as during the cycle of vegetative multiplication which follows induction of the heterogenotes (Morse *et al.*, 1956a, b). As shown by Weiglé (1957), the genetic material of phage λ and of the Gal+ determinant have multiplied together, just as they also multiply together when Gal− sensitive bacteria are infected with the bacteriophages λ of an Hft lysate. In lysogenic bacteria, the genetic material of a phage behaves as a genetic element of the bacterium; in the case of the transducing bacteriophage λ, it is a genetic determinant of the bacterium which behaves as a part of the genome of the phage.

Bacteriophages λ appear to be incapable of transducing any genetic characters of the donor bacteria other than the Gal character, the determinants of which are located on the bacterial chromosome close to the specific site occupied by prophage λ. Moreover, Gal transducing λ particles can be found only among bacteriophages λ obtained by induction of lysogenic bacteria, not among phages prepared by infection of sensitive bacteria. It appears, therefore, that a permanent association between the genetic material of the phage and of the adjacent segment of the bacterial chromosome is established when the genetic material of the phage is in the prophage state. The nature of this association has been clarified. The λ particles in an Hfr lysate that are able to transduce the Gal+ character are not normal λ bacteriophages, but defective ones (Arber, Kellenberger, and Weiglé, 1957; Campbell, 1957). An Hft lysate is in fact composed of a mixture, in about equal proportions, of normal infectious λ particles which are unable to transduce, and of defective phage particles able to transduce the Gal character. When Gal− sensitive bacteria are infected at low multiplicity (less than one infectious particle per bacterium), the Gal^+ bacteria isolated are all defective lysogenics: they are immune to λ but do not liberate infectious particles either spontaneously or after induction. However, when such bacteria are induced and then infected with a normal phage λ, they lyse and liberate a mixture of normal and defective particles in about equal proportions.

The defective bacteriophages λ which transduce the Gal character (λdg) have remarkable properties. They are permanently associated with a segment of bacterial chromosome which bears the Gal loci, but they are deprived concomitantly of a segment of the phage genome which amounts to about one-fourth of the length of the linkage group of λ. It appears, therefore, that, in the transducing bacteriophages λdg, a segment of the phage genome has actually been replaced by a segment of the bacterial genome (Arber, Kellenberger, and Weiglé, 1957; Arber, 1958).

Bacteria transduced by λdg are Gal^-/Gal^+ heterogenotes, which continuously segregate stable Gal^- nonlysogenic progeny. The added piece of genetic material, comprising the defective prophage and the transduced Gal segment accordingly behaves as a unit, being lost in its entirety. The heterogenotes are represented by the symbol Gal^-/ex Gal^+, which distinguishes between the genetic determinant of the bacterial chromosome (endogenote) and that borne by the defective prophage (exogenote) (Morse, Lederberg, and Lederberg, 1956a, b). Occasional recombinations may take place, however, between the exogenote and the bacterial chromosome. Stable nonlysogenic Gal^+ segregants can thus be isolated, as well as more rare Gal^+/ex Gal^- heterogenotes, or even Gal^-/ex Gal^- or Gal^+/ex Gal^+ homogenotes, all of which are defective lysogenics.

B. Interaction between the Sex Factor and the Bacterial Chromosome

The case of the transducing bacteriophage λ, in which recombination occurs between the genome of the phage and the bacterial chromosome, has helped to understand the behavior of certain atypical donor strains of *E. coli* K12, in which similar interactions appear to take place between the sex factor and the bacterial chromosome.

From an Hfr strain of type 2 (see Fig. 26), a variant has been isolated which exhibits properties intermediate between those of Hfr and of F^+ donor types (Adelberg and Burns, 1959). This *intermediate donor* (I) is similar to the Hfr type from which it arose, in the sense that it is able to transfer its chromosome in the same oriented sequence; but the frequencies of recombination observed are about one-tenth those in Hfr $\times$ F^- crosses. It resembles, however, F^+ donors in transferring the sex factor with high frequency; the recipients are converted not to F^+ but to I type donors, and these can in turn transfer serially the I donor character. The kinetics and efficiency of transmission of the I donor character and of the normal F factor are identical. These results indicate that I donors harbor a specifically modified sex factor, which apparently alternates between the autonomous and the integrated state and which has an affinity for a particular site of the bacterial chromosome. It would appear that although all donor cells are able to transfer the modified sex factor, only about 10 per cent of them have the Hfr phenotype at any given time (Adelberg and Burns, 1959, 1960).

The most remarkable feature of bacteria of the I type is that their autonomous sex factor, unlike that of F^+ strains, has acquired a unique specificity. It keeps the memory, so to speak, of the original location of the integrated sex factor from which it arose: upon transfer to F^- bacteria, it converts them to a special type of chromosomal donor. The most plausible hypothesis to account for this acquired specificity is that the integrated sex factor underwent genetic recombination with the bacterial chromosome in the original Hfr, thereby becoming partially homologous with a particular segment of this chromosome. This interpretation, which accounts for all the facts, is further strengthened by the results of experiments in which the original I donor type is converted to the recipient type by treatment with acridine dyes (Adelberg and Burns, 1960). The F^- recipients so isolated are converted to the I type by mating with either F^+ or I donors. It therefore seems not only that the sex factor has acquired a specificity for a defined region of the bacterial chromosome, but also that the chromosome has acquired a special affinity for the sex factor, as though a reciprocal recombination had taken place between the integrated sex factor and the adjacent region of the Hfr chromosome.

These findings allow a reinterpretation of the results of Richter which were mentioned above. In crosses between his unstable Hfr strain and F^- bacteria, the rare F^- recombinants formed at low frequency, which have inherited distal markers from the Hfr, would have inherited also part of the integrated sex factor, and thereby acquired a special affinity for the sex factor. This "Hfr_3 locus" would then segregate in further crosses (Richter, 1958). A striking feature of Richter's case is that the hypothetical recombination between the sex factor and the bacterial chromosome appears to have produced a new character in the strain, which changed from maltose$^+$ to maltose$^-$.

From different Hfr strains, Hirota (1959) has isolated intermediate donor types which have properties similar to those of the original strain studied by Adelberg and Burns.

Just as in the case of prophage λ, the sex factor in the integrated state appears to undergo occasional recombination with the neighboring region of the bacterial chromosome. As a result of this recombination, the sex factor acquires a specific affinity for the homologous region of the bacterial chromosome and the bacterial chromosome acquires concomitantly a special affinity for the sex factor.

C. Transfer of Genetic Characters by the Sex Factor: Sexduction

The hypothesis that an integrated sex factor may undergo recombination with the bacterial chromosome predicts that it should be possible to demonstrate the transfer of known genetic markers by the sex factor in the autonomous state. A necessary condition is the use of Hfr strains in which the integrated sex factor is closely linked to known genetic markers. Such situations have been obtained using Hfr types the distal markers of which are respectively the characters lactose, galactose, and proline (Jacob and Adelberg, 1959).

As an example, the characterization and properties of a sex factor that has incorporated the determinants of lactose fermentation will be described briefly. An Hfr strain of type 2 (see Fig. 26) injects its chromosome in the order O - Pro - L - T - B_1. . . . λ - Gal - Lac. The most distal marker known, Lac, which is located close to the integrated sex factor, is normally transferred only about 2 hours after the beginning of mating. In a cross between a Lac^+ S^s Hfr donor and a Lac^- S^r F^- recipient in which mating is interrupted after 30 or 60 minutes, rare Lac^+ S^r recombinants may, nevertheless, be selected. These recombinants, which are formed too early to be accounted for by the normal process of genetic transfer, exhibit very distinctive properties. They have received from the Hfr parent only the sex factor and the Lac^+ character and are donors of the intermediate type described above. Unlike the recombinants normally formed in Hfr $\times$ F^- crosses, they are unstable, and segregate bacteria which have the Lac^- phenotype of the recipient parent at a rate of about 10^{-3} divisions (see Fig. 30). They carry therefore both the Lac^+ and the Lac^- alleles, and are *heterogenotes* like the bacteria transduced for galactose by phage λ (see above). When mixed with F^- Lac^- recipients, they are able to transmit with high frequency both the sex factor and the Lac^+ character; the bacteria converted in this fashion are again Lac^-/F Lac^+ heterogenotes of the intermediate donor type (Jacob and Adelberg, 1959).

The autonomous sex factor and the chromosomal segment which

bears the Lac^+ determinants have therefore become permanently associated and behave as a single unit which can be transferred serially. Moreover, this modified sex factor has also acquired a specific affinity for the bacterial chromosome, since the recipient bacteria are converted not to the F^+ but to the I donor type. As such, they are able not only to

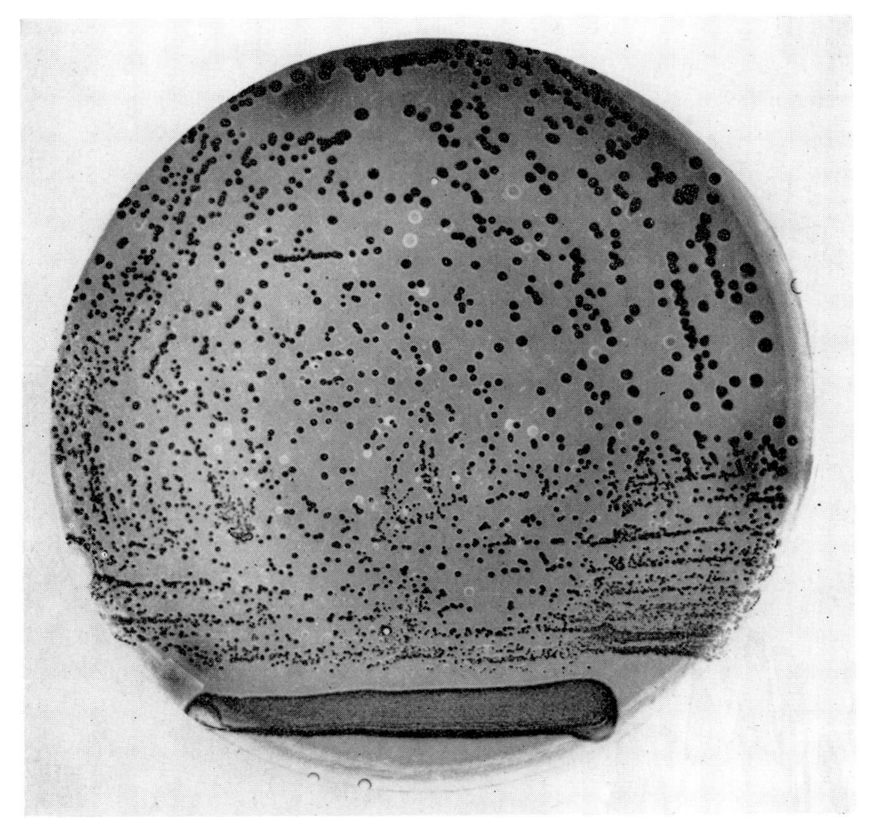

FIG. 30. Segregation of Lac^- bacteria from Lac^-/F^- Lac^+ heterogenotes obtained by sexduction. Heterogenotes are spread on EMB lactose agar. Dark colonies are Lac^+. The few clear colonies are Lac^- segregants.

transfer the F-Lac unit with high frequency, but also to transfer their chromosome with the same orientation as that of the original Hfr strain, although with one-tenth of the frequency. The amount of β-galactosidase produced by Lac^-/F Lac^+ heterogenotes is about three times that produced under similar conditions by haploid Lac^+ bacteria; this finding suggests that the heterogenotes may contain about three copies of the F-Lac^+ unit per chromosome.

From the unstable $Lac^-/F\ Lac^+$ heterogenotes, it is possible to isolate a variety of segregants which differ from them in sexual type, as well as in ability to ferment lactose. In addition to stable haploid Lac^- segregants, one can find stable Lac^+ haploid segregants and heterogenotes or homogenotes of all possible types (see Chapter XIV, page 252).

From other Hfr strains, in which the integrated sex factor is located close to the galactose and proline markers, respectively, heterogenotes which carry either the F-Gal or F-Pro units have also been prepared. Their properties are in every respect similar to those of the strains carrying F-Lac which have just been described. Given a suitable type of Hfr, it is clear, therefore, that any genetic locus of the bacterial chromosome can become incorporated in the sex factor and be transferred subsequently with high efficiency upon conjugation. This process, which is very similar to transduction by a bacteriophage, may be called *F-duction* or *sexduction* (see Fig. 31).

The exact size of the chromosomal segment which can be incorporated into the sex factor is not yet known. It is, however, generally small. The F-Pro factor does not include the closest known markers, T_1^r, Panto or Lac (see Fig. 27). The F-Lac factor carries all the linked loci which play a role in the utilization of lactose (see Chapters XIII and XIV), but not the T_6^r, Ad, or Pro markers. The size of the incorporated segment can vary somewhat, as shown by the analysis of several F-Gal factors isolated independently from the same Hfr strain. One of these F-Gal factors carries only the loci which control galactose fermentation. Another carries in addition the loci which control the synthesis of biotin, the requirement for succinate as a growth factor, and the specific sites of attachment for the three prophages 82, λ, and 434. Neither λdg, nor the transducing phage 363 which accomplishes generalized transduction, seems able to transfer simultaneously so large a segment.

Mutations of the sex factor are extremely difficult to detect among F^+ bacteria carrying a wild type F factor. They can be found more easily in a population carrying a sex factor which has incorporated a chromosomal segment. For instance, from a population of bacteria carrying an F-Lac factor and exposed to a heavy dose of ultraviolet light, clones can be recovered which exhibit some remarkable properties. These bacteria are still heterogenotes for the Lac segment and segregate Lac^- bacteria at the same rate as the original population. Yet they are unable to transfer their F-Lac factor or any chromosomal marker when mated with F^- recipients. When mated with Hfr cells, they do not form recombinants with high frequency and therefore do not behave as F^- recipients. During growth, however, they throw haploid F^- segregants which, in all

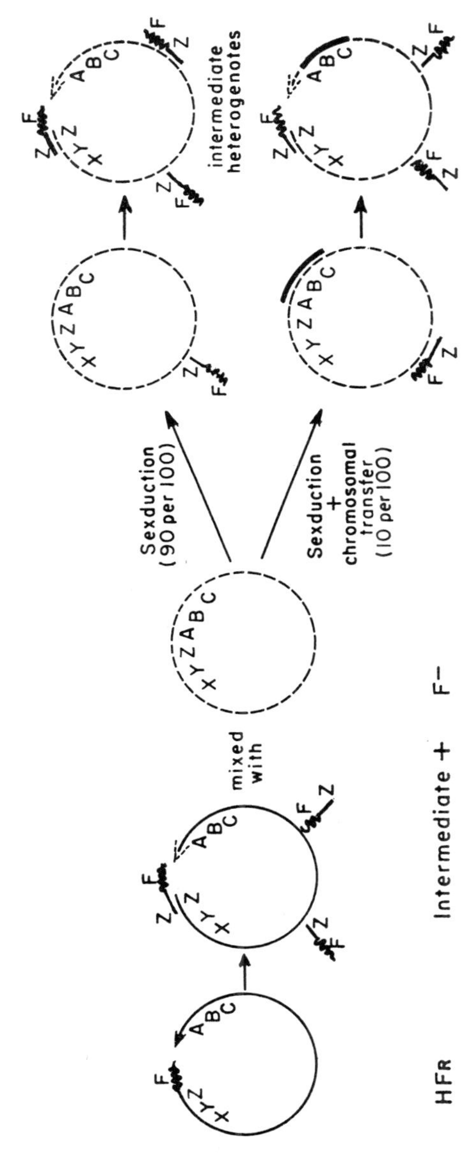

FIG. 31. Diagrammatic representation of the process of sexduction. In the original Hfr strain, the integrated sex factor becomes detached and incorporates the terminal marker Z. Thereafter the F-Z factor is transmitted and replicated as a single unit.

likelihood, have lost the defective sex factor. It seems clear therefore that the original sex factor has mutated toward a defective form which does not enable the carrier cell to behave as a donor. The presence of the defective sex factor is nevertheless manifested by the heterogenotic state of the carrier cell (Jacob and Wollman, 1961).

The ability of the sex factor to incorporate chromosomal segments which thereafter replicate autonomously with it and can be serially transferred, provides further evidence for the similarities in the genetic behavior of temperate bacteriophages and of sex factor and supports the concept of *episome,* which will be discussed in Chapter XVI. It also widens the scope of genetic analysis in bacteria, since it is now potentially possible to obtain any bacterial locus in heterozygous form, enhancing greatly thereby studies of the functions of genetic determinants. Examples of such functional analyses will be examined in Chapters XIV and XV.

* * *

Conjugation in *E. coli* K12 takes place between donor bacteria which can be considered analogous to males and recipient bacteria which can be considered analogous to females. The fact that in certain physiological states donor bacteria can play the role of recipients does not seriously affect this fundamental distinction. Such recipient phenocopies are indeed genotypically males and retain their donor potentialities.

Sexual differentiation is dependent upon a specific sex factor, the presence or absence of which conditions the male or female character of a strain. A peculiarity of the mating system of *E. coli* is the existence of different types of males, none of which has all the attributes of a male gamete. The two extreme types, F^+ and Hfr, are determined by the state of the sex factor in the cell: it is autonomous in F^+ bacteria, and integrated in the Hfr types. Any single Hfr type is in general able to transfer with high efficiency only part of its genome. The ability to transfer the total genome is the attribute of the aggregate of Hfr types. The formation of these varied Hfr types is, in turn, a potential property of F^+ bacteria.

From the comparison of crosses involving a variety of Hfr types, it may be concluded that whereas the F^- females and the F^+ males have a continuous linkage group, every Hfr type is characterized by a linear linkage group, the nature of which is determined by the position occupied by the integrated sex factor. When in the integrated state, the sex factor may undergo genetic recombination with the adjacent region of the bacterial chromosome, thereby giving rise to a new type of male which has properties intermediate between those of the F^+ and Hfr types. The modified sex factor alternates between the autonomous state and a fixed position on the bacterial chromosome. Segments of the chromosome may thus become incorporated into the sex factor and be transferred serially upon conjugation. The sex factor of bacteria has accordingly very special properties which differentiate it from the genetic determinants that are an integral part of the chromosome. In its behavior, it resembles the genetic material of temperate bacteriophages.

PART III

Bacterial Conjugation as a Genetic System

"Toutes choses étant causées et causantes, aidées et aidantes, médiatement et immédiatement, et toutes s'entretenant par un lien naturel et insensible qui lie les plus éloignées et les plus différentes, je tiens impossible de connaître les parties sans connaître le tout, non plus que de connaître le tout sans connaître particulièrement les parties."

PASCAL. *Pensées.*

CHAPTER XII

Meromixis and the Structure of the Genetic Material

One of the main conclusions which can be drawn from the genetic studies of microorganisms is that the basic mechanisms of heredity and variation are essentially similar in higher organisms and in bacteria and viruses. The genetic information of bacteria and viruses is stored in their nucleic acids, and their genetic determinants are arranged linearly in specialized structures similar to chromosomes. In bacteria, genomes from different lineages can be reassorted by certain highly distinctive processes of genetic transfer.

Bacteria differ from organisms more familiar to geneticists both by virtue of their generally haploid condition and by virtue of their special modes of genetic transfer. It was long believed that sexual reproduction as it exists in diploid organisms, with its alternation of karyogamy and meiosis, was the only possible process which allowed the reassortment, within one cell lineage, of determinants derived from distinct sources. Genetic studies in microorganisms have demonstrated that sexual reproduction, even though it may be the most perfect system of genetic transfer and hybridization, is not the only possible one. The genetic systems which have been discovered in bacteria also unite in one cell hereditary determinants derived from two different lines of organisms. They provide the same opportunity for genetic recombination as does sexual reproduction; but they do so by entirely different mechanisms, which have been vividly designated by Haldane (1955) as "alternatives to sex" and by Pontecorvo (1954, 1958) as "parasexuality."

The very peculiarities of the bacterial genetic systems, inherent in their lower degree of organization and complexity, are especially suitable for genetic analysis at the cellular level, as well as for studying the structure and functions of genetic material. In the first part of this chapter, the various modes of genetic transfer in bacteria will be compared and contrasted. In the second part, we shall summarize our knowledge concerning the structure of the genetic material of bacteria, and more especially the information concerning the structure of the bacterial chromosome obtained from the study of conjugation.

I. MEROMIXIS

Several processes of genetic transfer are known in bacteria. Bacterial conjugation, which involves contact between bacteria belonging to different mating types, is the one which may be formally considered to be most closely related to sexual processes as they occur in more complex organisms. Since sexual types in bacteria play different roles in conjugation, one is led to compare donors to males and recipients to females. A few years ago, when it was still believed that bacterial conjugation always leads to the formation of complete zygotes (karyogamy), J. Lederberg (1955a) proposed to describe all other kinds of bacterial gene transfer under the general term of *transduction,* which he defined as the transmission of a (nuclear) genetic fragment from a donor cell (which in every case so far is destroyed in the process) to a recipient cell (which remains intact). In this terminology, transduction was opposed to sexual reproduction, defined as "the formation of a hybrid zygote from the fusion of two intact gamete nuclei." It seems clear now that, in contrast to the zygotes which in higher forms result from the fusion of specialized gametes, bacterial conjugation gives rise in most instances to incomplete zygotes. In this respect, conjugation in bacteria resembles the other bacterial processes of genetic transfer, namely transformation by means of DNA and transduction by phage. Irrespective of mechanism, all these processes of genetic transfer in bacteria lead to the formation of *incomplete* zygotes, which are made up essentially of a recipient cell containing only a segment of genetic material from the donor cell. For this reason, it has seemed useful to unify under the general term of *meromixis* (from μερος: part and μιξις: mixture) those processes of partial genetic transfer, or partial fecundation, which result in the formation of incomplete zygotes or *merozygotes* (E. L. Wollman, Jacob, and Hayes, 1956; E. L. Wollman and Jacob, 1958b). According to this terminology, bacterial conjugation is a merozygotic process in the great majority of the pairs of a mating population. Only rare pairs give rise to holozygotes, or complete zygotes, which contain the whole genome of the male, and which thus resemble the product of the fusion of gametes in higher forms.

A. Mechanisms of Meromixis in Bacteria

Each mode of meromixis in bacteria can be defined in terms of the specific mechanism responsible for the transfer of fragments of genetic material from donor to recipient bacteria (Fig. 32).

In conjugation, it is as a consequence of a specific pairing between

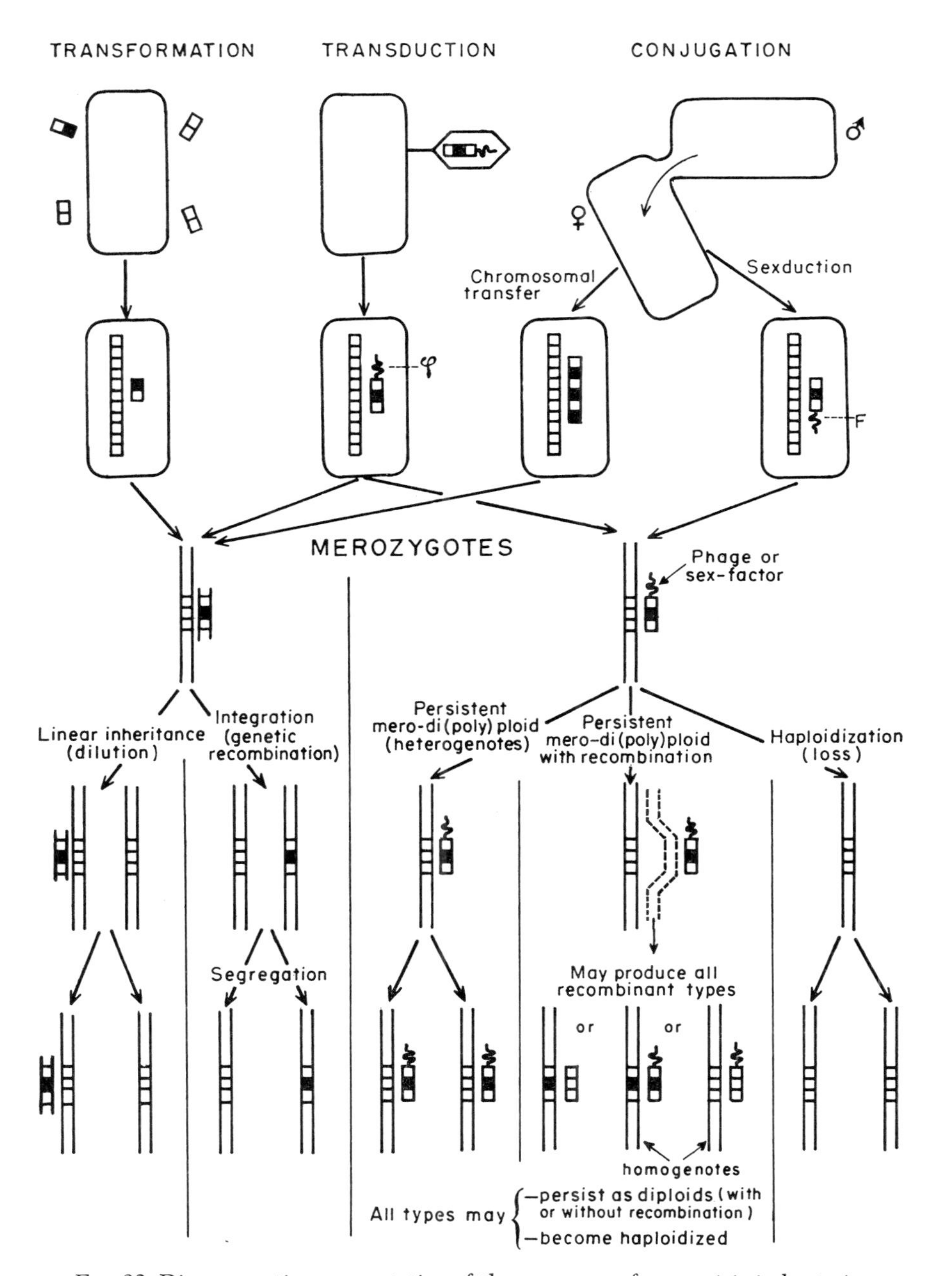

FIG. 32. Diagrammatic representation of the processes of meromixis in bacteria.

bacteria of opposite mating types that transfer of genetic material takes place. The material transferred from the donor consists of part of a chromosome (or of autonomous elements such as the sex factor, which may or may not be associated with a small chromosomal fragment). When it is the chromosome that is transferred, chromosomal rupture occurs at random during transfer: the fragmentation of the chromosome is, therefore, a secondary phenomenon. In transduction, a fragment of the donor bacterium becomes incorporated into a bacteriophage during the development of this phage in the donor bacterium. The chromosomal fragments incorporated in this fashion are transferred only secondarily by phage particles into recipient bacteria. Finally, in transformation, fragmentation of the genetic material of the donor bacteria is accomplished experimentally when the DNA of these bacteria is extracted. The DNA so obtained is able to penetrate into the recipient bacteria without the help of a vector. Whereas in conjugation the donor bacterium survives the mating act, in the two other cases of meromixis, genetic transfer can take place only after destruction of the donor cell.

The successive steps which lead to the formation of merozygotes are formally similar in each of these processes of genetic transfer although each may raise particular problems. These successive steps are: random collisions between the elements taking part in the process; fixation on the recipient bacterium of either the donor bacterium, the transducing phage, or the transforming DNA; and finally penetration into the recipient bacterium of the genetic material originating from the donor. In conjugation, the penetration of this genetic material takes place through the conjugation tube. In transduction, it is achieved by the injection of the content of the transducing phage particle. In transformation, the mechanism which allows the DNA of the donor to penetrate inside the recipient is not yet clearly understood.

The nature and size of the transferred genetic elements also differ in each mode of meromixis. In transformation, the contribution of the donor to each zygote is composed of a small number of DNA "molecules," with a molecular weight of about 6,000,000. In transduction, this contribution comprises short genetic segments which contain several functional units or "genes." The amount of chromosomal material which can be transduced by a phage particle varies with the transducing system concerned. In generalized transduction in *Salmonella*, the data of Demerec (1958) and his group indicate that it represents more than ten genes but probably not more than twenty; recent observations by Ozeki (1959) suggest that the transduced material consists of defined segments of predetermined size, rather than random fragments of a continuous structure. In conjugation, the contribution from the donor depends on the type of genetic element transferred. This contribution may comprise the sex factor alone. In the process of sexduction, the sex factor carries with it a small chromosomal segment which contains several functional units. When the chromosome itself is transferred, the chromosomal segment contributed by the donor bacterium to a merozygote, although of variable length, is generally larger than the segment transferred in other processes of meromixis.

Each of these modes of genetic transfer makes possible a particular type of genetic analysis and is therefore particularly suitable for the solution of certain classes of problems. In conjugation, chromosomal transfer offers the possibility of establishing chromosomal maps and of studying chromosomal segments of a considerable length. Sexduction, which gives rise to persistent heterogenotes, provides a convenient tool for a functional analysis of the genetic material. Transduction lends itself to an analysis of the fine structure of short chromosomal segments. Finally, transformation in principle permits the extension of genetic analysis to the molecular level. The possibility of using jointly conjugation and transduction which exists in some bacteria, such as *Escherichia, Shigella,* and *Salmonella,* should be very valuable in the study of many genetic problems. No system is yet known, however, in which transformation and any one of the other processes of genetic transfer may be studied concurrently.

B. The Genetic Events which Occur in Merozygotes

Whatever the mode of genetic transfer, the events which occur in a merozygote appear in every respect to be essentially similar. In all cases, a genetic segment derived from a bacterium of one lineage, the donor bacterium, has been transferred into a bacterium of another lineage, the recipient bacterium. Similar genetic problems, such as the phenotypic expression of the transferred genetic determinants, the mode of genetic recombination between material originating from the donor and a chromosome of the recipient, and the segregation of a recombinant bacterium from a zygote mainly constituted by a multinucleate recipient bacterium, may be laid in similar terms, whether one deals with transformation (Ephrussi-Taylor, 1955; Hotchkiss, 1956), transduction (Demerec, 1956; J. Lederberg, 1955a) or conjugation (E. L. Wollman, Jacob, and Hayes, 1956). It is therefore justifiable to make a distinction between those genetic processes which, in bacteria, lead to the formation of merozygotes, and the processes whether sexual or parasexual, which in higher forms involve full genetic complements from two different lineages.

In bacteria, as in most other lower forms, the vegetative cells are haploid and the merodiploid stage is usually restricted to the zygote, which undergoes reduction and gives rise to haploid progeny. With the exception of limited transduction and of sexduction, which will be discussed below, the genetic segment contributed by the donor bacterium does not replicate as such. The recipient bacteria, however, are generally multinucleate. When a merozygote gives rise to a recombinant type, a pure haploid clone of recombinants is segregated only after several generations. The short life of the heterozygotic phase, followed by a short stage of heterokaryosis, facilitates greatly genetic analysis. The possibility of obtaining large populations of merozygotes allows the selection of very rare recombinants, thereby increasing greatly the resolving power of recombinational analysis. As a matter of fact, both in bacteriophage (Benzer, 1957) and in bacteria (Demerec, 1956), the closest possible mutations may be separated in this fashion. This fact has made possible an analysis of the fine structure of the gene which could hardly have been achieved in other organisms.

Meromixis in bacteria is suitable also for a functional analysis of the genetic material. Recipient bacteria, although in some respects equivalent to female gametes, are not specialized cells as are the female gametes of higher forms. A particular genetic determinant, when present in a merozygote, is, therefore, potentially capable of expression in this merozygote or in its early descendants, without the interposition of such complex processes as germination, embryogenesis, and cellular differentiation. The merozygotes which are formed as a result of conjugation are particularly favorable for quantitative studies of the events which occur after genetic transfer. When bacteria of one sexual type are mixed with an excess of bacteria of the other type, practically the whole minority population undergoes conjugation. If the genetic characters under study are transferred with high frequency, almost the entire population of zygotes will have received the corresponding genetic determinants. Large populations of zygotes in which well defined genetic segments have been introduced may, therefore, be obtained.

Because of their early segregation, the merozygotes that are formed in conjugation between Hfr and F^- bacteria are convenient tools for the study of genetic recombination and of the expression of genetic determinants. Such merozygotes, which represent a partial diploid stage, may also be very useful for studies of physiological genetics which cannot be investigated unless a diploid heterozygous stage is available.

More lasting heterozygotes are formed in the processes of limited transduction and of sexduction which therefore lend themselves to the functional analysis of allelism. Although in limited transduction this analysis has been restricted so far to the determinants of galactose metabolism (E. M. Lederberg, 1960), it is potentially possible to obtain heterozygotes for any genetic character by sexduction. These partial heterozygotes (heterogenotes) are unstable. Genetic recombination can take place between the exogenotic segment and the bacterial chromosome, and reduction to the haploid state is also known to occur. From such heterogenotes, whether merodiploid as in limited transduction by λdg or meropolyploid as in sexduction, all possible segregants may be obtained, whether haploid or merodiploid (or meropolyploid) homogenotes or heterogenotes (see Fig. 32). The processes of recombination, segregation, and reduction which take place in these persistent heterogenotes are comparable in every respect to the processes of mitotic recombination which have been analyzed in *Drosophila,* in *Aspergillus* and in yeast and which have proved so useful in genetic analysis. It is for such mechanisms of genetic recombination that the term "parasexual" has been proposed by Pontecorvo (1954, 1958).

Another important characteristic of the different modes of meromixis in bacteria is that the contribution of the donor bacteria is primarily, if not exclusively, composed of genetic material. This is clearly the case for transformation and transduction, and appears also to be true for conjugation between Hfr and F^- bacteria. The processes of genetic transfer in bacteria appear therefore to be especially suitable for studying the structure of genetic material, as exemplified by the fact that the identification of DNA as the substratum of genetic information was first demonstrated in bacteria. Each mode of meromixis offers the possibility of investigating the structure of the genetic material at a different level of complexity and organization.

The information gained from these different aspects of genetic analysis in studies of bacterial conjugation will be examined in the following chapters of this monograph. Experiments bearing on the nature and structure of the genetic material transferred during conjugation will be first summarized in the concluding part of the present chapter.

* * *

Although bacteria reproduce asexually, a variety of phenomena have been discovered which all result in a reassortment of genetic characters. In spite of the diversity of the mechanisms involved, all these phenomena exhibit common characteristics: they consist almost exclusively in an unidirectional transfer of genetic material, and the zygotes formed are incomplete. The evolutionary value of these "alternatives to sex" is still difficult to assess, since the adaptability of bacteria to changes in environmental conditions appears to be amply satisfied by their almost infinite potentialities for variation. Mechanisms of genetic transfer do not, accordingly, seem to be important factors for the survival of the species in which they have been found. However, they may provide additional opportunities for varying the genome of a bacterial lineage.

From an evolutionary point of view, it may be wondered whether the different modes of meromixis might not represent intermediate stages —*attempts toward sex*—between vegetative reproduction and the restricted, but precise, mechanisms of sexual reproduction as they exist in higher forms. The examples of merodiploidy, or meropolyploidy, which have been found in bacteria might be considered likewise to represent intermediary stages between haploidy and diploidy. It is remarkable that, in these examples, the persistence of exogenotic segments seems to depend on the existence of self-reproducing genetic elements (episomes, see Chapter XVI) such as the genome of a phage or the sex factor, which, although independent of the bacterial chromosome, exhibit a special affinity for it.

II. THE STRUCTURE OF THE GENETIC MATERIAL

Genetic studies have shown that, in bacteria, genetic determinants are arranged in an orderly fashion along a single linkage group; it is this structure that we call a chromosome. Our knowledge of the bacterial chromosome is very indirect, however, and incomplete. We know that it is composed essentially of DNA, but we still lack information on the organization of the DNA in the chromosome. It has not yet been possible to isolate and characterize a bacterial nucleus or a bacterial chromosome. The DNA extracted from bacterial cells is not in the form of an organized cellular structure, but consists of DNA "molecules." In the last 10 years, the information gathered on the properties and structure of DNA in general, and on that of bacteria in particular, has developed strikingly. But between the extensive data on DNA on the one hand, and the genetic data on the bacterial chromosome on the other, there still exists a considerable gap.

A. DNA and the Bacterial Chromosome

On the basis of the results of chemical analysis (Chargaff, 1950) and of crystallographic studies (Franklin and Gosling, 1953; Wilkins, Stockes, and Wilson, 1953), Watson and Crick (1953a, b) have proposed a model for the structure of DNA. According to this model, a DNA molecule consists of two polynucleotide chains wound helically around a common axis. The backbone of each helix is constituted by phosphodiester bonds, and the bases at each level on one chain are hydrogen bonded to the bases at the same level on the other chain. For structural reasons, hydrogen bonding can take place only between the base pairs adenine-thymine and guanine-cytosine, which results in the complementarity of the two chains. As emphasized by Watson and Crick, this model has important biological implications: it can formally account for the molecular replication of DNA (duplication), for the storage of the information in DNA, and finally for the mechanism of mutations.

In view of the complementarity of the two elementary chains which compose the molecule of DNA, replication at the molecular level may be visualized as consisting of the unwinding and separation of these two chains, each chain serving thereafter as a template for the synthesis of its complement. After one replication, each "daughter" duplex is a hybrid; i.e., it is composed of one parental "old" chain and of one newly synthesized chain. Starting with the second replication entirely new molecules are constantly segregated, whereas the number of hybrid molecules remains constant, since each original single polynucleotide chain retains its integrity. Such a mechanism of replication is called semiconservative (Delbrück and Stent, 1957).

The model proposed by Watson and Crick imposes no restriction on the sequence of base pairs that can occur. Despite its regularity, this model permits an infinite diversity in the succession of base pairs, and it is this arrangement of base pairs which is assumed to account for the specificity of the genetic material. The information "coded" in the succession of base pairs could in turn be translated into the sequence of amino acids characteristic of the protein whose synthesis is controlled by a particular sequence of base pairs.

According to this model, a point mutation would correspond to a change in one base pair. At the time of replication of the DNA, a mistake could occur in the pairing of one of the bases (adenine pairing with cytosine instead of pairing with thymine for instance), this mistake being made possible by the occasional transition of the base from its most probable tautomeric form to a less probable one.

DNA preparations obtained from different sources appear to be rather homogeneous, any given preparation being composed of units of uniform particle size. If the concept of molecule applies to these units, then their molecular weight lies between 6,000,000 and 12,000,000.* The fate of

* Recent experiments indicate that the particle size of DNA is strongly dependent on the methods of preparation. These results suggest that DNA, at least in phage

DNA of *E. coli* during replication has been followed by Meselson and Stahl (1958a, b) by the elegant technique of equilibrium sedimentation in a density gradient of cesium chloride. These experiments have shown that, after one generation, DNA becomes hybrid, composed of two subunits, one old and one new, which can be separated by heat treatment. No further subdivision of the original DNA is found to occur in subsequent replications. The mechanism of replication of DNA in *E. coli* appears, therefore, to be semiconservative. If the subunits actually corresponded to single-stranded DNA, the mechanism of replication of DNA would be exactly that predicted by the model of Watson and Crick. The results of Meselson and Stahl point to the same conclusion as those obtained with entirely different methods for the replication of the DNA of bacteriophage T_2 (Levinthal, 1956). Similar results are also obtained in the case of the chromosomes of *Vicia faba* (J. H. Taylor, Woods, and Hughes, 1957): the study of the distribution of tritiated thymidine incorporated into the chromosomes indicates that these large structures also subdivide once and remain intact thereafter during subsequent replications.

Practically nothing is known about the mode of organization of DNA in a bacterial chromosome. In higher organisms, cytochemical investigations combined with electronmicroscopy have cast some light on the structure of chromosomes. Such structures appear to be constituted of a large number of more or less coiled fibrils, in which DNA seems to be associated with polyamines or small basic proteins including histones, while much thicker fibrils would be found when more complicated proteins are present (see Ris, 1957). Electronmicroscopical studies suggest that the chromosome of *E. coli* is multistranded (Kellenberger, 1960). It is likely however that this appearance does not correspond to a polytenic state, but rather to the folding and coiling of a single, double-stranded chromosomal structure. A suggested hypothesis would be that a chromosome consists of a linear array of DNA subunits, linked in an unknown way, the whole structure enjoying great flexibility. Several models have been proposed, the aim of which is to fulfill the basic requirements for such a structure, namely the linearity observed in the arrangement of the genetic determinants on a linkage group, the existence of discrete units (the DNA molecules), and the model of Watson and Crick for the structure of DNA (J. H. Taylor, 1958a; Freese, 1958; Kellenberger, 1960). All these models call for the

---

and in bacteria, might be a single continuous structure and that the "molecules" characterized in any given preparation might only be artificial subunits of such a continuous structure (Levinthal and Davison, 1961).

existence of small links, which might be protein in nature, placed between DNA molecules or DNA fragments and tying them two by two.

Whatever the organization of the DNA may be in the bacterial chromosome, even less information exists concerning the actual composition of this chromosome or its structure. Polyamines have been found in bacteria and in phage and it seems likely that they are in some way associated with DNA (Ames, Dubin, and Rosenthal, 1958). It is not known whether in bacteria as in higher organisms the chromosomal structure contains basic proteins.

Some information concerning the structure of the bacterial chromosome has been obtained through experiments on conjugation. The results obtained are summarized in the next sections.

B. The Nature of the Material Transferred during Conjugation

As already indicated in previous chapters, genetic transfer is unidirectional and, at least in Hfr $\times$ F^- crosses, nonchromosomal material does not appear to be transferred in measurable amounts during conjugation. There is direct evidence that the material transferred contains DNA, but it is not known whether the contribution from the donor parent also includes material other than DNA such as protein.

The first measurements of material transfer were performed by Garen and Skaar (1958), who estimated the amount of P^{32}-containing material transferred during conjugation by measuring the later incorporation of P^{32} atoms into T_2 bacteriophages grown on the F^- recipient bacteria. It is known that the only phosphorus-containing material in phage T_2 is DNA; and further, that when T_2 phage is grown on sensitive bacteria, most of the bacterial DNA is used as a source for the synthesis of the DNA of the phage, whereas the other phosphorus-containing constituents of the bacterium are not. In these experiments, P^{32}-labeled Hfr C donors, resistant to phage T_2, were mated with nonlabeled F^- recipients sensitive to T_2. After 1 hour of contact, the majority F^- population was multiply infected with phage T_2 under conditions of lysis inhibition and artificially lysed at an appropriate time, after which the amount of P^{32} incorporated into the phage progeny was measured. Adequate control experiments allowed the determination of the efficiency of P^{32} incorporation into phage DNA, the quantity of nonspecific incorporation, the recovery of progeny phage, and the various parameters needed for the calculations. From these indirect and rather complicated experiments, a certain number of conclusions could be drawn. Whereas practically no P^{32} is transferred from F^- to F^- bacteria or from F^- to Hfr bacteria, a measurable amount of P^{32} is transferred from Hfr to F^- bacteria. There is every reason to believe that this P^{32} is contained in DNA. The amount transferred under the conditions of the experiments was, however, relatively small, corresponding to about 3 to 6 per cent of the DNA of the minority Hfr population. From these results, it may be concluded that the transfer of DNA during conjugation is unidirectional and incomplete. If one makes the assumptions that all Hfr bacteria have actually conjugated, that there is an average of three chromosomes per Hfr bacterium, and that only one chromosome takes part in the process of transfer, the numerical value obtained implies that the Hfr bacteria have transferred, on the average, between one-tenth and one-fifth of one of their chromosomes. This estimate is compatible with the genetic results obtained under similar experimental conditions.

More direct evidence for the transfer of DNA during conjugation, as well as more precise quantitative estimations of the amount transferred, have been obtained in recent experiments (E. L. Wollman and Stent, 1961). Hfr H donor bacteria, labeled with tritiated thymidine, were crossed with unlabeled F^- recipient bacteria, and the amount of tritiated thymidine transferred to the zygotes was measured as a function of time after mating. It is known that thymidine is incorporated only into DNA. The measurement of the amount of thymidine transferred is, therefore, a direct estimate of the transfer of DNA. The only serious difficulty in such experiments is the quantitative elimination of the highly labeled Hfr bacteria. This was achieved by lysis from without with a high titer stock of bacteriophage T_6 inactivated by ultraviolet light. These experiments have confirmed that the transfer of DNA is unidirectional and partial. When labeled but carefully washed Hfr bacteria were mixed with an excess of F^- recipients and incubated with very gentle aeration, it was found that the amount of tritiated thymidine transferred to the T_6-resistant F^- bacteria increased as a function of time, reaching from 7 to 12 per cent of the total thymidine content of the Hfr bacteria after 2 hours of contact. This result would indicate that each Hfr bacterium has transferred on the average between one-fifth and one-third of one of its chromosomes, which is in agreement with calculations based on the gradient of transmission of genetic characters (see p. 148).

C. The Effects of the Disintegration of Incorporated Radioactive Phosphorus

Additional information on the structure of the bacterial chromosome has been gained by applying to bacterial conjugation the powerful method of analysis based on the disintegration of radioactive phosphorus atoms incorporated into the DNA. This method, which was first evolved in studies of bacteriophage and later extended to bacteria, lends itself to the investigation of a variety of problems (see Stent and Fuerst, 1960).

Bacteriophages which multiply in the presence of radioactive phosphorus P^{32} of high specific activity incorporate this radiophosphorus into their DNA. When such bacteriophages are subsequently kept in the frozen state in order to allow disintegration of the P^{32} atoms to take place, it is found that they are progressively inactivated as a function of time, that is, as a function of the number of atomic disintegrations. The inactivation follows an exponential course, and the rate of inactivation is proportional to the specific activity of the P^{32} in the presence of which these bacteriophages have multiplied (Hershey, Kamen, Kennedy, and Gest, 1951; Stent, 1953). In the model proposed by Watson and Crick for the structure of DNA, the backbone of each helical strand is maintained by phosphodiester bonds. The disintegration of a P^{32} atom contained in the DNA of a bacteriophage would bring about, therefore, the rupture of a phosphodiester bond. It is found experimentally that only a fraction of the $P^{32} \rightarrow S^{32}$ transmutations, about one in ten at 4°, inactivates the phage, and that this fraction depends on the temperature at which P^{32} disintegration is allowed to proceed. These facts may be interpreted in the following way. The disintegration of a P^{32} atom usually ruptures only one of the helices of the DNA molecule, without destroying the continuity of this molecule. In a certain fraction of the disintegrations, which becomes progressively larger with a rise in the temperature at which disintegration occurs, the energy liberated is large enough to rupture both polynucleotide chains, thus inactivating the phage (Stent and Fuerst, 1955).

Comparable phenomena are observed when *E. coli* is grown in the presence of P^{32} of high specific activity. The bacteria are inactivated exponentially as a function of P^{32} disintegration; the rate of inactivation, which is proportional to the specific activity of the medium in which the bacteria have been grown, depends also on the temperature at which P^{32} decay is allowed to proceed. Here again, only a fraction of the disintegrations (about one out of ten at 4° and one out of fifty at —196°) has a lethal effect, exactly as in the case of phage (Fuerst and Stent, 1956). These facts, as well as other evidence, indicate that in both bacteria and phage, the inactivation which results from P^{32} decay is caused essentially by disintegrations which take place in the DNA; disintegrations occurring in other compounds and ionizations play only a minor part in this phenomenon.

Since the effects of P^{32} disintegration on bacteria are caused predominantly by the decay of those atoms which have been incorporated into DNA, bacterial conjugation lends itself to a more refined analysis of these effects at the level of the bacterial chromosome. It should be pointed out that the mechanism by which genetic transfer is accomplished in conjugation is particularly favorable for the differential analysis of deleterious effects caused by chemical or physical agents. It permits one to dissociate effects on the genetic material and its organized support, the bacterial chromosome, from effects on other bacterial constituents. When P^{32} of high specific activity is incorporated into Hfr bacteria, its disintegration may be allowed to proceed either in the Hfr bacteria *before transfer* or in the zygotes *after transfer*; the effects of P^{32} decay on the outcome of crosses is strikingly different in the two cases. When it takes place in the Hfr bacteria before mating, P^{32} disintegration affects the process of transfer itself, producing chromosomal ruptures the genetic consequences of which are very similar to those resulting from the interruption of mating by mechanical treatment. When P^{32} decay is allowed to proceed in the zygotes after mating, the ruptures which occur have very definite effects on the process of genetic recombination (Fuerst, Jacob, and Wollman, 1956, 1961; Jacob and Wollman, 1958a). These two types of experiments will now be described, with particular emphasis on the effects of P^{32} decay on chromosomal transfer. The effects of P^{32} decay on genetic recombination will be discussed at greater length in the next chapter.

1. *The effects of P^{32} decay on chromosomal transfer.* All the experiments to be reported have been done with the nonlysogenic strains Hfr H S^s and F^- P678 S^r. The Hfr bacteria are grown for several generations in a medium containing P^{32} of high specific activity, then centrifuged, resuspended, frozen and stored at —196° in order to allow P^{32} decay to proceed for various lengths of time. From day to day, an aliquot is thawed and mated, under standard conditions, with nonlabeled F^- bacteria in a nonlabeled medium. Samples of the mating mixtures are plated on media selective for $T^+L^+S^r$, Gal^+S^r, and $T^+L^+Gal^+S^r$ recombinants. The recombinants are isolated and their genetic constitution is analyzed. In this way, one determines, as a function of P^{32} decay, the relative frequencies of transmission to recombinants of different markers from the Hfr donor (Fig. 33).

It may be seen (Fig. 33*A*) that, for each class of recombinants selected, the numbers formed decrease exponentially as a function of P^{32} disintegration. The slopes of these "inactivation"* curves differ, however,

* "Inactivation" is taken to mean inactivation of the *ability* of a certain class of recombinants to be formed.

for the $T^+L^+S^r$ recombinants on the one hand and for the Gal^+S^r and $T^+L^+Gal^+S^r$ recombinants on the other, the rate of "inactivation" of the $T^+L^+S^r$ recombinants being only one-third that of the two other classes of recombinants. This differential effect indicates that as P^{32} decay proceeds, an increasing fraction of the Hfr bacteria which are no longer able to transmit to recombinants the Gal^+ character can still transmit the T^+L^+ characters. Genetic analysis of the $T^+L^+S^r$ recombinants

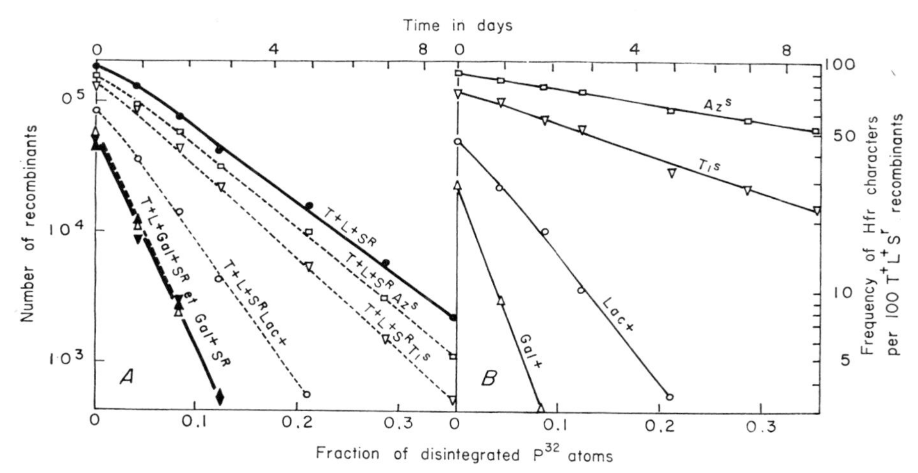

FIG. 33. The effects of P^{32} decay occurring in the Hfr donor bacteria before transfer. Hfr H S^s donor bacteria grown in a medium containing 70 mc/mg of phosphorus are centrifuged, washed, and resuspended in a protective medium. Samples are frozen in liquid nitrogen. Every day a sample is thawed, resuspended in buffer, and mixed in standard conditions with an excess of nonradioactive P678 S^r F− recipients (2.10^6 Hfr and 10^8 F−/ml). After 1 hour at 37°C, samples are diluted and aliquots are plated on selective media. The *numbers* of recombinants $T+L+S^r$, $Gal+S^r$, and $T+L+Gal+S^r$ (*left,* solid lines) and the *proportions* of $T+L+S^r$ recombinants having one of the Hfr characters Az^s, $T1^s$, Lac+, Gal+ (*right*) are plotted on a logarithmic scale versus the time in days and the fraction of disintegrated P^{32} atoms. On the left, are also plotted in dotted lines the numbers of $T+L+S^r$ recombinants having one of the Hfr characters Az^s, $T1^s$, Lac+ as calculated from curves on the right. (From Fuerst, Jacob, and Wollman, 1961.)

shows that this differential effect exists for the different characters of the O-T-L-Gal segment (Fig. 33*B*). The data of Fig. 33*B* have been used to establish the survival curves of the T^+L^+ recombinants which have inherited any given unselected marker of the Hfr bacteria (Fig. 33*A*). It is apparent that the transmission of any given marker of the Hfr is inactivated at a particular rate and that this rate depends on the position of this marker on the proximal segment of the Hfr chromosome: the more distant from the origin O of the Hfr chromosome, the faster the rate of elimination of the marker. The fact that Gal^+S^r and $T^+L^+Gal^+S^r$ recombinants are eliminated at the same rate indicates that the sensitivity of the transmission of the Gal^+ marker *is determined by its distance to the origin O of the Hfr chromosome.*

These results are analogous to those which are obtained when mating is interrupted as a function of time by mechanical treatment. They indicate that P^{32} decay occurring in the Hfr bacteria prior to mating affects mainly the transfer of chromosomal determinants. The disintegration of phosphorus atoms seems to produce breaks in the Hfr chromosome, and consequently the magnitude of the effect on the transfer of any particular determinant increases with its distance from the origin of the chromosome, i.e., with the number of phosphorus atoms that lie between the determinant and the proximal extremity of the chromosome.

These conclusions are strengthened when the effects of P^{32} decay occurring before transfer are compared with its effects after transfer.

2. *The effects of P^{32} decay occurring in the zygotes after transfer.* In these experiments, the highly labeled Hfr bacteria are mated immediately with unlabeled F^- recipients in a medium containing no radioactive phosphorus. After enough time has elapsed for transfer of the Gal^+ character, the Hfr H bacteria are destroyed by addition of ultraviolet-inactivated T_6 bacteriophage; the T_6 resistant recipients survive. Aliquots of the zygote population are then frozen and stored at —196°, P^{32} decay being allowed to proceed for various lengths of time. From day to day, aliquots are thawed and plated on selective media for $T^+L^+S^r$, Gal^+S^r, and $T^+L^+Gal^+S^r$ recombinants (Fig. 34).

It can be seen from Fig. 34 that the ability of different genetic determinants to be transmitted to recombinants is still sensitive to P^{32} decay after their transfer to zygotes. The results obtained are, however, very different from those which are observed when P^{32} decay takes place in the Hfr bacteria before mating. In the first place, both the $T^+L^+S^r$ and the Gal^+S^r recombinants are "inactivated" at about the same rate, whereas the $T^+L^+Gal^+S^r$ recombinants are inactivated at a much faster rate. Secondly, the rate of inactivation of any given class of recombinants is much lower when P^{32} decay takes place in the zygotes than when it takes place in the Hfr bacteria prior to mating.

Accordingly, the ability of an Hfr marker to be transmitted to recombinants is much more sensitive to P^{32} decay which occurs prior to transfer than to that which occurs after transfer. When P^{32} decay occurs before transfer, the transmission of a marker is dependent on its distance from the origin of the Hfr chromosome; when P^{32} decay occurs after transfer, the positional factor has no effect. These differences confirm that the main effect of P^{32} decay, when it occurs in the Hfr bacteria, is on *transfer*. When P^{32} disintegration takes place in the zygotes, it affects the *linkages between markers*, as can be seen by comparing the inactivation curves of $T^+L^+S^r$ and Gal^+S^r recombinants on the one hand with the inactivation curve of the $T^+L^+Gal^+S^r$ recombinants on the other. This effect will be discussed more fully in the following chapter.

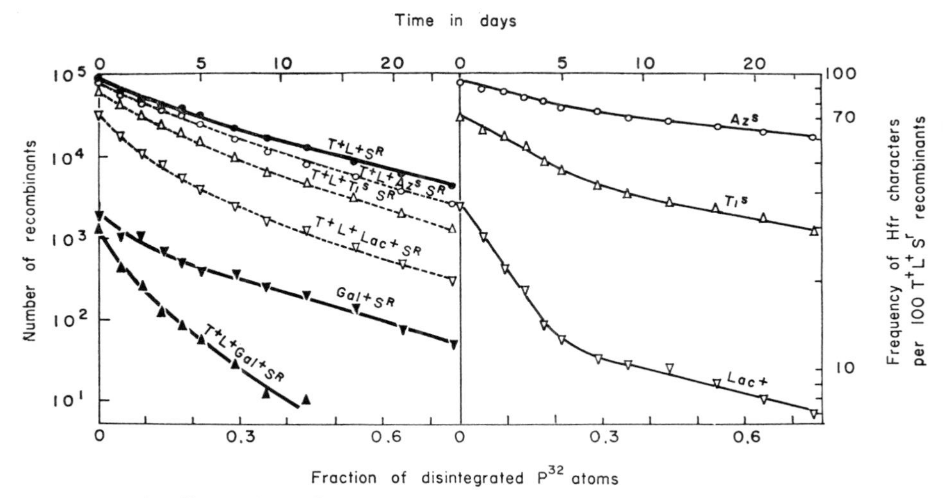

FIG. 34. Effects of P^{32} decay occurring in the donor chromosome after its transfer to the zygotes. Hfr H $T6^s$ S^s bacteria grown in a medium containing 110 mc/mg of radiophosphorus are washed, resuspended in buffer, and mixed with an excess of nonlabeled F^- P678 $T6^rS^r$, in a medium containing streptomycin in order to prevent the Hfr parent from synthesizing nucleic acids. After 40 minutes at 37°C, KCN $M/100$ and an excess of phage T6 are added to arrest conjugation. After 10 minutes at 37°C, the mixture is diluted in protective medium and samples are frozen in liquid nitrogen. Every day a sample is thawed and aliquots are plated on selective media. Plots as in Fig. 33. (From Fuerst, Jacob, and Wollman, 1961.)

These experiments confirm that phosphorus-containing material is transferred from donor to recipient bacteria during conjugation, and that this material is DNA, for it is the bearer of hereditary characters. They confirm also that the main effects of P^{32} decay on bacteria are due to the disintegration of those radioactive atoms which are incorporated into their DNA. As a matter of fact, as will be seen in the next section, it is these experiments that have given the strongest evidence in favor of the hypothesis that the effect of P^{32} incorporated into DNA is one of producing breakages in the continuity of the polynucleotide chains of DNA (Stent and Fuerst, 1960).

3. *Physical determinations of chromosomal segments.* The effect of P^{32} decay occurring in Hfr bacteria prior to mating may be ascribed to an effect on the transfer of genetic characters: the farther a genetic determinant lies from the origin of the Hfr chromosome, the greater becomes the probability that it will be excluded from the contribution of the Hfr bacteria to the zygotes. This fact may be most simply interpreted by assuming that, in a certain fraction of the cases, the disintegration of a P^{32} atom causes a rupture of the bacterial chromosome. Any genetic determinant located on the segment distal to the break can no longer be transferred, whereas the genetic determinants which are located between the break and the origin of the chromosome can still be transferred upon conjugation. The effect of P^{32} decay on the process of chromosomal

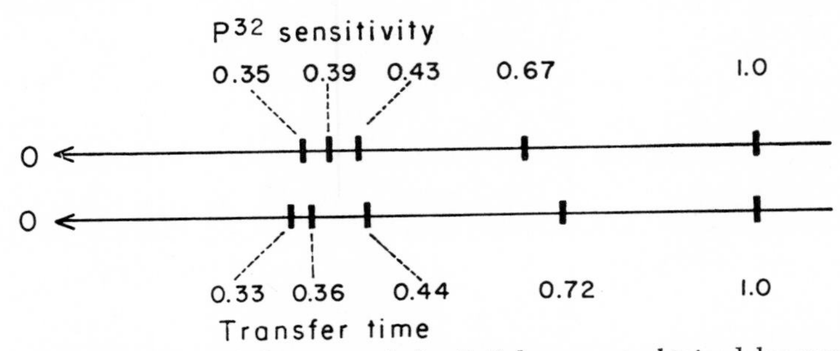

FIG. 35. Comparison of the maps of the O-Gal segment obtained by mechanical or by P^{32}-induced fragmentation. The characters represented are, from left (O) to right: TL, Az, T_1, Lac, and Gal. Figures represent: *above,* the relative sensitivities of the characters of the donor to P^{32} decay occurring in the donor before transfer; *below,* the relative time at which the markers penetrate into the recipient as measured in an interrupted mating experiment.

transfer is, therefore, very similar to the effect of mechanical treatment. In both cases, ruptures of the bacterial chromosome prevent the entry into the zygotes of those markers which are distal to the break. It is not surprising, therefore, that the genetic markers of an Hfr bacterium can be arranged in the same order on the basis of their times of entry into the zygotes and on the basis of the sensitivities of their transfer to P^{32} decay (Fig. 35). The agreement between the two sets of data is not only qualitative, but there is a surprising degree of quantitative agreement. The relative distances in time units of the markers of the O-TL-Gal segment and their relative sensitivities to P^{32} decay may be compared by assigning an arbitrary value of unity to the time of transfer of the Gal^{+} character and to its sensitivity to P^{32} decay. Two sets of marker "distances" are thus obtained for the O-TL-Gal segment, as indicated in Fig. 35. Each character is seen to occupy very nearly the same position on each of these two maps (Fuerst, Jacob, and Wollman, 1956).

The effects of P^{32} decay on the process of chromosomal transfer provide, therefore, a method of estimating genetic distances. The rates at which genetic markers are excluded from transfer are proportional to the distances of the corresponding determinants from the origin O of the bacterial chromosome, i.e., to the number of P^{32} atoms which lie between these determinants and O. The larger the chromosomal segment, and consequently the larger the number of P^{32} atoms incorporated into the DNA, the greater the probability that a break will occur between a given locus and O as a result of the random disintegration of a P^{32} atom. Assuming that the distribution of P^{32} atoms along the chromosome is homogeneous and that the probability for a disintegration to cause a rupture is independent of the position of a P^{32} atom along the chromosome, it should be possible to translate genetic distances into numbers of phosphorus atoms. To do so, however, it is necessary to know the probability of chromosome breakage per P^{32} disintegration. This probability can be estimated indirectly from the comparison of the efficiencies with which Hfr bacteria are killed and with which genetic markers are excluded from transfer. The content in phosphorus atoms of different regions of the O-TL-Gal segment of Hfr H bacteria can be calculated from the data of Fig. 33. These estimations (Table XXXIV)

TABLE XXXIV
PHOSPHORUS CONTENT OF DIFFERENT CHROMOSOMAL SEGMENTS ACCORDING TO THEIR SENSITIVITY TO P^{32} DECAY[a]

Segments	Estimated number of P atoms
O - Gal	27.6×10^5
O - TL	9.3×10^5
TL - Az	1.2×10^5
Az - T_1	1.4×10^5
T_1 - Lac	6.2×10^5
Lac - Gal	9.5×10^5

[a] From Fuerst, Jacob, and Wollman (1961).

should be considered to give only an order of magnitude, in view of the uncertainties which enter into the calculations (Fuerst, Jacob, and Wollman, 1961; Stent and Fuerst, 1960).

* * *

The processes of meromixis which exist in bacteria are very useful for studies on the nature and structure of the bacterial genetic material. The investigations which have been made of bacterial conjugation provide an additional confirmation, if necessary, that genetic information in bacteria is stored in a linear array of DNA, and that only segments of bacterial chromosome are transferred upon mating from donor to recipient bacteria. The observations on the effects of P^{32} decay which takes place in the donor bacteria before transfer are of particular interest. They bring further support to the hypothesis that the disintegration of P^{32} atoms incorporated into DNA actually causes ruptures of the continuity of the genetic material. The fact that chromosomal breaks are produced with an efficiency very comparable to that which is found for the inactivation of bacteriophages indicates that a bacterial chromosome is most probably a linear array of double stranded DNA molecules, rather than a complex polytenic structure. Finally, these experiments make it possible to translate genetic distances into chemical terms. As will be discussed in the next chapter, the very mechanism by which genetic transfer is accomplished in bacterial conjugation provides a unique opportunity for relating genetic determinations of linkages to physical and chemical measurements of the chromosomal structure which bears the genetic determinants of bacteria.

CHAPTER XIII

Genetic Recombination

Genetic analysis is based on the fact that, when individuals which differ in their hereditary characteristics are crossed, a reassortment of the characters of the parents is observed in the progeny of the cross. Linkage maps can be deduced from the frequencies of such reassortments. In animals and in plants, the linkage groups have been correlated with cytologically observable structures, namely the chromosomes. Such analysis has allowed a dissection of the genome into elementary units of heredity, the genes, each gene occupying a definite chromosomal location or locus. Until rather recently, it was generally thought that the elementary unit which determines a character (functional unit) behaves as a whole, both in mutation and in recombination.

During the last two decades, the principles of genetic analysis have been successfully extended to microorganisms, including bacteria and bacteriophages, and linkage maps have been determined in a variety of microorganisms. These studies, which have helped to establish the fundamental unity of the structure and function of genetic material throughout the biological world, have also widened considerably the scope of genetic analysis. The large numbers of microorganisms which can be handled and the possibility of using highly selective procedures have greatly increased the resolving power of genetic analysis. They have facilitated also the isolation of mutant types as well as the detection of rare recombinant types. Both the availability of large numbers of mutants and the increased sensitivity of recombinational analysis have brought refinement and greater precision to the definition of the elementary unit of heredity. As had already been foreshadowed by earlier though less extensive studies on higher forms, studies with microorganisms have shown that the criteria used in defining the unit of function, the unit of recombination, and the unit of mutation are not equivalent. The brilliant investigations of Benzer (1957) on bacteriophage, of Demerec (1956) on bacteria, and of Pritchard (1955) on *Aspergillus* have demonstrated that, within a single locus, mutations can occur at many different sites, separable by intragenic recombination. Genetic analysis now aims at interpreting these findings in molecular terms; i.e., at correlating genetic data with the available knowledge concerning the structure of DNA. In the molecular model of Watson and Crick, the smallest mutational unit could correspond to a single nucleotide pair and the smallest recombination unit to the distance between two nucleotide pairs or to a small multiple of this distance. The smallest recombination values obtained in phage would indeed correspond, according to Benzer's calculations, to the distance between only a few nucleotide pairs. Genetic analysis in microorganisms has also allowed an experimental approach to the problem of the very mechanism of genetic recombination and its relation to the duplication of the genetic material.

The processes of meromixis which exist in bacteria and, in particular, the oriented transfer of genetic material as it occurs in bacterial conjugation are especially suitable for the study of these problems. In the first part of this chapter, we shall describe the special features of genetic analysis pertinent to bacterial conjugation. We shall then compare the measurements of genetic distances obtained by genetic methods and by other methods, such as mechanical or P^{32}-induced breakages of the bacterial chromosome. Lastly, we shall summarize information concerning the mechanism of genetic recombination in merozygotes as obtained in the study of bacterial conjugation.

I. RECOMBINATIONAL ANALYSIS

Recombinational analysis, as developed in higher organisms, is based on the assumption that the probability of exchanges between two characters reflects the relative positions of their determinants in the genome. When two individuals which differ in two characters A and B are crossed, it is indeed found that the frequency of exchanges is dependent on the two specific characters chosen and varies from one pair of characters to another. If two characters are found to segregate independently, either they are located on two different linkage groups or, if located on the same linkage group, they are sufficiently distant from one another for the number of exchanges between them to be on the average greater than one. If the two characters do not segregate independently, they are located on the same linkage group and sufficiently close to one another for the number of exchanges between them to be on the average less than one.

Characters which are located on the same linkage group can be ordered with respect to one another. Let A, B, and C be three characters located on the same linkage group. The recombination frequencies between the pairs AB, AC, and BC are measured. If AC, for example, is found to exhibit the greatest recombination value, the order of the three characters is A, B, C. The order of other characters may then be determined with respect to these three. It is thus possible to place any number of linked characters in a linear order. It is important to stress that, in general, independent determinations of order give concordant results: a given character is always found to be located in the same position with respect to another given character.

In addition to establishing the existence of linkage groups and the order of genetic characters on these linkage groups, recombinational analysis permits the determination of genetic distances and consequently the construction of *genetic maps.* Indeed, the recombination frequencies between pairs of characters have a simple additive relationship. If B lies between A and C, then the recombination frequency for the pair AC is found to be roughly equal to the sum of the recombination frequencies between A and B on the one hand and between B and C on the other. This additivity makes it possible to represent graphically the relationships between markers as linear segments proportional to the recombination frequencies between these markers. Deviations from strictly additive relations are assumed to result from distortions or *interference* in the mechanics of recombination.

Recombinational analysis has been the instrument mainly responsible for the progress of classical genetics. In conjunction with cytological analysis, it made possible the construction of detailed chromosomal maps for animals and plants. It has been extended successfully to microorganisms, although in many of these forms the difficulties of cytological work preclude at present a correlation of the genetic data with cytological observations.

In bacteria and in bacteriophage, the recombinational process differs markedly from karyogamy. Despite this fact, the principles of recombinational analysis can still be fruitfully applied (J. Lederberg, 1947; Hershey and Rotman, 1948). In each specific case, however, the special features of the recombinational process involved have to be taken into account in the interpretation of the data. The theory of Visconti and Delbrück (1953) provided the necessary basis for the analysis of recombination in bacteriophage. For each process of bacterial meromixis, corresponding allowances must be made in evaluating the quantitative data obtained from crosses.

A. Measurements of Recombination Frequencies

One peculiarity is common to all modes of bacterial meromixis: the contribution of the donor parent is limited to a chromosomal segment.

The formation of recombinant types therefore always requires an even number of genetic exchanges (see Figs. 32 and 39). In bacterial conjugation, the frequency with which a given marker of the donor type appears among recombinants depends in the first instance on the probability of its transfer to the zygotes, and only secondarily on its distance from the selected and counterselected characters. Accordingly, the recombination frequencies observed show a marked dependence on the relative positions of the markers considered.

1. *Large chromosomal segments.* In a cross between Hfr H and F^- bacteria, when selection is made for the proximal characters T^+L^+ (the counterselected character S^r being distal), the different unselected markers of the Hfr parent appear with characteristic frequencies among the $T^+L^+S^r$ recombinants (see Table V and Table XXIII). These characteristic frequencies, which allow the ordering of the corresponding determinants on the Hfr chromosome, are not, however, equivalent to recombination frequencies between the characters involved. They reflect, as already indicated, the probability of breakage of the Hfr chromosome in the course of its transfer. On the assumption that the probability of transfer decreases exponentially along the Hfr linkage group (see page 148), the actual recombination frequencies could be calculated from the experimental values obtained. Such calculations, however, would be imprecise, since the frequency of breakage is the major factor influencing the values obtained. It is more reliable, therefore, to select for a rather distal character of the Hfr parent (the counterselected character being still more distal), and to score for the unselected markers located between the origin O of the Hfr chromosome and the character used for selection. In this fashion, attention is focused on an almost homogeneous class of zygotes which have received from the Hfr parent a chromosomal segment extending at least to the selected character. The results of such an analysis are presented in Table XXXV where it may be seen that the Hfr alleles of the proximal markers scored all appear in about equal proportions, these proportions being close to 50 per cent.*

The order of the markers may be established, however, by tabulating the different classes of associations found, and a rough estimate of the genetic distances may be obtained from the frequencies of exchanges between pairs of markers. It is also clear from Table XXXV that recombinants which result from several pairs of exchanges are more frequent

* In many experiments, and depending on the recipient strains used, these proportions may be definitely higher than 50 per cent (see Table V). Such results, if not due to technical flaws, could be interpreted as evidence for the existence of a polarity in the recombination process.

TABLE XXXV
GENETIC CONSTITUTION OF RECOMBINANTS SELECTED FOR A DISTAL MARKER[a,b]

Hfr		●		●		●		●		●		●		●	●
F−		○		○		○		○		○		○		○	○
O		T		L		T_1		Lac		Gal		Try		H	Sm
Region	1		2		3		4		5		6		7		8
Total number of crossing-over	92		18		19		26		57		65		89		

T	L	T_1	Lac	Gal	Try	No.	c-o	T	L	T_1	Lac	Gal	Try	No.	c-o
●	●	●	●	●	●	31	8 + 1	○	○	○	●	●	○	2	8 + 7 + 4 + 6
○	●	●	●	●	●	1	8 + 2	○	○	●	●	○	●	1	8 + 6 + 3 + 5
○	○	●	●	●	●	4	8 + 3	○	●	●	●	○	●	1	8 + 6 + 2 + 5
○	○	○	●	●	●	7	8 + 4	○	●	●	○	○	●	1	8 + 6 + 2 + 4
○	○	○	○	●	●	20	8 + 5	●	○	○	○	○	●	1	8 + 6 + 1 + 2
○	○	○	○	○	●	20	8 + 6	●	○	○	○	●	●	2	8 + 5 + 1 + 2
○	○	○	○	○	○	39	8 + 7	●	○	○	●	●	●	1	8 + 4 + 1 + 2
●	○	○	○	○	○	4	8 + 7 + 1 + 2	●	○	●	●	●	●	1	8 + 3 + 1 + 2
●	●	○	○	○	○	2	8 + 7 + 1 + 3	●	●	●	○	●	●	1	8 + 5 + 1 + 4
●	●	●	○	○	○	2	8 + 7 + 1 + 4	●	●	○	○	○	●	2	8 + 6 + 1 + 3
●	●	●	●	○	○	9	8 + 7 + 1 + 5	●	●	●	○	○	●	3	8 + 6 + 1 + 4
●	●	●	●	●	○	17	8 + 7 + 1 + 6	●	●	●	●	○	●	7	8 + 6 + 1 + 5
○	○	●	○	○	○	2	8 + 7 + 3 + 4	●	●	○	○	●	●	4	8 + 5 + 1 + 3
○	○	○	●	○	○	2	8 + 7 + 4 + 5	●	○	○	●	●	○	1	8 + 7 + 4 + 6 + 1 + 2
○	○	○	○	●	○	1	8 + 7 + 5 + 6	●	●	○	●	○	●	1	8 + 6 + 4 + 5 + 1 + 3
○	○	●	●	○	○	1	8 + 7 + 3 + 5	●	○	●	●	○	●	1	8 + 6 + 3 + 5 + 1 + 2
○	●	●	●	○	○	2	8 + 7 + 2 + 5	●	●	●	●	○	○	1	8 + 7 + 5 + 3 + 1 + 2
○	●	●	●	●	○	1	8 + 7 + 2 + 6	●	○	○	●	○	●	1	8 + 6 + 5 + 4 + 1 + 3
○	○	●	●	●	○	1	8 + 7 + 3 + 6	●	●	●	○	●	○	2	8 + 7 + 6 + 5 + 4 + 1

[a] Per cent Hfr alleles among H^+S^r recombinants: T^+: 47; L^+: 44; T_1^s: 45; Lac^+: 47; Gal^+: 49; Try^+: 57.
Number of double crossing-over: 122 Number of quadruple crossing-over: 71 Number of sextuple crossing-over: 7

[b] In a cross Hfr H S^s × F^- PA209 S^r, the genetic constitution of 200 H^+S^r recombinants is determined as to the unselected characters T^+, L^+, T_1^s, Lac^+, Gal^+, Try^+ of the Hfr parent.

than might be expected from random acts of recombination. This *negative interference* had already been noticed in early studies of bacterial recombination (Newcombe and Nyholm, 1950b; Rothfels, 1952). As suggested by Cavalli-Sforza and Jinks (1956), it could result from irregular pairing between parental chromosomal structures.

2. *Short chromosomal segments.* Although recombinational analysis is of little practical value when investigating large chromosomal segments, it becomes very useful when short chromosomal segments are considered. As an example, we shall discuss the mapping of the small region which comprises the determinants of lactose metabolism (Monod and Jacob, unpublished results).

In *E. coli,* the metabolism of lactose and of other β-galactosides requires the participation of two distinct factors: the *galactoside permease* which is responsible for the penetration of β-galactosides into the cell; and the β-*galactosidase* which accomplishes the hydrolysis of these β-galactosides. In wild type *E. coli* K12, both the permease and the β-galactosidase are inducible, i.e., their synthesis requires the presence of an inducer which must be a β-galactoside. Three main types of mutations which affect the metabolism of β-galactosides have been described (Rickenberg, Cohen, Buttin, and Monod, 1956; Monod, 1958):

$y^+ \rightarrow y^-$, resulting in loss of the capacity to synthesize the permease

$z^+ \rightarrow z^-$, resulting in loss of the capacity to synthesize the β-galactosidase

$i^+ \rightarrow i^-$, resulting in mutation from inducible (i^+) to constitutive (i^-) synthesis of both the permease and the galactosidase

All these mutations, as first shown by the work of E. Lederberg (1947), are located in a short region of the bacterial chromosome, the Lac region (Pardee, Jacob, and Monod, 1959). Known markers are located on each side of the Lac region, a proline marker (Pro) on one

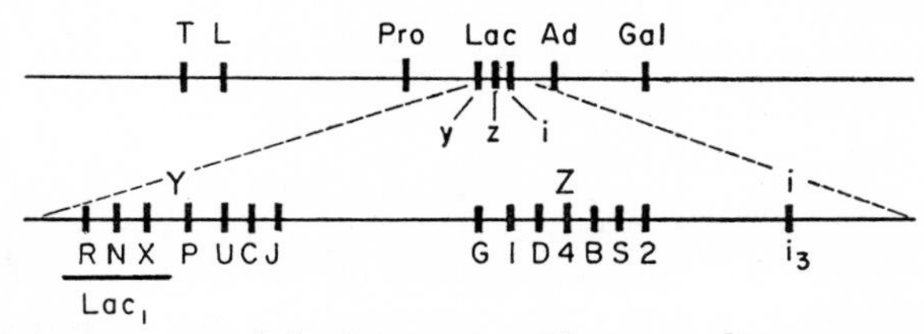

FIG. 36. Representation of the Lac region. The upper line represents the position of the Lac region in the TL-Gal segment. The lower line represents an enlargement of the Lac region. Additional z^- mutants have recently been isolated which map in the interval represented between the z and the y regions. The z and y loci are therefore adjacent.

side, and an adenine marker (Ad) on the other (Fig. 36). Interrupted mating experiments indicate unambiguously that Hfr H bacteria inject these markers in the order: O T L Pro Lac Ad Gal. Crosses involving adequate combinations of markers not only allow the measurement of recombination frequencies among the Pro, Lac, and Ad markers, but permit also the sequential ordering of the different mutations affecting the Lac region and the measurement of the genetic distances between them. The results of two reciprocal crosses between Hfr H and F^- bacteria differing not only in their adenine character but also in their y, z, and i characters are presented in Table XXXVI. In each cross Ad^+S^r,

TABLE XXXVI
MAPPING OF THE Lac SEGMENT[a]

Crosses	
Hfr y_R^- z_4^+ i_3^+ Ad^+ S^s	y_R^+ z_4^- i_3^- Ad^+ S^s
F^- y_R^+ z_4^- i_3^- Ad^- S^r	y_R^- z_4^+ i_3^+ Ad^- S^r
Region 1 2 3 4	1 2 3 4
Among recombinants Ad^+S^r (c-o in 4)	Among recombinants Ad^+S^r (c-o in 4)
22 per cent of z_4^- (c-o in 2 or 3)	26 per cent of z^+ (c-o in 2 or 3)
2.3 per cent of z^+y^+ (c-o in 1)	1.9 per cent of z^+y^+ (c-o in 2 or 3 and 1)
0.25 per cent of z^+i^- (c-o in 2 and 3) among which	1.6 per cent of z^+i^- (c-o in 2) among which
19 per cent y^- (extra c-o in 1)	14 per cent y^+ (extra c-o in 1)

[a] In the two reciprocal crosses, Hfr H $y_R^-z_4^+i_3^+Ad^+S^s \times F^-$ $y_R^+z_4^-i_3^-Ad^-S^r$ and Hfr H $y_R^+z_4^-i_3^-Ad^+S^s \times F^-$ $y_R^-z_4^+i_3^+Ad^-S^r$, Ad^+S^r recombinants are selected. The genetic constitution of more than 10,000 recombinants was analyzed by replica platings on suitable media and assay with papers impregnated with *o*-nitrophenolgalactoside. (From Monod and Jacob, unpublished.)

recombinants are selected and their genetic constitution with respect to the y, z, and i characters is determined by replica plating on suitable indicator media. It is apparent from Table XXXVI that the only order compatible with the results is (Pro)-y-z-i-Ad. Furthermore, it may be seen that for any given class of recombinants resulting from a cross-over in one of the regions indicated, there is an excess of cross-overs in adjacent regions. This negative interference suggests a clustering of exchanges in small chromosomal regions, as already demonstrated in *Aspergillus* (Pritchard, 1955), in phage (Chase and Doermann, 1958), and in other microorganisms. According to Pritchard, the "effective pairing" which allows crossing-over to take place would affect only a few small segments of a chromosome in each zygote, although the probability of occurrence of such effective pairings would be distributed along the chromosome for a population of zygotes. When effective pairing has actually occurred within a small region, the number of exchanges would, on the average, be greater than one.

The analysis just presented can be extended to crosses involving the proline (Pro) character located on the proximal side of the Lac region in Hfr H. A genetic map in recombination units of the Lac region is given in Fig. 37.

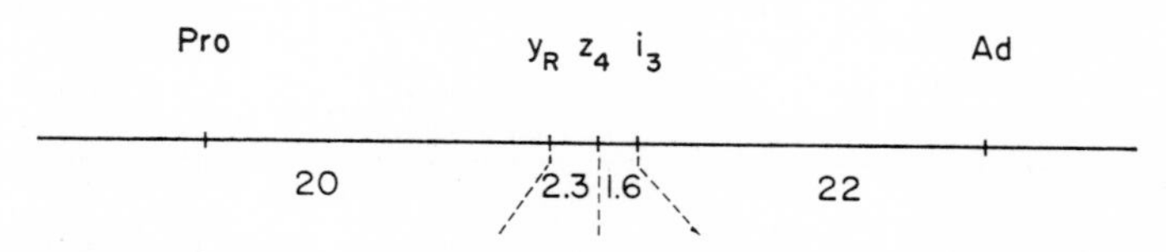

FIG. 37. Genetic distances in the Lac region. (From Monod and Jacob, unpublished.)

3. *Intragenic recombination.* The resolving power of recombinational analysis of bacterial conjugation is high enough to allow the mapping of mutations occurring at different sites within the same locus. A variety of z^- mutants, all lacking the ability to synthesize β-galactosidase, have been isolated. Mapping of the corresponding mutations has been attempted by intercrosses between pairs of such mutants. From the frequencies of z^+ recombinants obtained in these crosses, the relative distances between mutational sites can be determined, provided that fluctuations in efficiency from cross to cross are taken into account. This determination can be made by comparing, in different crosses, not the absolute frequencies of z^+ recombinants, but the fraction of such recombinants existing in a standard class of recombinants selected for another marker. For example, in crosses Hfr $T^+L^+z_A^-S^s \times F^-$ $T^-L^-z_B^-S^r$, or Hfr $z_A^-Ad^+S^s \times F^-$ $z_B^-Ad^-S^r$, the recombination frequency between any two z^- mutations may be estimated by taking in each case the ratios $T^+L^+z^+S^r/T^+L^+S^r$ or $Ad^+z^+S^r/Ad^+S^r$. Such recombination frequencies must of course be measured in reciprocal crosses, for the values obtained will depend on the relative order of the investigated mutations with relation to the selected character taken for reference (Fig. 38). It is evident that if the recombination frequency between z_A^- and z_B^- is greater in cross Hfr z_A^- $Ad^+S^s \times F^-$ $z_B^-Ad^-S^r$ than in cross Hfr $z_B^-Ad^+S^s \times F^-$ $z_A^-Ad^-S^r$, the order of the markers is z_A-z_B-Ad because an additional double cross-over within a short region is required in the second cross in order for $z^+Ad^+S^r$ recombinants to be

formed. Comparison of the recombination frequencies obtained in reciprocal crosses, therefore permits the ordering of the z^- mutations with respect to the Ad marker. The smallest recombination frequency measured in such crosses is about 3×10^{-5}.

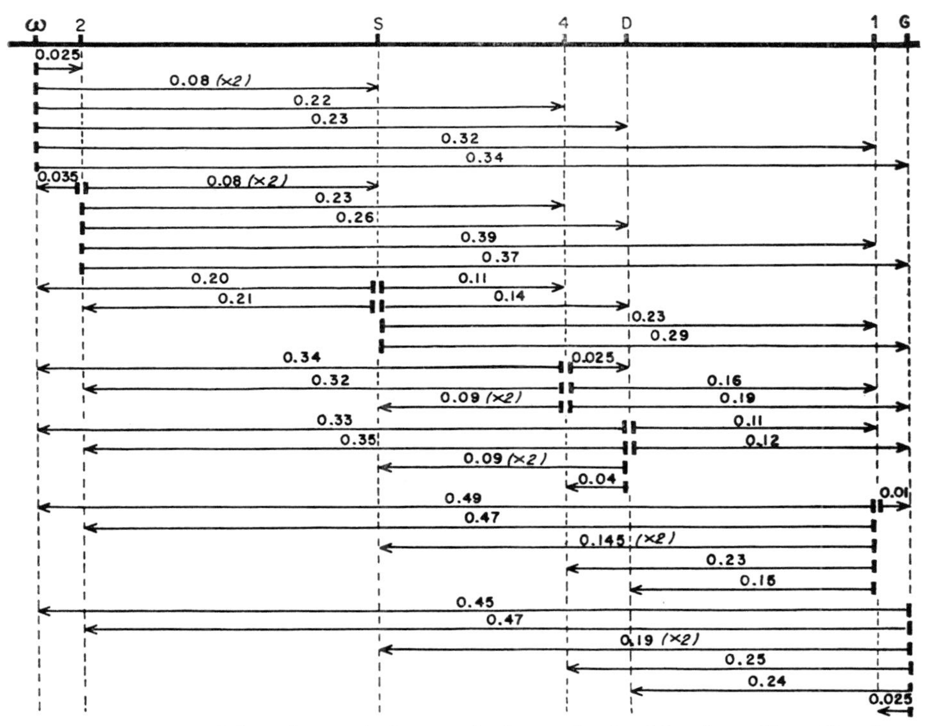

FIG. 38. Map of the z locus which controls the synthesis of β-galactosidase. Results of two factor crosses between z-mutants. The arrow indicates the polarity of the cross (Hfr → F−) between Hfr prototroph S^s donors and F− Ad−S^r recipients (except recipient z_s^- which is T−L−S^r). Recombination frequencies are calculated as the per cent of Lac+ among Ad+S^r recombinants (or T+L+S^r recombinants when the z_s^- recipient is involved; hence a correction by a factor of about 2). (Monod and Jacob, unpublished.)

Another and more reliable method of ordering intragenic mutations is to follow the segregation of an outside marker. Needless to say, this outside marker has to be very closely linked to the locus under study, since the segregation of more distant markers is obscured by negative interference. In crosses between pairs of z^- mutants, it is convenient to follow the segregation of the i marker (see Fig. 37) when one of the strains used in the cross is inducible (i^+) and the other one constitutive

(i^-). The results of such crosses, presented in Table XXXVII, allow the ordering of the z^- mutations (Fig. 38) (Monod and Jacob, unpublished results).

From the evidence just presented, it is clear that recombinational analysis can be successfully applied to bacterial conjugation, provided that the peculiarities inherent in the process are taken into consideration.

TABLE XXXVII
ORDERING OF Lac_z^- MUTANTS WITH RESPECT TO i[a]

		Ratio i^+/i^- among z^+ recombinants in crosses between						
		Constitutive Hfr			Inducible Hfr			
		O_2°	z_4^-	z_1^-	O_ω°	z_S^-	z_D^-	z_G^-
Inducible F−	O_ω°	0.1	0.05	0.025	—	—	—	—
	z_S^-	4	0.16	0.16	—	—	—	—
	z_D^-	7	4.5	0.16	—	—	—	—
	z_G^-	9	10	8	—	—	—	—
Constitutive F−	O_2°	—	—	—	0.1	10	15	6
	z_4^-	—	—	—	0.04	0.14	8	10
	z_1^-	—	—	—	0.08	0.1	0.25	4

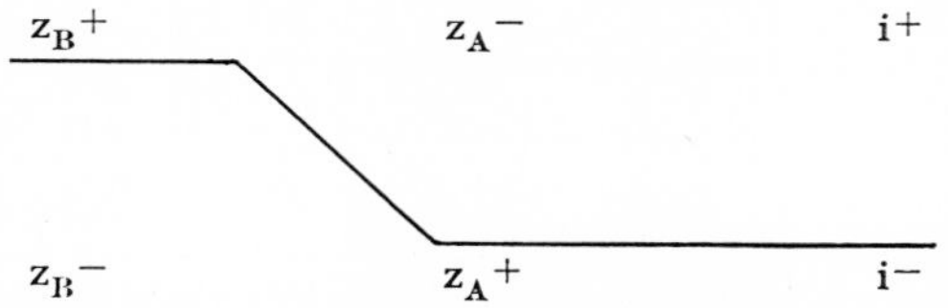

z_B^+ z_A^- i^+

z_B^- z_A^+ i^-

[a] In crosses between constitutive (i^-)Hfr and inducible (i^+)F−, or vice versa, carrying two different z^- mutations, z^+ recombinants are selected. Their genetic constitution with respect to the i character is determined by replica-plating on glucose medium and assay with paper impregnated with *o*-nitrophenol-galactoside. In these conditions, only the constitutive (i^-) clones synthesize enzyme and give a yellow spot. Results are expressed by the ratio i^+/i^- observed among the z^+ recombinants. The order thus deduced is identical to that represented in Fig. 38. (From Monod and Jacob, unpublished.)

This method is of little practical value when large chromosomal segments are involved, since other methods of evaluating genetic distances are available, and also because the results are distorted by negative interference. For small chromosomal segments on the contrary, and in particular for intragenic analysis, this method is extremely useful and may even be the only one possible. It provides a high degree of resolution which allows one to distinguish mutations occurring at neighboring sites of the same locus.

B. Genetic and Physical Determination of Chromosomal Segments

In most organisms, recombinational analysis is the only method which allows a determination of the position of genetic loci and of the distances between them. In *E. coli*, the mechanism of genetic transfer makes possible other methods of analysis, and the results obtained by these methods can in consequence be compared with the results of recombinational analysis. As already indicated, the distances between bacterial markers may be expressed in three different types of units: recombination units, time units, and "chemical units" (number of phosphorus atoms, for example).

1. *Recombination units.* Recombination units express the frequencies of genetic exchanges between markers as measured by classical genetic analysis. Such measurements, as discussed above, provide reliable information only for markers which are closely linked. To assess by this method the number of recombination units which corresponds to the entire linkage group of *E. coli* K12 would require rather elaborate determinations.

2. *Time units.* Time units are determined by measuring the relative times of entry of Hfr markers into recipient bacteria in interrupted mating experiments. The validity of this representation depends on the assumption that, in a population of conjugating cells, the transfer of the Hfr chromosome proceeds, on the average, at a constant rate. Experiments with Hfr strains which transfer the same chromosomal segment at very different times during conjugation indicate that this assumption is correct at least for the first half of the linkage group. For markers located on the distal part of the chromosome, the rate of transfer appears to decrease and the dispersion in the time of their entry becomes greater. If the rate of progression of the chromosome were constant, it can be estimated that the whole chromosome would be transferred in about 100–110 minutes when conjugation takes place at 37°.

3. *"Chemical units."* Chemical units are estimated from the relative sensitivities of Hfr markers to P^{32} decay occurring before transfer. Although such calculations are based on several assumptions which have already been discussed (see Chapter XII, page 221), the general validity of this approach appears justified in view of the remarkable correlations found between the genetic maps deduced from interrupted mating on the one hand and from P^{32} induced fragmentation on the other (see Fig. 35).

An attempt can be made to establish a relation between these three types of units, although as yet such translations are rather imprecise. It may be assumed that all the DNA of *E. coli* is contained in its chromosomal bodies. Biochemical estimates would indicate that one of these bodies, i.e., one linkage group, contains about 10^7 nucleotide pairs. One minute of transfer, which corresponds to the transfer of about one hundredth of a linkage group, would therefore represent about 10^5 nucleotide pairs. This estimate, which is based on the assumption that P^{32} atoms incorporated into *E. coli* DNA are regularly distributed along the chromosome, does not presuppose the actual arrangement of DNA "molecules" in the chromosome or the structure of the chromosome itself. If one were to assume that the chromosome of *E. coli* is constituted by a single continuous DNA duplex conforming to the Watson-Crick model, then the amount of DNA transferred during 1 minute of conjugation would correspond to a length of 34 μ of such a structure.

A relation between time units and recombination units can also be established although determination of the former is more accurate for large chromosomal segments, whereas determination of the latter is more accurate for small chromosomal segments. When closely linked markers such as T, L, and Az or Pro-Lac-Ad are considered, it can be calculated that a chromosomal length transferred in about 1 minute corresponds to about 20 recombination units. The total map length of *E. coli* K12 would thus amount to about 2000 units, one map unit being equivalent to about 5×10^3 nucleotide pairs. Similar calculations for a variety of organisms can be found in Pontecorvo's illuminating essay (1958). It is worth mentioning that one recombination unit would correspond to 2.5×10^2 nucleotide pairs in bacteriophage T4 (Benzer, 1957) to 7×10^4 in *Aspergillus* and to 3×10^5 in *Drosophila* (see Pontecorvo, 1958).

* * *

One of the ultimate aims of genetics is to assign a structural meaning to the numerical data embodied in linkage maps. Genetic studies of microorganisms and, in particular, of the processes of meromixis in bacteria provide means of approaching this goal. In bacterial conjugation several methods exist for relating genetic and physical measurements. The interpretation of genetic data in structural terms would be greatly facilitated if a system were available in which the transfer of genetic information could occur both by conjugation and by transformation with extracted DNA. A valuable contribution toward this end has been made recently by Kaiser and Hogness (1960), who have transferred genetic characters to *E. coli* K12 by means of DNA extracted from a transducing Hft lysate of bacteriophage λ.

II. THE PROBLEM OF GENETIC RECOMBINATION

Recent developments in the field of genetics have brought new possibilities of investigating the process of genetic recombination. However, although a great number of facts have been gathered, it has not yet been possible to integrate them into a general and comprehensive picture. Genetic research on microorganisms has played a major role in the evolution of ideas concerning genetic recombination and has opened the possibility of posing this problem in biochemical terms. The model proposed by Watson and Crick for the structure of DNA leads to the establishment of a relationship between replication and genetic recombination at the molecular level. It is difficult, however, to extend these considerations to the mechanism of recombination at the chromosomal level, because of our lack of knowledge concerning the structure of chromosomes. These limitations should be kept in mind when analyzing the process of recombination in any given system.

The processes of meromixis in bacteria offer many possibilities for investigating the problem of genetic recombination. The series of events which takes place in a merozygote must be very similar whether transfer is accomplished by transformation, transduction, or conjugation, because in all cases, recombination occurs with a certain probability between the genetic fragment derived from the donor and a chromosome of the recipient. A recombinant chromosome is formed, the genetic determinants of which are mainly those of the recipient, some of them, however, being those of the donor. As the recipient bacterium is, in general, multinucleate, a bacterium of recombinant type will emerge after the recombinant chromosome has segregated from the chromosomes of the recipient type.

It should be pointed out that bacterial conjugation offers a unique opportunity for dissociating the genetic effects of external agents, whether physical or chemical, from their purely physiological effects. When Hfr bacteria are subjected to a given treatment before mating and then allowed to conjugate, the effects of the treatment on genetic recombination may be assessed by examining the progeny of the merozygotes.

We shall consider in this section the relevant information concerning the process of recombination. The methods used, the results obtained, and the bearing of these results on the mechanism of recombination will be discussed first. In the second part of this section, the available information on the kinetics of recombination will be examined.

A. The Mechanism of Genetic Recombination

In sexual reproduction of higher forms, recombination is generally described as resulting from a reciprocal exchange of homologous segments between homologous chromosomes. The results of quantitative genetic analysis, correlated with the cytological observation of chiasmata between homologous chromosomal structures, have led to the notion that genetic exchange is a consequence of crossing-over which results

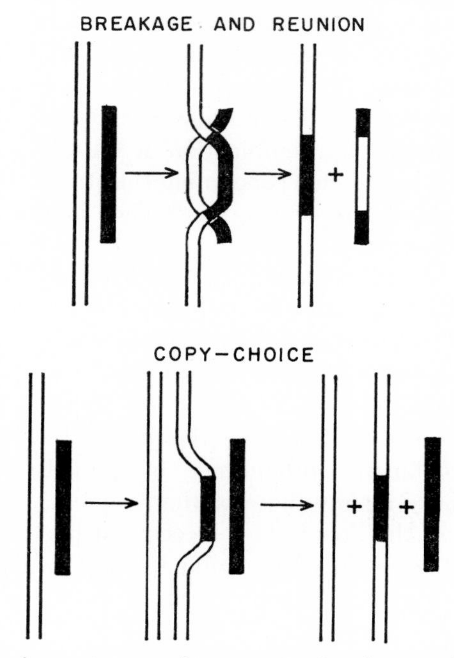

Fig. 39. Models of genetic recombination: By breakage and reunion; By copy-choice.

in a precise breakage and reunion of preexisting structures. Such a mechanism would be, a priori, difficult to visualize in the case of merozygotes since odd exchanges would inevitably result in the formation of non-viable products (see Fig. 39). Unless a precise mechanism of double breaks, even in very small regions, is postulated, it seems unlikely that recombination in microorganisms can be a consequence of breakage and reunion of preexisting structures. For these, and for other reasons, the hypothesis has been advanced that, in microorganisms, genetic recombination is closely related to replication of the genetic material, and takes place by a mechanism of "copy-choice" or "alternate copy." A model connecting recombination with chromosome duplication was proposed by Belling in 1931. Since then it has been extended and developed to account for genetic recombination in bacteriophage (Sturtevant, 1949; Levinthal, 1954) and in bacteria (Lederberg, 1955a; Demerec and Demerec, 1956). According to this model, a copy started on one of the parental structures may switch to the other parental structure and be continued on it. A recombinant linkage group would be a completely new structure synthesized partly along one of the parental structures, partly along the other (see Fig. 39). Most features of recombination in bacteriophage are explained by such an hypothesis which appears also to apply to genetic recombination in bacteria.

1. *The effect of ultraviolet light on genetic recombination.* In crosses between bacteriophages, ultraviolet (U.V.) treatment of the infecting particles results in a remarkable increase in the observed frequencies of genetic recombination. For small doses of U.V. light, the increase is roughly proportional to the dose up to a saturation level. The treatment does not alter the relative distances between linked markers but increases the absolute distances between them. Its over-all effect is, therefore, to stretch out the linkage group of the phage. Irradiation of only one of the parental types introduces a polarity in the cross, the irradiated parent behaving as a donor of small genetic segments. The genetic recombinants formed inherit only a limited number of markers of the irradiated phage. The most likely interpretation of these facts is that the lesions occasioned by irradiation in the genetic material of the phage greatly enhance the probability of switches from the treated to the untreated phage type at the time of DNA replication (Jacob and Wollman, 1955b).

Similar results are observed when donor Hfr bacteria are exposed to small doses of U.V. light and then immediately mated with untreated recipient bacteria. Doses of U.V. light which only have a limited effect on the processes of conjugation and of genetic transfer affect to a much greater extent the process of genetic recombination. When Hfr H bacteria are submitted before mating to increasing doses of U.V. light, the numbers of $T^+L^+S^r$ and Gal^+S^r recombinants formed decrease exponentially as a function of the dose and at about the same rate, as can be seen in Fig. 40. The number of the $T^+L^+Gal^+S^r$ recombinants, on the contrary, decreases at a much faster rate, evidencing a decrease in the apparent linkage between T^+L^+ and Gal^+. The analysis of the $T^+L^+S^r$ and of the Gal^+S^r recombinants (Table XXXVIII) reflects in similar fashion the effect of U.V. light on genetic linkages. Exposure of the recipient bacteria alone, as indicated in Table XXXVIII, also affects to some extent the process of genetic recombination, although the effect encountered is much less pronounced than when Hfr donor bacteria are submitted to the same dose of U.V. light.

The effect of U.V. light on genetic recombination in bacteria appears to be interpreted best by the same hypothesis which had been already proposed in the case of recombination in phage. The random lesions of

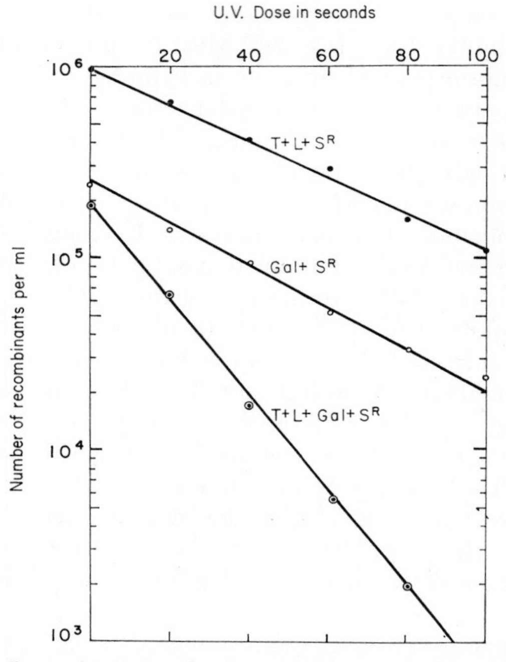

Fig. 40. The effects of U.V. irradiation on genetic recombination. Hfr H bacteria are exposed to increasing doses of U.V. light. The irradiated samples are mixed under standard conditions with nonirradiated F− P678 recipients and aliquots are plated on selective media. The numbers of T+L+S^r, Gal+S^r, and T+L+Gal+S^r recombinants are plotted on a logarithmic scale versus the dose of U.V. light in seconds.

the irradiated genetic material would interfere with its normal replication, thus favoring switches from the treated to the untreated chromosome. This phenomenon would result in a decrease in size of the genetic segments contributed by the irradiated parent to the recombinants, and hence lead to the apparent stretching of genetic linkages (Jacob and Wollman, 1955a, 1958a).

2. *The effects of P^{32} decay on genetic recombination.* Genetic effects very similar to those of U.V. light are observed when highly P^{32} labeled

Hfr donors are mated with unlabeled F^- recipients and the disintegration of the radiophosphorus atoms allowed to proceed in the zygotes immediately after mating. These experiments have already been described in Chapter XII, and it has been shown (see Fig. 34) that the transmission to recombinants of the genetic markers of the donor decreases as a function of P^{32} decay. The "inactivation" of Hfr markers is less pronounced, however, and follows different kinetics when the disintegration of radiophosphorus atoms occurs *in the zygotes after transfer,* than when it takes place *in the Hfr donors before transfer,* as can be seen by comparing Figs. 33 and 34. In the former case, P^{32} decay affects the very process of genetic recombination, whereas in the latter case, its effects are primarily on the process of genetic transfer (see p. 218).

TABLE XXXVIII
EFFECT OF ULTRAVIOLET LIGHT ON GENETIC RECOMBINATION

	Genetic constitution of recombinants							
	$T^+L^+S^r$				Gal^+S^r			
Crosses[a]	Az	T_1	Lac	Gal	TL	Az	T_1	Lac
Hfr × F^- control	91	73	49	26	57	52	59	71
Hfr U.V. × F^-	56	31	9	3	14	23	31	37
Hfr × F^- U.V.	83	54	37	18	44	49	53	64

[a] Crosses Hfr H S^s × P678 S^r are performed under usual conditions. In the last two crosses, one of the parental cultures is submitted, just before mating, to a standard dose of U.V. light which leaves about 30–50 per cent survivors. The figures represent the percentage of recombinants having inherited the unselected characters from the Hfr parent.

The susceptibility to P^{32} decay decreases progressively as a function of time as seen in Fig. 34. The transmission to recombinants of the Hfr markers T^+L^+ on the one hand and Gal^+ on the other decreases at about the same rate. Once the genetic loci of the donor have been transferred to the zygotes, their sensitivity to P^{32} decay thus no longer depends on the particular position they occupied on the Hfr chromosome. The simultaneous transmission of the T^+L^+ and Gal^+ markers, however, is much more sensitive to P^{32} decay than is the transmission of either T^+L^+ or Gal^+ separately. The disintegration of radioactive P^{32} occurring in the zygotes after transfer accordingly has a marked effect on genetic linkages. Analysis of the $T^+L^+S^r$ recombinants formed in the course of P^{32} decay leads to the same conclusion. As seen in Fig. 34, the initial rates at which different unselected characters disappear from the genetic constitution of $T^+L^+S^r$ recombinants increase as a direct function of their distance from the T^+L^+ selected characters. The different curves, however, achieve a final slope which is the same for all and similar to that of the curve which expresses the decrease of the $T^+L^+S^r$ recombinants themselves.

The best interpretation of these findings appears to be the following one. The disintegration of radiophosphorus atoms causes interruptions in the continuity of the transferred Hfr chromosome. Two linked markers have the greatest chance of becoming simultaneously integrated if both are attached to the same chromosomal fragment: the more distant the two markers, the greater the probability that a P^{32} disintegration will interpose a break between them and hence the greater the sensitivity of the linkage to P^{32} decay. Any chromosomal locus can however become integrated independently of other loci as long as the fragment in which it is located exceeds a critical minimum size: the larger the size of the fragment, the greater the probability for the marker to become integrated. This interpretation accounts for the general shape of the curves of Fig. 34 and for the fact that the ultimate slopes of the "inactivation" curves reach a common value (Fuerst, Jacob, and Wollman, 1961; Stent and Fuerst, 1960).

The genetic effects of ultraviolet light and of the disintegration in the zygotes of P^{32} atoms introduced by the Hfr chromosome can therefore both be interpreted as manifestations of the effects on replication of lesions induced in the DNA of the donor bacteria.

3. *Analysis of the progeny of individual zygotes.* The high efficiency of bacterial conjugation makes it possible to detect individual pairs of mating bacteria under the microscope. Hence, individual zygotes can be isolated by micromanipulation and their progeny can be analyzed (Anderson and Mazé, 1957; J. Lederberg, 1957; Anderson, 1958).

In order to distinguish the two parental types, it is necessary to use donor and recipient bacteria which differ morphologically, for example in cell form or in motility. Cultures of Hfr and F^- bacteria are mixed in liquid medium in order to allow conjugation to occur and samples are examined at intervals. Conjugating pairs of bacteria are visible shortly after mixing of the parental cultures. The members of such pairs move through the microscopic field as single units and appear to be connected by invisible fibers. The period during which they remain attached is variable, but can often exceed 1 hour. Individual pairs can be isolated with a micromanipulator and placed in individual droplets of medium. After the members of a pair have separated, each ex-conjugant is placed in a separate droplet and allowed to multiply. Whenever recombinants are formed, they always arise in the progeny of the recipients. These direct observations accordingly confirm the findings that the transfer of genetic material is unidirectional and that the zygotes are essentially constituted by the recipient bacteria.

The segregation pattern of individual zygotes has been analyzed by separating the daughter bacteria formed at each division during the first 5–10 divisions. The isolated bacteria are left overnight in individual droplets, where each cell forms a clone, the genetic characters of which can then be determined. Such experiments show that recombinants are formed in only a fraction of the zygotes and that the size of this fraction depends on the parental strains used. When recombinants occur, they usually inherit from the donor only a limited number of genetic characters located near the origin of the donor chromosome. In the progeny of the zygotes, a majority of the clones exhibit the genotype of the recipient. Segregation of pure recombinant clones occurs only after several divisions. These results are easily explained by the fact that the recipients are multinucleate. A pure recombinant clone arises from a homokaryotic cell in which recombinant chromosomes have segregated from the several chromosomes of the recipient type present in the zygote.

In the two studies published so far on the pattern of segregation from individual zygotes, differences have been observed which appear to be attributable to differences in the strains used. In the pedigree analysis reported by J. Lederberg (1957), division of the zygotes is regular. Segregation of recombinant types occurs rather early, at the third or fourth generation, and only rarely does a single zygote give rise to more than one recombinant type. In the other series of investigations (Anderson and Mazé, 1957; Anderson, 1958), on the contrary, division of the zygotes is irregular as compared with that of normal unmated recipient cells, and a sizeable fraction of progeny bacteria are nonviable. Pure clones of recombinants segregate rather late, between the third and the ninth generation. A remarkable finding is that different recombinant types not infrequently arise from the same zygote (see Fig. 41). These results can be explained by assuming that the chromosomal fragment derived from the donor persists in one of the cell lines originating from the zygote and can therefore recombine more than once with the genome of the recipient. This interpretation implies that the integrity of the chromosomal fragment of the donor is preserved in the process of recombination, an hypothesis that is compatible with a mechanism in which genetic recombination is correlated with the replication of the genetic material.

Tomizawa (1960) has recently designed a simple and elegant experiment which allows the main features of the recombinational act to be deduced from the kinetics of segregation of bacterial recombinants.

Hfr Lac+ and F− Lac− bacteria are mixed in liquid medium. Samples are removed after various intervals of time and Hfr bacteria are eliminated with phage, after which the zygotes and their progeny are plated on a complete, nonselective medium which contains an indicator of

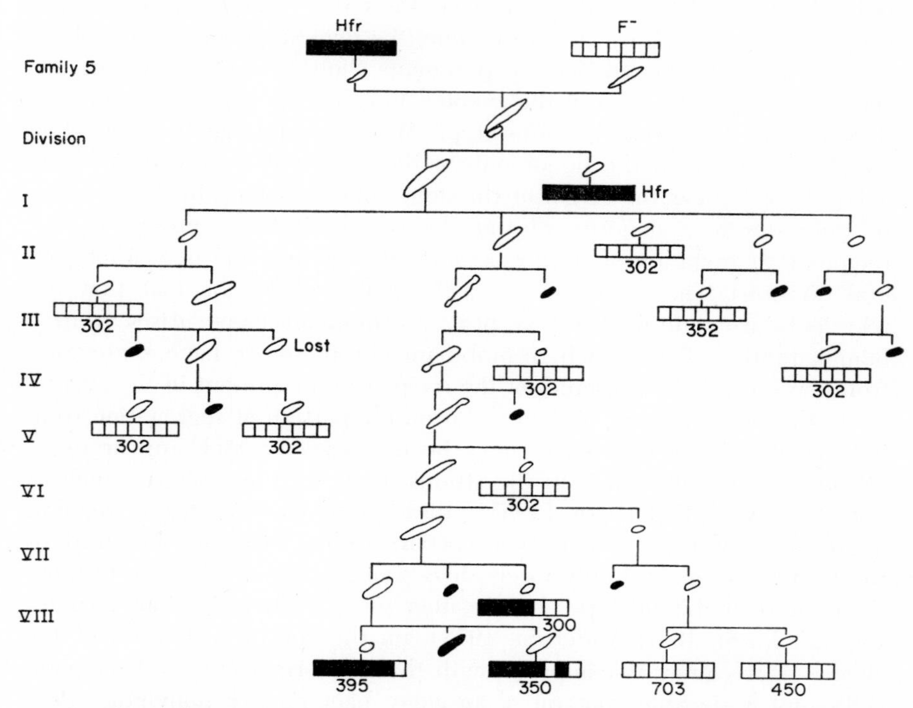

FIG. 41. Pedigree of the progeny issued from a single zygote isolated by micromanipulation. From a mating mixture of Hfr H and F− P678 bacteria, a conjugating pair is isolated in a microdroplet of broth, in an oil chamber at 37°C. After separation, the two exconjugants are placed in two different microdroplets. At each further division, each daughter bacterium is isolated in a microdroplet. After 8 divisions, the clones are allowed to multiply and their genetic constitution is determined. The relative size, shape, and viability of the bacteria are represented (nonviable bacteria in black). The genetic constitution is represented by small squares (from left to right T, L, Az, T_1, Lac, Gal, Sm), in white if they are issued from the F− recipient, in black if they are issued from the Hfr donor. (From Anderson and Mazé, 1957.)

lactose fermentation. The kinetics of segregation of pure Lac+ colonies are compared to the kinetics of formation of Lac variegated colonies, i.e., of colonies which contain both Lac+ and Lac− bacteria. Such experiments show that, with the strains used, segregation of Lac+ recombinants occurs very early, and that the kinetics of this segregation are incompatible with the existence of any kind of heterozygous stage in which a recombinant chromosome is composed of one Lac^+ "subunit" and of one Lac^- subunit which would have to segregate in order for a pure Lac^+ recombinant clone to arise. For the sake of simplicity, it may be assumed that the subunits which could be responsible for a heterozygous stage in bacteria are the two strands of the Watson-Crick helix. Tomizawa's results, although they do not imply any mechanism of genetic recombination, place important restrictions on the possible models which may be considered. According to these results, a genetic locus which takes part in recombination behaves as a whole. In the model of the double stranded DNA duplex, this inference would indicate that both strands of a locus are either of the original recipient type or of the donor (recombinant) type. If recombination were to consist of a direct incorporation of a chromosomal segment of the donor into the recipient's chromosome, by breakage and reunion for example, this substitution ought to be complete as far as the locus considered is concerned. If, alternatively, recombination were to take place by a copy choice mechanism, no hybrid stage would be involved in the recombination process and a recombinant chromosome would be, at the outset, an entirely new structure.

These conclusions are still difficult to reconcile with other lines of evidence bearing on the replication of genetic material (see p. 212) and would imply that different mechanisms might be involved in the process of normal replication and in the process of genetic recombination.

B. The Duration of Genetic Recombination

The types of experiments which have been described in the preceding section also provide some information about the time at which genetic recombination occurs, i.e., about the time interval between the moment when a genetic determinant of the donor penetrates into the recipient and the moment when a new, recombinant structure is formed. This problem had been previously explored only at the level of populations of zygotes, and the data obtained were rather imprecise. Since both the process of conjugation and the process of chromosomal transfer have a considerable time spread in a mating population, it is to be expected that the process of recombination will show a similar time spread. Recombination can only be detected, therefore, when it has occurred in a sizable fraction of the zygotes. Three lines of observation nevertheless give some indication of the duration of the recombinational process.

1. *Kinetics of segregation of recombinants.* The kinetics of formation of recombinants may be followed in crosses between Hfr and F^- bac-

teria (see Fig. 14). The time at which the recombinants begin to multiply gives a maximal estimate of the time required for segregation of a recombinant genome from the multinucleate recipient. More precise results can be obtained if conjugation is allowed to proceed for a fixed and limited period, being terminated by destruction of the Hfr donors, for example with a virulent phage (Hayes, 1957). The experiment can be still further refined if platings are made on a nonselective medium, on which zygotes and heterokaryotic or heterozygous segregants can be distinguished from pure recombinant clones (Tomizawa, 1960). The results obtained vary with the strains used in the cross; roughly speaking, however, the time that elapses between the penetration of a genetic determinant into a recipient and the segregation of a pure recombinant clone lies between 40 minutes (Tomizawa, 1960) and 100 minutes (Hayes, 1957). When extrapolating from these data to the time required for a recombinant chromosome to be formed, one has to keep in mind that at least two divisions are necessary for segregation of a recombinant genome. If the time required for each of these divisions is the normal generation time of the recipient (or of the recombinant itself), the time that elapses between the transfer to the zygote of a genetic determinant and its appearance in a recombinant chromosome may be estimated to lie between 10 and 40 minutes.

2. *Ultraviolet irradiation of the zygotes.* As described earlier in this chapter (see page 237), the administration of small doses of ultraviolet (U.V.) light to Hfr bacteria prior to mating strongly decreases the apparent linkage between markers contributed by the donor bacteria to recombinants. The same effect is observed when newly formed zygotes are submitted to the same dose of U.V. light. By irradiating zygotes at intervals after the transfer has been accomplished, it is possible to determine changes of the U.V. effect as a function of time, and thus to explore the sequence of events which leads to the formation of recombinants (Jacob and Wollman, 1955a; E. L. Wollman, Jacob, and Hayes, 1956). With this technique, it is found that the effect of U.V. light on genetic recombination changes very little until 50 minutes after transfer and then begins to decrease, disappearing at about 100 minutes. It can be inferred from these results that a stage in recombination which is insensitive to U.V. light (perhaps the appearance of the first recombinant chromosomes) is reached about 40 minutes after transfer.

3. *Decay of radioactive phosphorus after transfer.* As already discussed, the disintegration of radiophosphorus atoms in the chromosome of Hfr bacteria, when it takes place in the zygotes immediately after transfer, has marked effects on the process of genetic recombination (see

p. 239). By sampling the zygotes at various intervals after transfer and allowing P^{32} decay to occur in every sample, it is possible to follow the variations in sensitivity of the Hfr markers to the disintegration of the P^{32} atoms contained in the segment originally transferred. The results of such an experiment are shown in Fig. 42. It can be seen that less than 1 hour after the T^+L^+ determinants of the donor have been transferred to the recipient, the sensitivity of these markers has noticeably decreased while complete resistance to P^{32} decay is attained less than 2 hours after the onset of mating (Jacob and Wollman, 1958a; Fuerst, Jacob, and

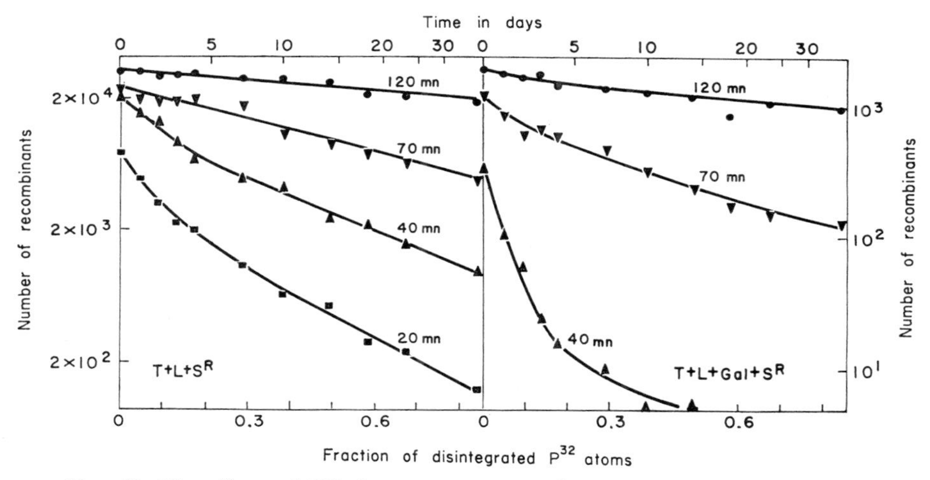

FIG. 42. The effects of P^{32} decay occurring in the zygotes at various times after transfer of the labeled Hfr chromosome. The experimental procedure is the same as that described in Fig. 34, except that samples of the mating mixtures are taken and frozen at various times after the onset of mating. The numbers of recombinants are plotted versus time and fraction of disintegrated P^{32} atoms: *left,* $T^+L^+S^r$ recombinants; *right,* $T^+L^+Gal^+S^r$ recombinants. (Fuerst, Jacob and Wollman, 1961.)

Wollman, 1961). Although detailed kinetic studies of this process have not yet been made, it may be assumed that about 40 minutes after transfer, the genetic information borne by the chromosomal segment derived from the donor has been transmitted to structures no longer susceptible to the disintegration of the P^{32} atoms in the transferred segment.

Despite their incompleteness and imprecision, the three types of experiments just described all give concordant information and indicate that about 40 minutes elapse between the penetration of a genetic determinant of the donor and the formation of a recombinant structure. This corresponds approximately to the time of one generation of the recipient. Little is known as yet about the events which occur during this period. However, the available information suggests that, in bacteria as in bacteriophage, recombination does not involve a reciprocal exchange of preexisting structures by a mechanism of breakage and reunion but rather takes place by a process of copy choice in which the material integrity of the parental elements is preserved. Different models in which genetic recombination is associated with the replication of the genetic material have been proposed (see Levinthal, 1954; J. Lederberg, 1955a; Penrose and Penrose, 1957; Delbrück and Stent, 1957; Stent, 1958).

At the molecular level, the mechanism of copy choice could be either entirely conservative (i.e., the material integrity of the DNA molecules is preserved) or semiconservative (daughter molecules are formed with one old DNA strand and one newly synthesized). For normal replication, the available evidence obtained in phage (Levinthal, 1956) and in bacteria (Meselson and Stahl, 1958a, b) points to a semiconservative mechanism. In bacterial recombination, Tomizawa's results would rather suggest a conservative mechanism. For the moment, no decision can be made.

The evidence from Anderson's pedigree experiments suggests that the chromosomal segment derived from the donor is not directly incorporated in the hybrid chromosome as a result of recombination. This segment appears to persist in one line of cells derived from the zygote. Being unable to multiply as such, it is diluted out in the course of bacterial division. The insensitivity of the Hfr markers to further P^{32} decay after transfer of a labeled chromosomal segment to the zygote also points to the absence of direct incorporation.

* * *

If genetic recombination in bacteriophage and in bacteria takes place by a mechanism of copy choice, how can this be reconciled with the mechanism of genetic recombination in higher forms, classically interpreted as resulting from a reciprocal exchange between preexisting structures? The main argument in favor of such a mechanism of reciprocal exchange through breakage and reunion is the formation of reciprocal recombinant types, easily demonstrable whenever all the products of the same zygote can be analyzed. Conversely, it is the lack of correlation in the numbers of reciprocal recombinants produced in crosses of bacteriophages and the impossibility of their formation in the processes of bacterial meromixis which first indicated the existence of another mechanism of genetic recombination in these cases.

Recent studies with organisms such as *Neurospora* and yeast, where tetrad analysis permits investigation of all the products of meiosis, have revealed instances of recombination in small chromosomal regions which appear to be nonreciprocal. Such instances mainly involve recombination between extremely closely linked but nonidentical alleles (heteroalleles) (Mitchell, 1955; Case and Giles, 1958; Roman, 1956). They have led to the revival of the "gene conversion" hypothesis, which was first proposed by Winkler in 1930 as an alternative to crossing-over for recombination between closely linked markers, and later used by Lindegren (1953) to interpret irregular segregations observed in the tetrad analysis of yeasts. They have also given rise to the suggestion that in such organisms as *Neurospora* and yeast, there might be two distinct mechanisms operating at different levels of genetic organization: conventional crossing-over for large chromosomal segments; and miscopying, analogous to that postulated for bacteriophage and bacteria, for small genetic segments (see Beadle, 1957). In fact, as Pontecorvo (1958) clearly stated, there are three possible ways of explaining the present facts about genetic recombination in lower and higher forms. First, the mechanism of recombination in phage and in bacteria may be basically different from that of higher forms. Second, the mechanism of genetic recombination may be basically similar in all living forms; in this event, the differences observed are only apparent and result from analysis of different levels of organization. Lastly, it is possible that in organisms such as yeast and *Neurospora*, and perhaps in other higher forms, there are two different mechanisms of genetic recombination: an elementary mechanism, similar to that of phages and of bacteria when small regions (for instance the same DNA "molecule") are involved; and a chromosomal mechanism (crossing-over) when large regions are concerned. The third possibility, which was originally proposed by Winge (1955), implies that a complex structure such as a chromosome may consist of DNA molecules tied together by a nongenetic backbone, and that crossing-over affects exclusively this backbone.

It is not yet possible to decide among these three alternative hypotheses, mainly for lack of suitable experimental approaches. If they can be associated with genetic or cytogenetic data, chromosome labeling experiments such as those already initiated by Taylor and his colleagues (see Taylor, 1958a, b), should provide valuable information. The remarkable effect of U.V. light on genetic recombination in phages and in bacteria might also prove to be useful as a tool. It has already been applied to the study of mitotic recombination in yeast (Roman and Jacob, 1957, 1958). Exposure of diploid yeasts to small doses of U.V. light increases markedly the frequency of allelic recombination and affects only slightly recombination between distant markers. Moreover,

U.V.-induced recombination between alleles does not appear to be correlated with recombination between outside markers. It is possible that recombination between alleles in yeast, which resembles recombination in phage and in bacteria in its susceptibility to U.V. light, may likewise be associated with DNA replication, whereas recombination between more distant markers, which is much less sensitive to U.V. light, may occur by the more conventional mechanism of crossing-over at the level of the chromosomal backbone.

To conclude this chapter, it must be pointed out that the evidence presented in favor of a model of copy choice in bacteria is as yet by no means conclusive. Genetic recombination constitutes the main tool of genetic analysis; but its very mechanism still remains obscure. The observations reported above concerning bacterial recombination can be easily interpreted by a copy choice model; but with a few additional assumptions, they might also be explained by a mechanism of breakage and reunion. A decisive solution of this problem will be obtained only through correlated physical and genetic analyses of crosses; i.e., through a determination of the molecular structure of recombinant chromosomes.*

* Recent experiments along these lines indicate that, even in bacteriophage, genetic recombination is correlated with material reassortment of DNA of preexisting genetic structures (Meselson and Weiglé, 1961; G. Kellenberger, Zichichi and Weiglé, 1961).

CHAPTER XIV

The Phenotypic Expression of the Genetic Material

The concept of a functional relationship between genes and proteins developed largely from the study of biochemical mutants in *Neurospora*. The loss of enzymatic activities observed as the result of mutations—more precisely, the loss of a single enzymatic activity as the result of a single mutation—led to the "one gene–one enzyme" hypothesis (Beadle, 1945). In the last decade, the concept of functional relationship between gene and protein has been replaced progressively by the notion of a structural relationship. This change in outlook is the consequence of advances in the fields of biochemistry and genetics: notably, the model for DNA proposed by Watson and Crick (1953b); the analysis of the fine structure of genetic material by Benzer (1955); and the finding that mutations may result not in a loss of the ability to synthesize a given protein but in the synthesis of an altered protein (Horowitz and Fling, 1956; Yanofsky and Crawford, 1959). The new concept aims at interpreting the genetic control of protein specificity at the molecular level. All the information necessary for the determination of the specific structure of a protein is assumed to be contained in the gene, the sequence of amino acids in the proteins being in some way determined by the sequence of nucleotides in the DNA molecule (see Crick, 1958). This notion implies that a small alteration in the fine structure of a gene may produce a small change in the sequence of amino acids in the corresponding protein, an hypothesis supported by observations concerning some mutations which affect the structure of human hemoglobin (Ingram, 1957).

As a result of studies on the genetic fine structure of viruses and bacteria, the concept of the gene as a unit which is at the same time the ultimate unit of mutation, of recombination, and of function can no longer be maintained (Benzer, 1957). A functional unit can be defined only by the classical test of allelism or complementarity (E. B. Lewis, 1951; Pontecorvo, 1956). This test is used to determine whether or not two mutants which exhibit similar phenotypes are defective in the same elementary function. In cells containing two homologous chromosomes (diploids or heterokaryons or cells mixedly infected with two viruses), the two mutations under investigation can be located either on the same chromosome (— —/+ +, position *cis*) or on two different chromosomes (— +/+ —, position *trans*). If the two mutations affect different independent functions, the diploid in configuration *trans* exhibits the wild phenotype; if they affect the same function, the diploid in configuration *trans* exhibits the mutant phenotype. In such noncomplementary mutants, the corresponding mutations have always been found to be located in a very limited segment of the genetic map. According to the terminology of Benzer (1957), such a map segment, corresponding to a function which is unitary by the *cis-trans* test, is referred to as a "cistron." The test of complementarity, however, does not constitute an absolute criterion. In several instances, pairs of mutants in which the same enzyme is altered and which, in all likelihood, are affected in the same cistron, still give rise to partial complementation (Giles, 1958). At the present time, however, the *cis-trans* test provides the only operational criterion of a functional unit.

The role of the genetic material in determining the specific structure of individual proteins is now firmly established; however, this finding does not exclude the possibility that the genetic material might also perform other tasks. In addition, the fact that the activity of a gene may depend on its localization on the chromosome remains unexplained. The existence of "a hierarchy of different field orders" in the chromosomes (see Goldschmidt, 1955), that is, of interactions along the length of a chromosome, is suggested by such position effects, as well as by the groupings of genes controlling related reactions. Recent work with various organisms has shown that the cistrons which control different reactions of the same biochemical pathway may not be randomly distributed over the genetic map but may rather tend to be closely associated, although the degree of association varies from one organism to another (see Pontecorvo, 1950, 1958). The most striking examples have been reported by Demerec and Hartman (1959) in *Salmonella,* where the cistrons controlling the sequential reactions of a pathway such as the biosynthesis of an amino acid are often located in a cluster on the chromosome.

In the study of gene expression, several experimental approaches may be distinguished. The first one is a direct consequence of the notion of a structural relationship between gene and protein, or between cistron and polypeptide chain. It aims at breaking the genetic code, by attempting to correlate the map of mutational sites—or more specifically the sequence of base pairs in the DNA—with the sequence of amino acids in the corresponding polypeptide chain. Another line of experiments deals with the study of the biosynthesis of macromolecules. Since it is virtually established that proteins are synthesized in the cytoplasm rather than directly at the genetic site, the transfer of structural specificity from gene to protein requires some chemical intermediate(s). The recognition of these intermediates is essential for the understanding of the mechanism of gene action. Finally, another type of research aims at analyzing the processes which regulate gene expression. A cell is able to regulate specific syntheses in conformity with its requirements and with the environmental conditions. This fact implies the existence of precise mechanisms that determine both qualitatively and quantitatively the phenotypic translation of the genetic message.

Bacterial conjugation provides a system suitable for the study of the relations between the genetic material and the cytoplasm and, therefore, for the study of the functional potentialities contained in the genome and of their phenotypic expression. The introduction of a chromosomal segment from a donor into a recipient corresponds not only to a fertilization but also, in some ways, to a nuclear transplantation. The high efficiency and the orientation of genetic transfer offer an opportunity for investigating the mechanism by which a genetic determinant, introduced into a recipient lacking it, makes its impact on the bacterial phenotype. In addition, the phenotypic effect of the newly introduced determinant can be detected directly without the delay required in higher organisms by morphogenetic processes. In this chapter, we shall describe the method of functional analysis by sexduction and summarize the information obtained from the study of the phenotypic expression of various characters. The genetic aspects of regulating mechanisms involved in protein synthesis will then be considered. This analysis leads to the recognition of new types of genetic units, the functions of which do not seem to determine protein specificity. In addition, the results obtained in such a study are not compatible with current ideas concerning the mechanism which allows the transfer of structural specificity from genes to proteins. They require a new model for gene action, which will be discussed in the last part of the chapter.

I. FUNCTIONAL ANALYSIS BY SEXDUCTION

Our ability to correlate map regions of the chromosome with physiological activities depends on the criteria used for defining the phenotype. For instance, many mutations are known which destroy the capacity of *E. coli* to utilize lactose as a carbon source. As discussed in Chapter XIII, these mutations may be distinguished and mapped by recombination. Most of them are found to be located within a small segment of the linkage group, the Lac region. Gross physiological criteria, such as growth on synthetic medium containing lactose as the sole source of carbon or fermentation of lactose on indicator agar, would suggest that all these mutants are alike. However, it is known from biochemical work that this system involves the sequential participation of two distinct catalytic entities: the galactoside permease, responsible for the concentration of galactosides inside the bacterium; and the β-galactosidase which hydrolyzes β-galactosides (see G. N. Cohen and Monod, 1957). Recently, the permease activity has been correlated with the presence of a protein which catalyzes the acetylation of certain galactosides (Zabin, Kepes, and Monod, 1959). Several independent criteria, such as heat stability, behavior during purification and antigenic properties, show that galactoside-transacetylase is different from β-galactosidase. When the Lac mutants are analyzed for permease (or transacetylase) and galactosidase properties, they may be arranged in three classes: some (designated as y^-) have lost the capacity to synthesize the permease (transacetylase); others (z^-) have lost the capacity to synthesize an active β-galactosidase; finally, a third group of single point mutants (o°) has lost the capacity to synthesize both the transacetylase and the galactosidase.

A functional analysis of these mutants has been undertaken with the persistent merodiploids obtained by sexduction with a sex factor carrying the Lac region of the wild type (Jacob and Monod, 1961). When an F-Lac^+ factor is introduced into most of the mutants studied so far, the phenotype of the resulting heterogenotes Lac^-/F-Lac^+ is Lac^+. Such Lac^- mutations are, therefore, recessive. During growth, the heterogenotes Lac^-/F-Lac^+ segregate a few bacteria which exhibit the Lac^- phenotype of the parental recipient. The genotype of these segregants can be determined by appropriate tests involving matings with a variety of Lac^- mutants. Such tests show that the segregants belong to two distinct types. A minority are haploid, possessing the Lac^- genotype of the original recipient parent, and having lost the F-Lac factor. The majority still carry an F-Lac factor which, as a result of some kind of "mitotic recombination," carries a Lac^- mutation, identical to that of the chromosome. Such segregants are therefore homozygous for Lac (homogenotes), and have the constitution Lac^-/F-Lac^-. They can transfer their F-Lac^- factor to F^- recipients.

It is accordingly possible to obtain heterogenotes carrying a specific Lac^- mutation, $Lac_A{}^-$, in the chromosome, and another one, $Lac_B{}^-$, in the sex factor. Such heterogenotes have the genetic constitution $Lac_A{}^-$ $Lac_B{}^+$/F-$Lac_A{}^+$ $Lac_B{}^-$. A variety of heterogenotes can be prepared which contain different combinations of pairs of available mutations in position *trans*. The phenotype of such heterozygotes is either wild (Lac^+) or mutant (Lac^-) depending on the pair of mutations involved. The high efficiency of the sexduction process allows a simple routine test: on indicator plates seeded with a recipient Lac^- mutant (for instance Lac_A^-), drops of cultures of various homogenotes able to transfer F-Lac^- factors (for instance F-Lac_B^-, F-Lac_C^-, etc.) are spotted. Complementary mutants produce a dense culture of heterogenotes, whereas noncomplementary mutants give rise only to rare colonies of recombinants carrying the wild alleles in position *cis* (see Fig. 43).

On the basis of this complementation test, the Lac^- mutants investigated so far fall into three distinct groups (see Fig. 48, p. 273).

a. One group contains the mutants classified as y^-, i.e., unable to synthesize galactoside permease (acetylase). These mutants are most generally complemented by the z^- mutants but not by other y^- mutants.

b. A second group contains the mutants classified as z^-, i.e., unable to synthesize β-galactosidase. These mutants are complemented by the y^- mutants but not, as a rule, by other z^- mutants, with the exception of certain pairs which produce various degrees of complementation.

c. A third group contains the mutants classified as o°, i.e., unable to synthesize both the permease and the galactosidase. Such mutants are complemented neither by other mutants of the same group nor by y^- or z^- mutants.

From these results one may conclude that the Lac region contains a cistron controlling the synthesis of the acetylase-permease, a cistron controlling the synthesis of the galactosidase and another genetic unit which is involved in some way in both syntheses. As will be discussed in a later section of this chapter (see page 262), it contains also another cistron which plays a role in the regulation of the system (Jacob and Monod, 1961). That the z cistron actually determines the structure of β-galactosidase is evidenced by the finding that certain z^- mutants produce, instead of the enzyme, a protein which is devoid of enzymatic activity but which cross-reacts specifically with an anti-galactosidase serum (Perrin, Bussard, and Monod, 1959). The heterogenotes z^+/z^- carrying such a mutant allele synthesize simultaneously both the active enzyme and the cross-reacting protein (Perrin, Jacob, and Monod, 1960).

The molecule of β-galactosidase seems to be a polymer, made up of six identical polypeptide chains, each with a molecular weight of about 135,000 which corresponds to some 1000 amino acid residues (see M. Cohn, 1957). The size of the z cistron may be roughly estimated from the maximum recombination values obtained in crosses between z^-

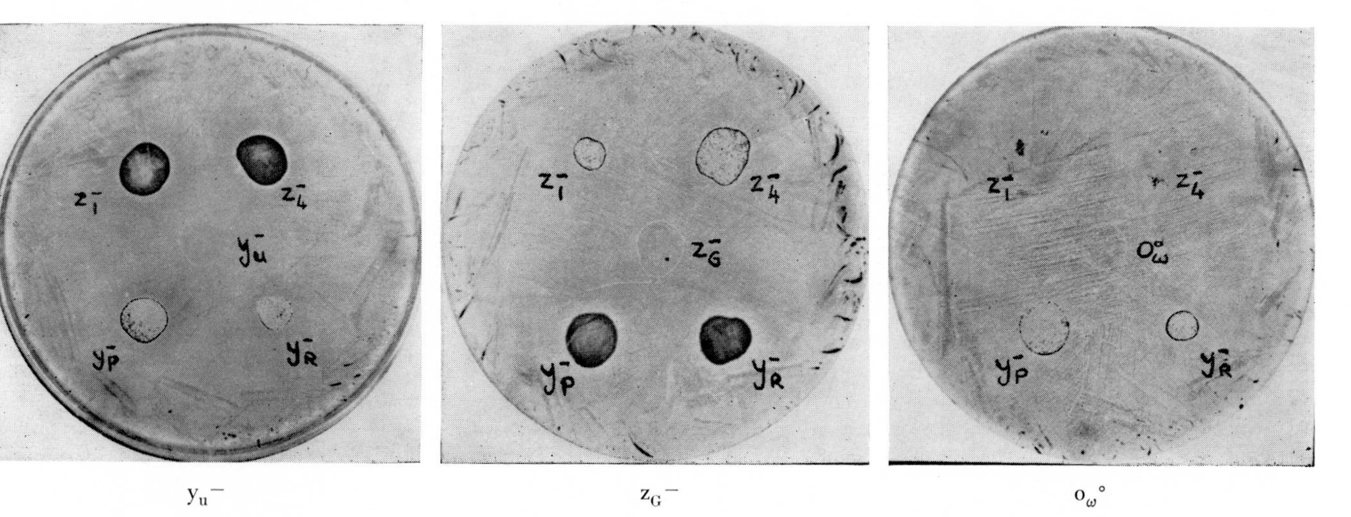

FIG. 43. Functional test by sexduction. Indicator plates containing lactose, streptomycin, and phenyltetrazolium are seeded with 10^7 F− Lac− S^r recipient bacteria. Different types of Lac−/F-Lac− S^s homogenotes are spotted on the plate (each drop contains about 10^7 bacteria). Complementary mutants produce homogeneous dark spots. Noncomplementary mutants produce only a few colonies of Lac+ recombinants. The three plates from left to right are seeded with a y− mutant, a z− mutant, and an o° mutant respectively. They are spotted with z− or y− homogenotes, and in the center a control with an homogenote carrying the same mutation as the strain under study.

mutants located farthest apart. This maximum value is of the order of 0.7 units, a figure which may be converted into about 3500 nucleotide pairs by the use of the conversion ratio of 5000 nucleotide pairs per one recombination unit described in the previous chapter (see page 234). If it is assumed that the 3500 nucleotide pairs specify the sequence of the 1000 amino acids of the enzyme, then one reaches a coding ratio of about 3.5 nucleotide pairs per amino acid, a figure similar to that calculated for the alkaline phosphatase of *E. coli* by Levinthal (1959), on the basis of similar assumptions. It should be pointed out that such a calculation involves a series of assumptions and rough estimates; accordingly, the resulting value cannot yet be taken too seriously.

This study of the lactose system shows that the heterogenotes formed by sexduction provide a valuable tool for functional analysis. Although only a few variant sex factors carrying known markers have been isolated as yet, it seems likely that any segment of the bacterial chromosome can be incorporated into a sex factor and, therefore, that sexduction offers the possibility of analyzing the functions of any system.

II. PHENOTYPIC EXPRESSION OF GENETIC DETERMINANTS UPON TRANSFER BY CONJUGATION

In order to investigate the mechanism by which genetic material controls cellular activities, one may analyze the phenotypic changes which result from the introduction of a genetic determinant into a cell which lacks this determinant. Such attempts have already been made through investigation of bacterial mutations (Witkin, 1951). However, the low frequency of mutations, as well as the difficulty of establishing the exact time of the mutational events, constitute serious disadvantages. The processes of meromixis, which ensure the transfer of material almost exclusively genetic, provide suitable systems for introducing a given genetic determinant into a bacterium. More especially in bacterial conjugation, it is possible to relate the time of penetration of the genetic determinant into the recipient and the time of its subsequent expression in the zygote or its progeny.

The procedure in such experiments consists in mixing two bacterial populations: a donor carrying a given genetic determinant and a mutant recipient. Upon mating, the donor will transmit to a fraction of the recipient population a chromosomal fragment carrying the factor under investigation. The aim of the experiment is to determine, as a function of time, how the new information introduced by the genetic factor of the donor will be phenotypically expressed after transfer.

Several conditions are required for such experiments. Suitable combinations of genetic characters must be used both in donor and in recipient cells, so that the genetic factor to be transferred can be expressed within the recipient phenotype. In order to determine the appearance of the new phenotype with sufficient accuracy, a large fraction of the recipient population must receive the genetic determinant. Hfr strains must be chosen in which the determinant under study is located close to the origin, and is therefore transmitted with high efficiency (see chapter X). Finally, since the expression of a given character is to be followed in the population of merozygotes and their progeny, it is necessary to prevent any disturbing effect due to the presence of the parental populations, and especially of the donors. This can be achieved either by choosing conditions in which the donor population cannot express the character under study while the zygotes and the recombinants can, or by the selective elimination of the donor population after conjugation, for example with an agent, such as phage or streptomycin to which the donor but not the recipient population is sensitive.

A merozygote is a differentiated organism, the phenotype of which is initially that of the recipient. It possesses not only the genetic material but also the cytoplasm and the cell wall of the recipient. Our ability to detect the phenotypic expression of a genetic determinant transferred from the donor can therefore be expected to depend not only on the dominant or recessive nature of the character, but also on the degree of cellular reorganization required for the new phenotype to manifest itself (E. L. Wollman, Jacob, and Hayes, 1956; Hayes, 1957; Jacob, 1958).

A. Expression of Complex Characters

The kinetic analysis of phenotypic expression after conjugation was first carried out by Hayes (1957), who studied rather complex characters such as resistance to phage T_1 (T_1^r) or to the drug sodium azide (Az^r). When the character Az^r is transferred from donors to sensitive recipients, it begins to be expressed within the zygotes after a lag of a few minutes. Expression is achieved in the whole population before the recombinants have started to divide. In contrast, when the character T_1^r is transferred from donors to sensitive recipients, the zygotes remain sensitive, and expression of the character "resistant" begins only after segregation of the recombinants. Expression is not completed in the whole population until several divisions have occurred. From these experiments, Hayes concluded that resistance to sodium azide is a dominant character, whereas resistance to phage T_1 is recessive.

These two examples illustrate the point that the detection of a new phenotype depends largely on the degree of cellular alteration required for a given character to manifest itself. In the case of resistance to phage T_1, it seems likely that a sensitive bacterium carries on its surface many receptor sites which allow the fixation of the virus. After segregation, the recombinants still possess several of these receptors, which become diluted out in the course of subsequent bacterial multiplication. The phenotypic effect that one is able to detect here, resistance to phage, is certainly a late aspect of gene action. It requires the rearrangement of a complex structure, the cell wall, through the disappearance, or the replacement, of all the specific receptor sites. The expression of resistance to sodium azide is certainly a more direct consequence of gene activity. It must be pointed out, however, that in both cases the exact nature of the physiological process involved in phenotypic expression is still unknown. The methods of analysis are not yet quantitative; they allow a distinction between two classes of bacteria, resistant and sensitive, but not the recognition of intermediate states.

For these reasons, it seems clear that a more direct and a more quantitative insight into the functioning of the genetic material should be obtained by the study of the phenotypic expression of a determinant which is known to specify the structure of an easily detectable protein.

B. Expression upon Transfer of a Gene Determining the Structure of a Protein

Functional analysis of the lactose system has shown that the synthesis of the enzyme β-galactosidase is controlled by one functional unit, the z cistron. Furthermore, the fact that several of the z^- mutants produce an immunologically similar protein devoid of enzymatic activity (CRM) in place of the active enzyme clearly indicates that the z cistron does determine the structure of the enzyme. This system may therefore be used to study enzyme synthesis following transfer of the genetic determinant in the process of conjugation.

Such experiments involve the transfer of the z^+ gene from Hfr donors to z^- mutant recipients, and the subsequent determination of kinetics of enzyme synthesis in the population of merozygotes and their progeny. The merozygotes formed in this mating have initially the cytoplasm of the female, which carries an inactive allele of the z gene, and have received from the donors a chromosomal segment carrying the wild z^+ allele. The time at which the z^+ gene begins to penetrate into the recipients can be accurately determined. Mating is performed under such condition that only the zygotes and their progeny, but not the parental populations, can actually synthesize enzyme. In the experiment described in Fig. 44, an Hfr donor which transfers the Lac region about 15 minutes after the onset of mating was used. It can be seen that the formation of β-galactosidase can be detected a few minutes after the time of appearance of the first z^+ containing zygotes. If conjugation is allowed to proceed, β-galactosidase accumulates at a rate which increases with time for about an hour (Pardee, Jacob, and Monod, 1959).

In the population of zygotes, the gross rate of enzyme formation de-

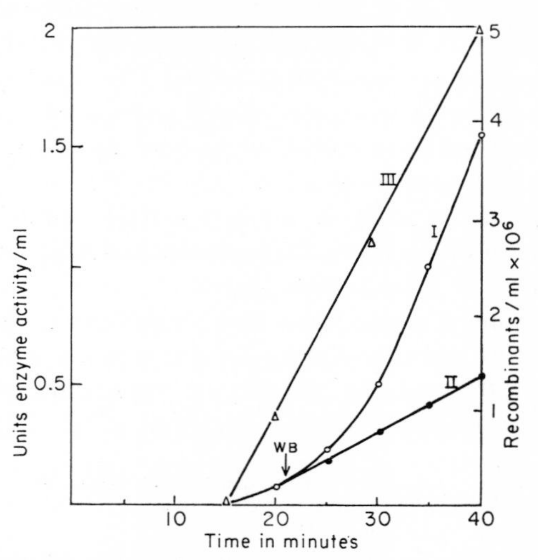

Fig. 44. Kinetics of β-galactosidase synthesis in merozygotes. Donor (Hfr $i^+z^+T6^sS^s$) and recipient (F^- $i^+z^-T6^rS^r$) bacteria, grown in a synthetic medium with glycerol as the carbon source, are mixed in the same medium (time 0) and gently shaken at 37°C. As a function of time after the onset of mating, the following measurements are performed.

1. The transfer of the z^+ determinant is determined in samples taken at various time intervals, treated in a Waring blendor to interrupt mating and plated on lactose-streptomycin MA medium (curve III).

2. The synthesis of β-galactosidase in the mating mixture is followed by assay of the enzyme in samples taken at various time intervals and incubated at 37°C after addition of streptomycin (500 γ/ml), which prevents enzyme synthesis by donor bacteria, and addition of the inducer thiomethyl-β-D-galactoside (10^{-3}M) (curve I).

3. The synthesis of β-galactosidase by the early zygotes is followed in a fraction of the mating mixture treated in the Waring blendor at 20 minutes to interrupt mating after the formation of the first zygotes. Streptomycin and phage T6 are added to prevent Hfr donors from further mating and the mixture is shaken at 37°C. Samples are then taken at various time intervals and treated as previously for enzyme assay (curve II).

Enzyme activity is expressed as mμmoles of *o*-nitrophenyl-β-D-galactoside hydrolyzed per minute per ml of culture. (After Riley, Pardee, Jacob and Monod, 1960.)

pends, not only on the individual rate of synthesis in every zygote, but also on the kinetics of zygote formation. The effect of the latter factor can be eliminated by interrupting the mating process a few minutes after the appearance of the first z^+ zygotes which makes it possible to follow the production of enzyme in the class of zygotes formed early (see Fig. 44). As shown in curve II of Fig. 44, the rate of enzyme synthesis after interruption of mating is constant and equal to the rate attained at the time of interruption. Furthermore, from a comparison with the amount of enzyme formed by z^+ bacteria under similar conditions, after correction for differences in the number of genes, it can be concluded that upon transfer of the z^+ determinant, the rate of β-galactosidase synthesis by the merozygote is not only constant but maximal from the start (Riley, Pardee, Jacob, and Monod, 1960).

The examples discussed in this chapter illustrate clearly the differences in the time at which various characters are expressed after genetic transfer. Expression is delayed for several divisions in the case of resistance to phage T_1, where the appearance of the new phenotype requires elimination of a cellular structure through bacterial multiplication, whereas expression is virtually instantaneous for the synthesis of an enzyme.

Since cytoplasmic constituents do not seem to be transferred during conjugation between Hfr and F^- bacteria, kinetic studies of enzyme synthesis following the entrance of the gene into the recipient bacterium may be expected to provide a valuable tool for investigating the sequence of biochemical steps involved in gene expression. The finding that in the merozygote the z^+ gene functions at maximal rate without significant delay places some restrictions on the possible models depicting its mode of action. This problem will be discussed in more detail at the end of this chapter.

III. GENETIC CONTROL OF REGULATION MECHANISMS

The genetic information contained in the chromosome is only potential and may not always be expressed. Furthermore, the expression of certain genetic characters can depend on the environment. In bacteria, it has been known for a long time that the synthesis of individual proteins can be evoked or suppressed through the influence of specific external agents and, more generally, that the relative rate at which different proteins are synthesized may be markedly dependent on external conditions. There are two situations in which the synthesis of a protein is controlled by specific agents: induction and repression of enzyme synthesis.

As shown a long time ago by Duclaux (1899), the synthesis of certain enzymes of microorganisms depends on the presence of the substrate. This effect has been called enzymatic adaptation (Karström, 1938) or induction of enzyme biosynthesis (Monod and Cohn, 1952). In bacteria, for example, the synthesis of most enzymes which attack exogenous substrates has proved to be inducible (see Stanier, 1951). Many of the characteristics of the induction process have been established through the study of the lactose system of *E. coli* (see Monod and Cohn, 1952). In the absence of β-galactosides, the enzyme β-galactosidase is not formed by wild *E. coli*. If a suitable concentration of inducer is added to the medium, synthesis of the enzyme begins immediately, and the quantity

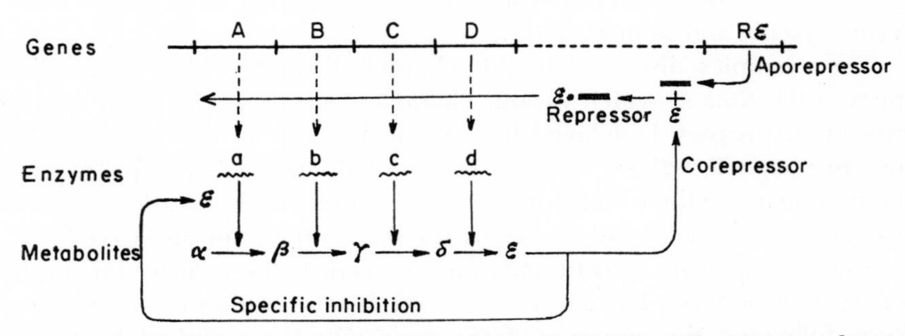

FIG. 45. Diagrammatic representation of the regulation mechanism in a biosynthetic pathway. A, B, C, D represent linked structural genes determining the synthesis of a series of enzymes a, b, c, d, which control the production of a metabolite ε. R_ϵ represents the regulator gene, which controls the synthesis of the aporepressor. This aporepressor in turn reacts with the end product ε of the pathway to form the repressor which inhibits the synthesis of the whole series of enzymes.

of enzyme increases linearly with the increase of total mass of bacteria. If the inducer is removed from the medium, enzyme formation stops at once.

In many of the so-called constitutive systems, the synthesis of enzyme is specifically inhibited by some metabolite (see Fig. 45). More particularly, the synthesis of the enzymes required for the production of an essential metabolite can be specifically inhibited by the end-product of the pathway (M. Cohn and Monod, 1953). The original observations of Monod and his collaborators on the inhibition of the synthesis of tryptophan synthetase and of methionine synthetase by tryptophan and by methionine respectively have been followed by a number of similar observations. In the case of the arginine pathway, studied in detail by Vogel (1957) and by Gorini and Maas (1958), arginine inhibits the synthesis not only of the last enzyme, but of many (probably of all) the enzymes of the pathway, even when the biochemical sequence is interrupted by a genetic block. The term *repression* has been coined by Vogel (1957) to describe this effect of a metabolic end-product on enzyme *synthesis*, and to distinguish it from another phenomenon, the control of enzyme *activity* by a metabolic end-product (Novick and Szilard, 1955; Umbarger, 1956). The phenomenon of repression seems to be a widespread means for the regulation of biosynthetic pathways: it has been demonstrated to operate in the pathways for biosynthesis of several amino acids, and also of pyrimidines (Yates and Pardee, 1957) and of purines (Magasanik, 1957). During growth, the rate of enzyme formation is regulated by the endogenous level of the end product of the pathway as elegantly shown by Gorini and Maas (1958) using continuous cultures in a chemostat.

The action of environmental conditions on gene expression appears itself to be genetically controlled, since mutations are known which affect the inducible or the repressible character of a system. The analysis of such mutations may be expected to give some insight into the mechanisms which, in bacteria, regulate the transfer of structural specificity from genes to proteins.

A. Regulator Genes

1. *Induction of enzyme synthesis.* Many inducible systems can be transformed into constitutive ones by single step mutations (J. Lederberg, 1951c; Cohen-Bazire and Jolit, 1953; Kogut, Pollock, and Tridgell, 1956). Such mutations do not affect the nature and properties of the enzyme itself: these remain the same by all criteria, whether the enzyme is synthesized constitutively or inducibly (M. Cohn and Monod, 1953; Kogut, Pollock, and Tridgell, 1956).

The properties of constitutive mutants should reflect the mechanism by which the mutated factor influences enzyme synthesis. The constitutive mutations might either affect the very genetic determinant which controls the structure of the enzyme or another genetic factor. In the latter case, two alternative interpretations are possible.

(1) The mutation "inducibility" → "constitutivity" corresponds to the acquisition of the capacity to produce an "internal inducer" as a result of a change in metabolism. The "constitutive" allele would then behave as dominant over the "inducible" allele.

(2) The mutation "inducibility" → "constitutivity" corresponds to the loss of the capacity to produce an inhibitor, the action of which is antagonized by external inducers in the inducible strains. The "inducible" allele would then be dominant over the "constitutive" allele.

An investigation of these alternatives has been undertaken in the system controlling lactose utilization in *E. coli.* It is worth recalling that, in wild *E. coli,* the syntheses of both the β-galactosidase and the galactoside permease (acetylase) are inducible (i^+) and depend on the presence of a β-galactoside in the culture medium. In constitutive (i^-) mutants, the mutations $i^+ \rightarrow i^-$ always affect both the permease and the β-galactosidase (G. N. Cohen and Monod, 1957). As described in Chapter XIII, the i mutations fall in the Lac segment of the chromosome, close to the z and y mutations which affect, respectively, the synthesis of the β-galactosidase and of the permease (see Fig. 36, page 228). The interaction of these factors as well as the dominance relations between the i^+ and the i^- alleles may be studied in merodiploids, either persistent ones formed by sexduction, or transient ones formed by chromosomal transfer during conjugation.

Using suitable strains, one can isolate double heterogenotes of the constitutions $i^+z^-/F\ i^-z^+$, $i^-z^+/F\ i^+z^-$, $i^+y^-/F\ i^-y^+$, and $i^-y^+/F\ i^+y^-$. Whatever the combination of markers in such heterogenotes, every time the cell contains one dose of the i^+ allele the syntheses of the β-galactosidase and of the permease are inducible (see Table XXXIX, lines 4 and 5). Only the homogenotes $i^-/F\ i^-$ are able to perform these two syntheses constitutively. In addition, in heterogenotes z^+/z^-_{CRM} carrying a z^- mutation which results in the formation of an altered protein (CRM) instead of active enzyme, both the enzyme and the CRM are synthesized in a parallel manner, either constitutively in the i^-/i^- homogenotes or inducibly in the i^+/i^- heterogenotes (Perrin, Jacob, and Monod, 1960).

These results show clearly that the "inducible" (i^+) allele is dominant over the constitutive (i^-) and that it is active both in the *cis* and *trans* configurations with respect to z and y. The i mutations affect, therefore, an independent functional unit which governs the synthesis of both β-galactosidase and permease via a cytoplasmic component. The dominance of the "inducible" allele over the "constitutive" one indicates that the former represents the active form of the i gene. This conclusion is also supported by the fact that strains carrying an F-i^- and a deletion of the whole Lac region in the chromosome behave as constitutives (see Table XXXIX, line 7). Two different interpretations of the function of the i^+ gene may be considered (Pardee, Jacob, and Monod, 1959).

a. The i^+ gene determines the synthesis of a repressor which inhibits specifically the synthesis of both β-galactosidase and galactoside-permease. In the inducible strains, the addition of an external inducer

TABLE XXXIX
SYNTHESIS OF GALACTOSIDASE AND GALACTOSIDE-TRANSACETYLASE BY HAPLOIDS AND HETEROZYGOUS DIPLOIDS OF REGULATOR MUTANTS[a]

Strain N°	Genotype	Galactosidase		Galactoside-transacetylase	
		Noninduced	Induced	Noninduced	Induced
1	$i^+z^+y^+$	< 0.1	100	<1	100
2	$i_6^-z^+y^+$	100	100	90	90
3	$i_3^-z^+y^+$	140	130	130	120
4	$i^+z_1^-y^+/Fi_3^-z^+y^+$	< 1	240	1	270
5	$i_3^-z_1^-y^+/Fi^+z^+y_U^-$	< 1	280	< 1	120
6	$i_3^-z_1^-y^+/Fi^-z^+y^+$	195	190	200	180
7	$\Delta_{izy}/Fi^-z^+y^+$	130	150	150	170
8	$i^sz^+y^+$	<0.1	< 1	< 1	< 1
9	$i^sz^+y^+/Fi^+z^+y^+$	<0.1	2	< 1	3

[a] Bacteria are grown in glycerol as carbon source and induced, when stated, by isopropyl-thiogalactoside $10^{-4}M$. Values are given as per cent of that observed with induced wild type; Δ_{izy} refers to a deletion of the whole Lac region. It will be noted that organisms carrying the wild allele of one of the structural genes (z or y) in the F factor form more of the corresponding enzyme than the haploid. This is presumably due to the fact that several copies of the F-Lac unit are present per chromosome. In i^+/i^- heterozygotes, values observed with uninduced cells are sometimes higher than in haploid control. This is due to the presence of a significant fraction of i^-/i^- homozygous recombinants in the population. (From Jacob and Monod, 1961.)

would then be required to antagonize the action of the repressor whereas in the constitutive mutants, the i^- mutation would result in the loss of the capacity to synthesize an active repressor.

b. The i^+ gene determines the synthesis of an enzyme which destroys an internal inducer produced by an independent pathway. The i^- gene would result in the loss of the capacity to synthesize the inducer-destroying enzyme.

The first interpretation is the simpler one, and it is supported by all available evidence. The most direct evidence comes from the study of a particular mutant (i^s) which exhibits remarkable properties. This mutant has lost the capacity to synthesize *both* galactosidase and permease. It does not carry a deletion, however, since it recombines with all z^- and y^- mutants, and the mutation falls in the i locus. Finally, the i^s allele turns out to be dominant, since the diploids of the constitution $i^sz^+y^+/F\ i^+z^+y^+$ are unable to synthesize galactosidase and permease (see Table XXXIX, lines 8 and 9). The unique properties of this mutation which results in a *dominant loss of several functions* cannot be explained by the assumption that the i gene controls the synthesis of an inducer-destroying enzyme. In contrast, they can be easily explained by the assumption that the i^s mutation results in the production of a "super-repressor," i.e., of an altered repressor which cannot be antagonized by external inducers (Jacob and Monod, 1961).

Some information concerning the product of the i^+ gene may be obtained by kinetic study of the expression of the i^+ gene when it is introduced by conjugation into cells carrying the "inducible" inactive allele. Such experiments consist in matings between bacteria of opposite genetic constitution allowing the formation of transient merozygotes z^+i^+/z^-i^-. The constitutive synthesis of β-galactosidase is measured in the populations of merozygotes thus formed, *in the absence of inducer.* Under such conditions, neither of the parental strains is able to form enzyme, the z^+i^+ being inducible, the z^-i^- carrying a mutation which prevents the synthesis of β-galactosidase. The results of reciprocal crosses are completely different. When a z^+i^+ recipient receives from a donor a chromosomal segment carrying the z^-i^- alleles, no trace of constitutive synthesis of β-galactosidase is observed in the population of zygotes, a result which confirms that the "constitutive" allele i^- is recessive. In contrast, when i^-z^- recipients receive from a donor a chromosomal segment carrying the z^+i^+ alleles, penetration of the z^+i^+ genes is immediately followed by enzyme synthesis in the zygotes, in the absence of inducer (see Fig. 46). During the initial period, the zygotes behave, therefore, like constitutive cells. Approximately 60 minutes later, however, the rate of enzyme synthesis falls off to zero. If at that time inducer is added, enzyme synthesis is restored to its maximal rate. The originally constitutive phenotype of the zygote is, therefore, converted into an inducible phenotype. This experiment shows clearly that the "inducible" state is associated with the presence, at a sufficient level, of a cytoplasmic substance synthesized under the control of the gene i^+ (Pardee, Jacob, and Monod, 1958, 1959).

Some indication on the chemical nature of the repressor has been obtained by similar experiments performed in the presence of inhibitors.

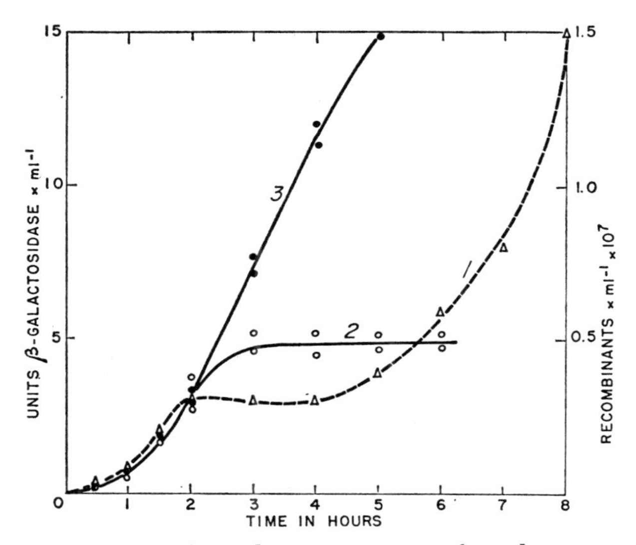

Fig. 46. Synthesis of β-galactosidase in merozygotes formed in a cross between inducible galactosidase-positive donors and constitutive galactosidase-negative recipients.

Donor (Hfr $i^+z^+T6^sS^s$) and recipient (F^- $i^-z^-T6^rS^r$) bacteria grown in a synthetic medium containing glycerol as the carbon source are mixed in the same medium (time 0) and shaken gently at 37°C. Phage T6 (multiplicity of 15 per Hfr bacterium) is added after 70 minutes and streptomycin (500 γ/ml) 10 minutes later in order to prevent further mating and eliminate the Hfr population. At various time intervals, samples are taken, on which are determined (1) the number of z^+S^r recombinants, by plating aliquots on lactose-streptomycin-MA medium; (2) the activity of β-galactosidase. At 115 minutes, thiomethyl-β-D-galactoside ($10^{-3}M$) is added to a sample of the culture and β-galactosidase activity is determined as a function of time.

The number of recombinants (curve 1) and the activity of β-galactosidase with no inducer (curve 2) or with inducer added at 115 minutes (curve 3) are plotted against the time of sampling in hours. Enzyme activity is expressed as mμmoles *o*-nitrophenyl-β-D-galactoside hydrolyzed per minute per ml of culture. (From Pardee, Jacob and Monod, 1959.)

For example, it has been shown that upon transfer into a constitutive recipient, the "inducible" i^+ allele becomes expressed even in the presence of 5-methyltryptophan or chloramphenicol, which are known to inhibit protein synthesis (Pardee and Prestidge, 1959). This result leads to the conclusion, not only that the repressor is not a protein, but that the functional expression of the i^+ gene does not involve the synthesis of a specific protein, a conclusion which again excludes the hypothesis that the i^+ gene controls the synthesis of an inducer-destroying enzyme. Conceivably, the repressor might be the direct product of the i gene, perhaps a polynucleotide.

2. *Repression of enzyme synthesis.* The results obtained from the study of the lactose system suggest that the repression of inducible systems by internal repressors could be basically similar to the repression effect observed in constitutive systems. If this is so, a common feature of many protein-synthesizing systems would be inhibition by repressors formed under the control of specific genes. One could then expect to find a genetic control of the class of repressions in which the end product of a biosynthetic pathway, such as an amino acid or a base, inhibits the synthesis of the specific enzymes of the pathway. This expectation has been fulfilled by the isolation of "constitutive" or "derepressed" mutants in several such repressible systems.

Derepressed mutants can be selected by the use of certain analogs of the repressing metabolite. For instance wild type *E. coli* does not grow in the presence of 5-methyl-tryptophan. A small fraction of the resistant mutants able to grow in the presence of this analog prove to be derepressed for several (if not all) enzymes involved in the biosynthetic pathway of tryptophan. Not only does the mutant form as much of the enzymes whether grown in the presence or in the absence of tryptophan but it forms more of the enzymes than the wild type does. Actually, the mutant produces more of the enzymes in the presence of tryptophan than does the wild type in its absence. The loss of sensitivity to the repressing action of tryptophan can be attributed neither to a change in the concentration mechanism for tryptophan nor to the destruction of tryptophan by increased tryptophanase activity since the mutant and the wild type are similar in these respects. The properties of the mutant must therefore result from an alteration of the regulation mechanism (G. N. Cohen and Jacob, 1959).

Several independent mutants of the same type have been isolated and all these mutations (R_{try}^-) are located in a small segment of the chromosome, close to the character threonine and far from the cluster of genes which has been shown (Yanofsky and Lennox, 1959) to control the capacity to synthesize the enzymes of the tryptophan pathway (see Fig. 27, page 165). One of the genes in this cluster has been shown by Yanofsky (1960) to be composed of two parts, each of which determines the structure of one component of tryptophan synthetase, and it seems reasonable to assume that the remaining genes in the cluster determine the structure of the other enzymes of the sequence. It appears, therefore, that the gene R_{try} determines the rate of synthesis of several and probably of all the enzymes of the sequence, whereas the cluster of genes determines the structure of the enzymes. Since R_{try} is located far from the cluster of structure-determining genes, it must operate through a cytoplasmic compound. The transient heterozygotes R_{try}^{+}/R_{try}^{-} formed by conjugation are sensitive to 5-methyl-tryptophan, which indicates that the "repressible" allele R_{try}^{+} is dominant over the "nonrepressible" one R_{try}^{-}. This finding suggests that tryptophan itself is not the repressor, but that the repressor is made under the control of the gene R_{try}^{+} in the presence of tryptophan (G. N. Cohen and Jacob, 1959).

Similar observations have been made in the case of the biosynthetic pathway of arginine (Gorini, unpublished results; Maas, Lavallé, Wiame, and Jacob, unpublished results). This pathway involves several known enzymes. The genes which control these enzymes are dispersed at various loci on the chromosome of *E. coli* (see Fig. 27). In mutants that are resistant to the analog, canavanine, the synthesis of several, and perhaps of all these enzymes, is no longer sensitive to the inhibitory action of arginine. These mutations (R_{arg}^{-}) occur at a locus close to the locus of streptomycin resistance, far from most of the genes that control the synthesis of the enzymes responsible for arginine formation. The dominance relationship between the "repressible" and "nonrepressible" alleles has not yet been analyzed.

Finally, a similar type of mechanism has recently been found to operate in the synthesis of the alkaline phosphatase of *E. coli.* The gene which controls the structure of the enzyme has been analyzed in detail, and several mutants at this locus have been shown to synthesize an altered protein (Levinthal, 1959). The synthesis of the enzyme is repressed in the presence of orthophosphate (Torriani, 1960). Derepressed mutants have been isolated which, in the presence of orthophosphate, synthesize an alkaline phosphatase undistinguishable from the normal enzyme of repressible strains. These mutations occur at two different loci, not closely linked to the gene determining the structure of the enzyme. The constitutive alleles for these two loci are recessive with respect to the wild alleles (Echols, Garen, Garen and Torriani, 1961).

The striking similarities observed in the systems analyzed so far, both inducible and repressible, suggests that the synthesis of many proteins is governed by two types of genes with two distinct functions (see Fig. 45, p. 260):

1. A *structural gene* determines the specific structure of the protein molecule.

2. A *regulator gene* determines the synthesis of an intracellular substance, or repressor, which inhibits the expression of the structural gene. A regulator gene does not determine the structure of a protein and, in contrast to a structural gene, it may affect the synthesis of several proteins (Jacob and Monod, 1959, 1961).

Regulation of protein synthesis appears, therefore, to involve a system of intracellular signals composed of two parts: a "genetic" or "apo" moiety synthesized under the control of a specific regulatory gene and a "metabolic" or "co" moiety constituted by a specific metabolite involved in the system (see Fig. 45). These signals keep the cell informed of the cytoplasmic level of various metabolites and thereby allow the cell to adjust its synthetic activities in response to its actual requirements. In the case of induced enzyme synthesis, the aporepressor appears to be active by itself, preventing synthesis of the corresponding enzymes until it is inactivated by an external inducer. Of its various potentialities, the cell thus selects and expresses those which are required to meet a specific environmental situation. In the case of the repression of enzymes operative in the biosynthesis of essential metabolites, the aporepressor seems to be inactive by itself and to be activated by the metabolic moiety, the end product of the pathway. The enzymes are synthesized, therefore, as long as the level of the end product in the cytoplasm remains low. Their synthesis is repressed only when the intracellular concentration of the end product reaches a certain level; i.e., when the cell has already a sufficient amount of enzymes to cover its present needs. Nothing is known yet about the processes which allow the coupling of the product of the regulator gene with the specific metabolite involved in the system.

B. Operators

The finding that the transfer of structural information from genes to protein is regulated by the intermediacy of specific repressors synthesized by regulator genes raises the problem of the site of action of the repressors.

The effect of a repressor is specific, since it affects exclusively a given biochemical sequence; it is also often pleiotropic, since it may affect the synthesis of several and, sometimes of all the enzymes of the sequence. The specificity of repressor action has a corollary: it implies that the repressor is able to combine specifically with a particular structure required for enzyme synthesis, and that this combination inhibits enzyme synthesis. The entity on which the repressor acts and which in some way commands the expression of the structural gene has been called *operator* (Jacob, Perrin, Sanchez, and Monod, 1960; Jacob and Monod, 1961). Whatever their actual nature, the existence of operators implies that their specific structure must be genetically determined and, therefore, subject to mutations. In particular, mutations altering the affinity of the operator for the repressor should result in a constitutive, or derepressed, synthesis of enzyme. Such mutations ($o^+ \rightarrow o^c$) should be readily distinguishable from constitutive mutations affecting the regulator gene, both by their location on the chromosome and by their properties. As shown in the previous section, the mutations which affect the regulator gene and result in the *synthesis of an inactive repressor* behave as *recessive* in heterogenotes. In contrast, mutations affecting an operator and resulting in a *decreased sensitivity to the repressor,* should manifest themselves in heterogenotes o^+/o^c irrespective of the presence of the wild allele o^+ and should therefore be *dominant.*

In the lactose utilizing system of *E. coli,* such mutants have been isolated by selecting for constitutive lactose fermenters in bacteria carrying an F-Lac factor, homozygous i^+/i^+. In contrast to the i^- mutation, the o^c mutations thus isolated manifest themselves in heterogenotes o^+/o^c as shown in Table XL. The constitutive (o^c) allele is, therefore, dominant over the wild (o^+) allele (Jacob, Perrin, Sanchez, and Monod, 1960).

If, as expected, the constitutivity of the o^c mutants results from a loss of the sensitivity of the operator to the repressor, the o^c bacteria should also be insensitive to the action of the altered repressor synthesized by the dominant (i^s) allele of the i gene (see page 264). That this is indeed the case, as shown by the constitutive behavior of heterogenotes of the constitution $i^s o^+/Fi^+ o^c$ (see Table XL, line 12), is a strong confirmation of the interpretation of the effects of both mutations (i^s and o^c).

The interest of such mutants lies in the fact that their properties may be expected to provide some information on the mode of action of the repressor. More particularly, they make it possible to investigate how a single repressor influences the synthesis of several proteins belonging to a single biochemical pathway. It should be recalled that the structures of such proteins are often controlled by closely linked genes in bacteria. The pleiotropic action of the repressor implies that the operator is a structure either repeated in, or common to, the systems determining the synthesis of the individual proteins of the sequence. We may consider

TABLE XL

SYNTHESIS OF GALACTOSIDASE, CROSS-REACTING MATERIAL AND GALACTOSIDE-TRANSACETYLASE BY HAPLOID AND HETEROZYGOUS DIPLOID OF OPERATOR MUTANTS[a]

Strain N°	Genotype	Galactosidase		Cross-reacting material	
		Noninduced	Induced	Noninduced	Induced
1	o^+z^+	< 0.1	100	—	—
2	$o^+z^+/Fo^+z_1^-$	< 0.1	105	< 1	310
3	o^cz^+	15	90	—	—
4	$o^+z^+/Fo^cz_1^-$	< 0.1	90	30	180
5	$o^+z_1^-/Fo^cz^+$	90	250	< 1	85
		Galactosidase		**Galactoside-transacetylase**	
		Noninduced	Induced	Noninduced	Induced
6	$o^+z^+y^+$	< 0.1	100	< 1	100
7	$o^cz^+y^+$	25	95	15	110
8	$o^+z^+y_U^-/Fo^cz^+y^+$	70	220	50	160
9	$o^+z_1^-y^+/Fo^cz^+y_U^-$	180	440	< 1	220
10	$i^+o^\circ_{84}z^+y^+$	< 0.1	< 0.1	< 1	< 1
11	$i^+o^\circ_{84}z^+y^+/Fi^-o^+z^+y^+$	1	260	2	240
12	$i^so^+z^+y^+/Fi^+o^cz^+y^+$	190	210	150	200

[a] Bacteria are grown in glycerol as carbon source and induced when stated, with isopropyl-thiogalactoside $10^{-4}M$. Values of galactosidase and acetylase are given as per cent of that observed with induced wild type. Values of CRM are expressed as antigenic equivalents of galactosidase. Note that the proteins corresponding to the alleles carried by the sex factor are often produced in greater amount than that observed with induced haploid wild type. This is presumably due to the existence of several copies of the F^- Lac factor per chromosome. In o^c mutants, haploid or diploid, the absolute values of enzymes produced, especially in the noninduced cultures, varies greatly from day to day depending on the conditions of the cultures. (From Jacob and Monod, 1961.)

three different models, each of which leads to different predictions for the properties of the dominant constitutive, or derepressed, mutations.

1. The repressor acts individually on the synthesis of every enzyme of the sequence (Fig. 47, I). The operator is repeated, therefore, in every system determining the synthesis of individual proteins. In this model, a

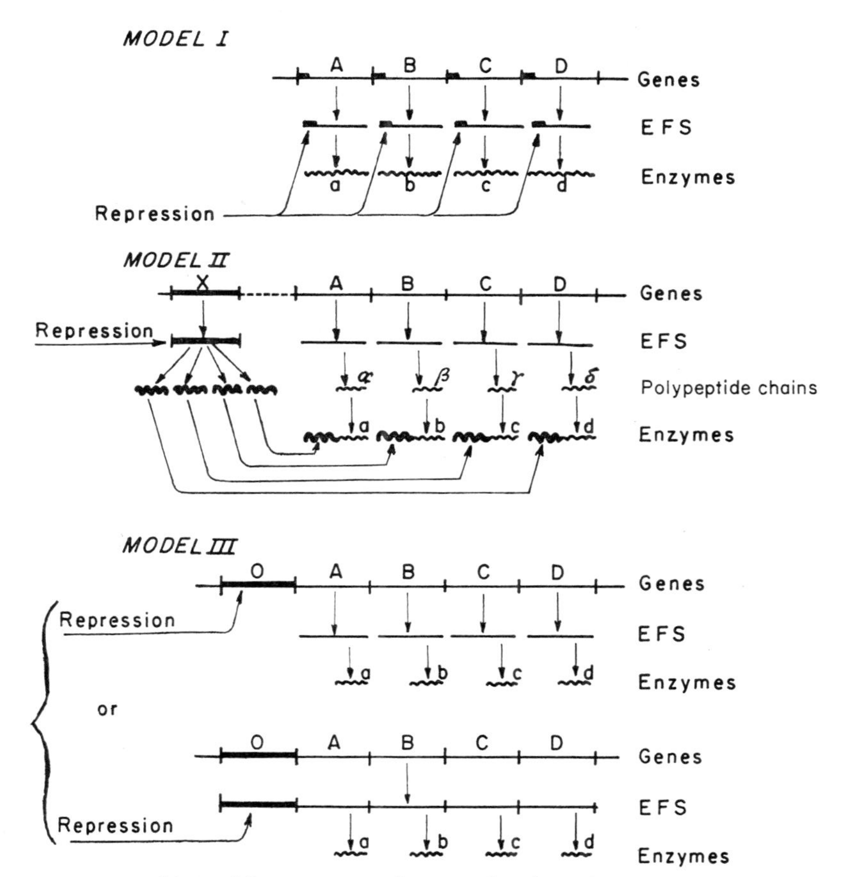

FIG. 47. Models concerning the site of action of the repressor.

dominant (o^c) mutation is *nonpleiotropic:* it alters the repressibility of one protein independently of the others, and it affects the corresponding structural gene.

2. The repressor acts on the synthesis of a cytoplasmic component common to all syntheses, for example an element common to the series of templates, or a polypeptide chain common to the series of proteins (Fig. 47, II). There exists a single operator for the whole system. In this

model, the dominant o^c mutation is *pleiotropic*: it alters the repressibility of the whole group of proteins simultaneously. This mutation affects, therefore, a functional unit which is different from the series of structural genes and which is cytoplasmically expressed. In heterogenotes o^+/o^c phenotypic mixing occurs and the o^c mutation acts on the expression of the structural genes of the sequence *located in both the cis and the trans positions.* In addition, other point mutations in the same locus ($o^+ \rightarrow o^\circ$) might result in a defective synthesis of the common element, and, therefore, in a physiological deletion of the whole series of enzymes. Such o° mutants would be complemented by mutants carrying a defect in any structural cistron of the sequence.

3. The repressor acts on the expression of the group of linked genes as a whole, the functional relationship of the genes being the reflection of a structural association (Fig. 47, III). The operator is an element common to the whole system and it constitutes, with the group of structural genes, an *integrated unit of activity.* In this model, the dominant o^c mutation is *pleiotropic.* It affects a locus different from the structural genes. This unit, however, has no independent cytoplasmic product but controls the expression of the group of structural genes associated with it on the same chromosomal segment. In heterogenotes o^+/o^c, the o^c mutation affects only the expression of the structural genes *located in position cis,* i.e., in the same chromosome. In addition, certain mutations at the same locus might modify the operator in such a way as to prevent permanently the expression of the whole group of genes, with resulting loss of the capacity to synthesize the whole series of enzymes. Mutants carrying such an inactivated operator would not be complemented by other mutants carrying a defect in any of the structural genes (Jacob and Monod, 1959).

The properties observed in the study of the dominant constitutive (o^c) mutations which affect the lactose system of *E. coli* are given in Table XL. It can be seen that the results obtained are compatible only with the third model. First, the o^c mutations are pleiotropic: they result in the constitutive formation in similar amounts, of the two proteins β-galactosidase and acetylase. This result excludes model 1. In order to distinguish between models 2 and 3, heterogenotes of the following constitution have been isolated: o^+z^-/Fo^cz^+, o^+z^+/Fo^cz^-, o^+y^-/Fo^cy^+, and o^+y^+/Fo^cy^-. In all cases, the galactosidase as well as the acetylase are synthesized constitutively only when the wild allele is located in position *cis* with respect to the o^c allele. In addition, heterogenotes of the constitution $o^+z_1^-/Fo^cz^+$ and $o^+z^+/Fo^cz_1^-$, which are able to synthesize both the active enzyme and an enzymatically inactive but cross-reacting protein, produce constitutively only that protein which is controlled by the allele located in position *cis* with respect to the o^c allele (see Table XL, lines 4, 5). This result is not compatible with model 2.

The predictions of model 3 concerning the properties of mutations resulting in an inactive operator are also fulfilled in the lactose system. As discussed in the first section of this chapter (see page 253), the analysis of the Lac region has revealed the existence of a cluster of mutations (o°) which result in the loss of the capacity to synthesize *both* β-galactosidase and acetylase. The o° mutants revert to the wild type, and they produce wild type recombinants in mating with any of the z^- or y^- mutants. In heterogenotes o^+/o°, the wild allele is dominant over the mutated allele and the o° mutants are not complemented by any of the z^- or y^- mutants, which have lost the capacity to synthesize the galactosidase or the acetylase (permease), respectively (see Fig. 43). Finally,

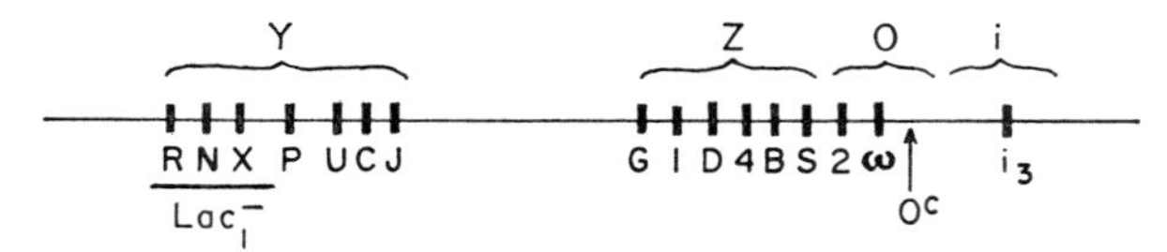

FIG. 48. Schematic representation of the functions recognized in the Lac region. Additional z^- mutants have recently been isolated which map in the interval represented between the z and the y regions. The z and y cistrons are therefore adjacent. (After Jacob and Monod, 1961.)

recombination analysis indicates that the o° and o^c mutations are extremely closely linked: they are all located in a short segment of the Lac region between the i and z loci (see Fig. 48).

The properties of the o^c and o° mutations are remarkable: they are pleiotropic and they affect the expression of the loci structurally associated with them in the same chromosome. These properties cannot be explained by the classical concept of the structural gene, which is assumed to specify a protein molecule. They differ also from the properties of a regulator gene which is assumed to control the synthesis of a cytoplasmic repressor. In contrast, the o° and o^c mutations appear to affect a genetic unit which is expressed not by an independent cytoplasmic product but rather by control of the expression of a limited chromosomal segment.

It must be pointed out that genetic analysis does not distinguish between regulation operating at the level of the genetic material itself and regulation operating at the level of a cytoplasmic intermediate in the synthesis of the series of enzymes (see Fig. 47, III). It indicates only that the operator controls the expression of an integrated chromosomal segment when the genetic information for the synthesis of a series of proteins is structurally associated. The operator is attached either to the cytoplasmic product of the linked genes or to the genes themselves. In the former case, the cytoplasmic product must be assumed to form an integrated structure, functioning as a single template for the synthesis of the series of proteins. In the latter case, the operator must be identical with the o locus and must directly govern the activity of the group of genes (Jacob, Perrin, Sanchez, and Monod, 1960; Jacob and Monod, 1961).

In other systems, dominant constitutive, or derepressed mutants have not yet been isolated. Mutants similar to the negative operators (o°) have been observed in the system controlling galactose fermentation by *E. coli* (E. M. Lederberg, 1960; Kalckar, Kurahashi, and Jordan, 1959). Mutations affecting the synthesis of galactokinase and galactose-transferase are clustered in a small segment of the chromosome. The functional analysis of this segment, carried out by means of heterogenotes obtained by transduction with phage λ, led to the recognition of several functional units. One, A, seems to determine the structure of the kinase and another, B, the structure of the transferase. Mutants of group A complement mutants of group B. A third group of mutations, C, results in the more or less complete loss of the capacity to synthesize both enzymes. Although such mutants C revert to the wild type and produce wild type recombinants in mating with A or B mutants, they fail to complement any mutants of either group A or B.

In the system involved in the synthesis of histidine in *Salmonella,* the specific genes determining the structure of the eight enzymes are located in a cluster on the chromosome (P. E. Hartman, Loper, and Serman, 1960). Elegant experiments by Ames and Garry (1959) have shown that expression of the series of genes, i.e., the synthesis of the whole series of enzymes, is regulated by a mechanism of coordinated repression by histidine. Although pleiotropic noncomplementable mutations leading to loss of the capacity to synthesize the sequence of enzymes have not been found, the quantitatively coordinated expression of the genes suggests that their activity may be regulated by a common operator.

* * *

Genetic analysis of regulation in bacteria has allowed the recognition of two new elements: regulator genes and operators. In many systems, the product of a regulator gene, eventually coupled with some specific metabolite, combines with the corresponding operator and thereby determines the rate at which genetic information contained in structural genes is expressed. The properties of the mutations affecting the operator indicate that between the cistron, defined as an independent unit of biochemical function, and the chromosome, there exists an intermediate "order of integration," according to the terminology proposed by Goldschmidt (1955). This intermediate element can be visualized as an *integrated unit of activity* or *operon* (Jacob, Perrin, Sanchez, and Monod, 1960; Jacob and Monod, 1961) containing an operator locus and the group of structural genes, the expression of which is controlled by the operator. There is not yet any interpretation of the role of the operator at the molecular level. The expression of the operon, either at the genetic level or at the level of a cytoplasmic delegate of the whole operon, may be polarized, always starting from the same end. The operator might be located at the starting end and might either allow or prevent the beginning of the synthesis and thereby switch on or off the expression of the whole operon.

An operator can be recognized only if the operon contains several structural genes, controlling the synthesis of several individual proteins which can be studied independently. If the concept of operon may be applied to various systems, it seems likely that the size of an operon might be expected to vary from one system to another and from one organism to another, depending on the complexity of the regulation involved. In bacteria, the tendency for genes controlling the successive steps of a biochemical sequence to remain closely linked may well be due to the persistence of large operons for whole pathways as a result of simple systems of regulation. Certain chromosomal rearrangements resulting in the separation of structural genes from their operator locus might produce a disturbance in the functioning of the displaced determinants, an alteration which would correspond to a position effect by chromosomal rearrangement. It is clear, therefore, that wild type bacteria in which the structural genes remain associated in an operon would have a selective advantage over bacteria carrying such a rearrangement (Jacob, 1960). In higher organisms, more delicate systems of regulation might result in smaller operons containing only a few structural genes, and, therefore, in a more random distribution, among the chromosomes, of the loci controlling the various steps of a same pathway. At the limit, one might conceive of operons containing one structural gene and one operator locus acting as a switch on the structural gene. At the present time, there is no operational way of distinguishing such a unit from the structural gene itself.

IV. ACTIVITY OF STRUCTURAL GENES

In the previous sections of this chapter, we have discussed the results obtained in the study of phenotypic expression upon transfer of genetic material and in the genetic analysis of regulation of protein synthesis. Although this study does not give any direct information concerning the process of protein synthesis, the findings place some restrictions on the possible models to be considered.

The genetic control of protein specificity raises the obvious question of whether structural genes act directly, or indirectly via cytoplasmic intermediate templates. Operationally, this question may be stated in slightly different terms by considering the two following hypotheses.

1. The gene forms *stable cytoplasmic intermediates* which in turn ensure the synthesis of the protein.

2. *No stable intermediates* are formed. The gene acts either directly as a template or indirectly via unstable intermediates.

The first hypothesis is the most widely accepted. On the one hand, many indirect indications suggest that RNA may be involved in protein synthesis as an intermediate template (see Brachet, 1955). On the other hand increasing evidence suggests that proteins are synthesized in the cytoplasm and that the so-called ribosomal particles, composed of protein and RNA, may well be the site of protein formation (see Roberts, 1958). These particles, or at least their main components, are stable, in the sense that they do not undergo continuous breakdown and resynthesis. Ribosomal RNA, in particular, has been demonstrated to be extremely stable under the conditions of growth (Davern and Meselson, 1960). It is generally believed that the base sequence of the RNA contained in a ribosome determines the amino acid sequence of the protein which the particle is producing (see Crick, 1958). A cell would therefore contain as many different species of ribosomes as the number of different protein species that it synthesizes, a scheme which might be epitomized as the one gene–one ribosome–one protein hypothesis.

The validity of this hypothesis has not, however, yet been demonstrated experimentally. Recently complications have arisen. For example, the wide variation of DNA base ratios observed in different bacterial species is not reflected in the base ratios of the corresponding ribosomal RNA (Belozersky and Spirin, 1960), as it could be expected if ribosomal RNA were the intermediate between gene and protein. Similarly, some of the findings reported in this chapter seem hardly compatible with the hypothesis of stable intermediate templates.

First, the kinetic study of β-galactosidase synthesis after transfer of the gene has shown that enzyme synthesis follows almost immediately the entry of the gene into the cell, and that the rate of synthesis is constant and maximal from the start (see page 259). This finding is hardly compatible with the model of stable intermediate templates, which would predict an accumulation of such templates and, therefore, a progressive increase of enzyme synthesis. The observations can however be reconciled with this model by making the additional assumption that the gene very rapidly forms a limited number of stable intermediates and then stops operating.

Second, the genetic analysis of regulation has led to the concept of the operator, a *common* structure which controls the activity of several genes. As discussed in the previous section of this chapter, the results of genetic analysis do not allow a distinction between repression operating at the genetic level and repression affecting a cytoplasmic delegate of the operon, which would correspond, on the current hypothesis, to the ribosomal RNA. The latter possibility, however, appears rather unlikely in view of the characteristics of ribosomal RNA. Whereas the size of various operons must be expected to vary widely, the size of ribosomal RNA seems to be remarkably homogeneous. In addition, it appears too small to account for the structural information of the series of three (or more) enzymes which, in all likelihood, may belong to a single operon in the case of biosynthetic pathways. Although not yet demonstrated directly, the hypothesis of a repression operating at the genetic level seems to be more compatible with the results of genetic analysis. Regulation at the genetic level means that protein synthesis may be switched on or off through the actual functioning of the genetic material itself. It is not compatible, therefore, with the existence of stable cytoplasmic templates containing all the information for protein synthesis (Jacob and Monod, 1961).

The ideal experiment to determine whether stable cytoplasmic intermediates exist would consist of introducing a structural gene into a cell that lacks it, letting the gene express itself, and then removing it. The presence of stable intermediates would be evidenced by the ability of the cell to continue synthesizing the enzyme after the removal of the structural gene. In bacteria, we know how to introduce a gene into a cell but not how to remove it. One can, however, introduce a chromosomal segment that contains a high proportion of radiophosphorus and subsequently let it be destroyed by P^{32} decay. Experiments of this type have been attempted to determine whether or not synthesis of β-galactosidase can proceed in the absence of the structural gene. In such an experiment, z^+ Hfr donors which are heavily labeled with P^{32} are mated with nonradioactive z^-F^- recipients. At different times after the onset of mating, samples of the mating mixture are frozen in order to allow P^{32} decay to occur and damage the transferred genetic material. After various periods of time, samples are thawed and assayed both for the number of recombinants in which the z^+ gene of the donor appears and for the initial rate at which the merozygotes synthesize β-galactosidase. Preliminary experiments of this type indicate that, even when P^{32} decay is allowed to occur after the z^+ gene has begun to express itself, the ability of the zygotes to form enzyme decreases in parallel with the capacity of the gene to appear among recombinants as a result of progressive P^{32} damage. These results suggest that the integrity of the gene is essential for the persistence of enzyme synthesis (Riley, Pardee, Jacob, and Monod, 1960).

This finding appears to exclude the hypothesis that the transfer of structural specificity from gene to protein involves the formation of a stable intermediate. Although the assumption that the gene itself is the template for the synthesis of the enzyme would account for the experimental results, it cannot be reconciled with the increasing number of observations which indicate that the ribosomes are involved in protein synthesis. The only remaining hypothesis is that ribosomes do not contain any stable genetic information for protein synthesis, but receive it from the gene in the form of a functionally *unstable* intermediate. In other words, a ribosome is not a structure specialized for the synthesis of one particular species of protein, but an unspecialized machine able to make any kind of protein; the genetic specificity is brought from the gene by a *messenger* molecule which acts as template for the synthesis of a small number of protein molecules, perhaps only one (Jacob and Monod, 1961). Let us consider the implications of this hypothesis. It implies the existence among cellular components of a messenger molecule, probably RNA, with molecular size sufficient to carry the information for protein specificity. This messenger molecule should have a rapid turnover. Ribosomal RNA, although of large molecular size, appears to be stable during bacterial growth. In contrast, the so-called soluble RNA, which accepts activated amino acids, exhibits a rather high rate of turnover but seems too small to carry all the information required for the synthesis of long peptide chains. A possible candidate might be the species of RNA observed by Volkin and Astrachan (1957) in *E. coli* infected with phage T_2. This RNA has not yet been isolated, and its molecular weight is unknown. However, it exhibits a fast turnover and the ratio of its bases is different from that found in the whole bacterial RNA and is closer to that observed in the DNA of phage T_2.

In fact, the synthesis of phage proteins by bacteria infected with T–even phages constitutes in many respects a remarkable situation. It has been known for a long time that upon infection, the over-all synthesis of proteins proceeds linearly at the rate existing at the time of infection (S. S. Cohen, 1947), although specific bacterial proteins are no longer synthesized (Monod and Wollman, 1947). In addition, there appears to be no synthesis of stable RNA similar to ribosomal RNA. This last fact raises an important question concerning the mechanism of synthesis of phage proteins. Are such syntheses performed in the bacterial ribosomes present at the time of infection, in new ribosomes of a different type, or in a nonribosomal fraction of the cell, for instance directly on the genetic material.

This question can be answered by experiments based on the following principle. Bacteria are grown in a medium containing heavy isotopes so that all their constituents are labeled "heavy." They are then washed, infected with phage T_2, and resuspended in a medium containing light isotopes so that all constituents synthesized after infection are "light." The RNA synthesized during phage development is labeled by pulses of radioactive phosphorus or uracil and the protein by pulses of radiosulfur. After extraction and purification of the ribosomes, the fate of the RNA and of the protein is followed by centrifugation of the purified ribosomes in a density gradient of cesium chloride. The results of such experiments show that no structures similar to ribosomes are made after infection. The radioactivity both of the RNA and of the protein synthesized after infection is associated with the old ribosomes, from where it can be displaced if the pulses are followed by the addition of nonradioactive phosphorus or sulfur. This experiment shows clearly that the bulk of the sulfur ultimately destined to appear in the phage proteins passes through the ribosomes which existed in the bacteria *before infection.* It shows, therefore, that the phage proteins are indeed synthesized in the ribosomes that are present in the bacterium at the time of infection and which, in all likelihood, were previously synthesizing specific bacterial proteins. It appears likely that the ribosomes are not structures specialized for the synthesis of a particular species of protein, but are rather able to synthesize a variety of polypeptide chains depending on the information they receive (Brenner, Jacob, and Meselson, 1961).

The fact that the species of RNA which was shown by Volkin and Astrachan to exhibit a fast turnover also passes through the ribosomes gives some support to its postulated role as intermediate messenger from the gene. A similar type of RNA should exist in normal, noninfected cells.

Some indication of its presence has been obtained in yeast. Experiments involving short pulses of radiophosphorus have revealed the existence of a type of RNA characterized by a fast rate of renewal and by a base ratio closer to the base ratio of yeast DNA than to that of the bulk of RNA (Yčas and Vincent, 1960). More recently, in growing *E. coli,* extremely short pulses of radioactive phosphorus or uracil have allowed the detection of a new species of RNA, in many respects similar to that de-

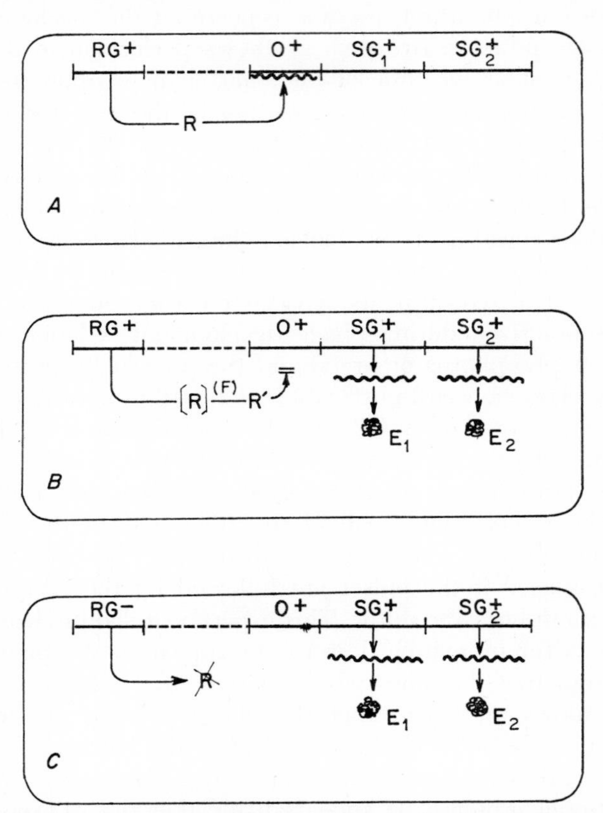

FIG. 49. Schematic representation of the effects of induction on a normal (wild type) cell and on a mutation resulting in inactivation of the regulator gene.

A. Induced wild type cell. The repressor (R) synthesized by the regulator gene (RG) attaches to the operator (o) and thereby blocks the expression of both structural genes (SG_1+, SG_2+).

B. In presence of inducer (F), the repressor is converted to the inactive form (R′). Expression of both SG_1+ and SG_2+ is allowed; both enzymes E_1 and E_2 are synthesized.

C. The mutated regulator gene (RG−) produces an inactive repressor which does not interact with the operator (o). Both enzymes are produced constitutively.

scribed by Volkin and Astrachan in bacteria infected with T_2. This RNA, which seems to have a minimum molecular weight of 300,000, exhibits a fast rate of renewal, and it has the remarkable property of attaching itself reversibly to the ribosomes depending on the magnesium concentration (Gros *et al.*, 1961). In view of these characteristics, the RNA in question appears to be a reasonable candidate for the messenger molecule carrying specific structural information from genes to ribosomes.

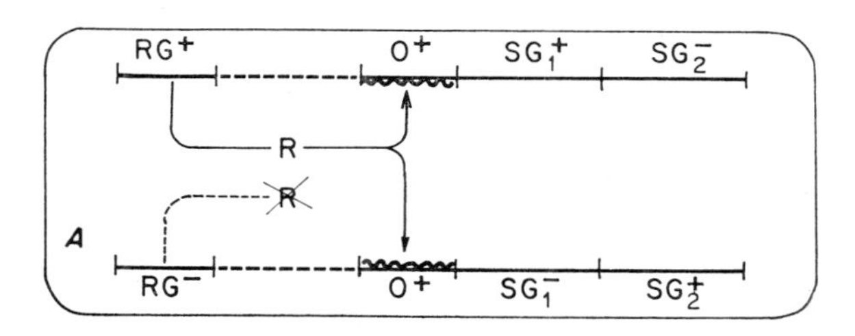

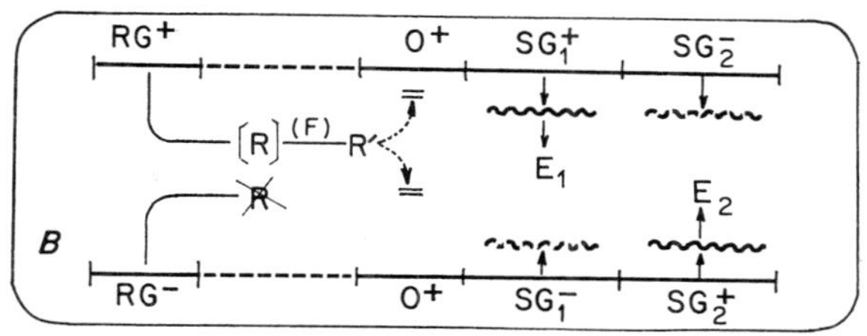

FIG. 50. Schematized behavior of a diploid heterozygous for the regulator and for both structural genes.

A. The mutated regulator gene (RG−) produces an inactive repressor while the normal regulator gene (RG+) produces the repressor which blocks both operators (o). No enzyme is synthesized.

B. In presence of inducer (F), gene activity is allowed. SG_1+ on one chromosome produces E_1, and SG_2+ on the other chromosome produces E_2. The diploid therefore behaves in every respect like an haploid wild type.

It must be pointed out that if individual structural genes do not specify the RNA of individual ribosomes, then the question of the origin of ribosomal RNA must be raised. It might either be synthesized under the control of a specific gene or else be a self-replicating unit, like the RNA of small viruses, although submitted to cellular control.

* * *

Although complex in its genetic potentialities, the bacterial cell provides highly suitable material for studying the transfer of information from the stable genome to the cytoplasm. Experiments reported in this chapter show that bacterial conjugation provides a versatile tool for the study of cellular genetics.

The high resolving power both in genetic and in functional analyses which can be attained with bacteria offers the possibility of studying the relationship between gene and protein. Theoretical and experimental

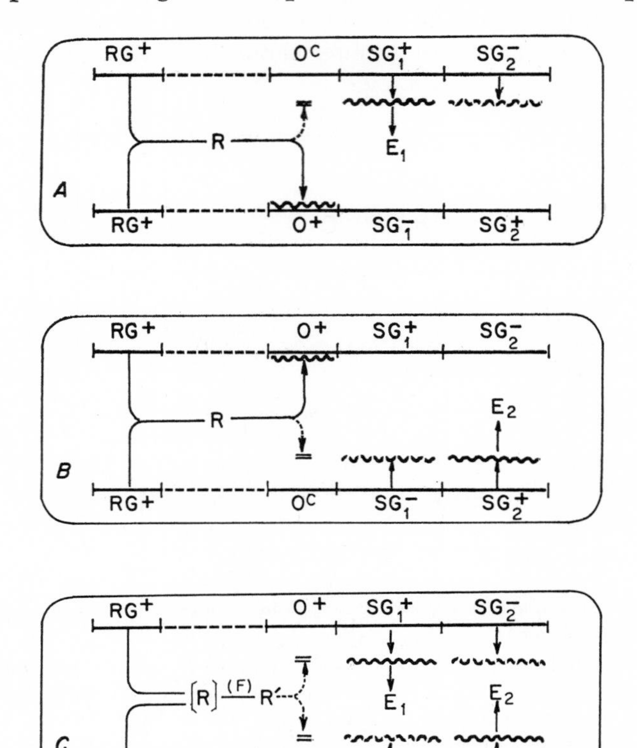

FIG. 51. Schematized behavior of diploids heterozygous for the constitutive operator (o^c mutation) and for each structural gene.

A. In the presence of inducer, the repressor made by the regulator gene blocks gene expression in the lower chromosome which carries a normal operator. It does not act on the upper chromosome which bears the o^c mutation of the operator and therefore does not combine with the repressor. Only enzyme E_1 is produced constitutively.

B. Same situation, but the mutated (o^c) operator is supposed to be present on the lower chromosome. Only enzyme E_2 is now produced. These two schemes illustrate the fact that an operator mutation affects only the activity of the genes placed on the same chromosome.

C. In the presence of inducer (F), both enzymes are produced.

advances have reinforced, with some minor modifications, the one gene–one enzyme hypothesis advanced by Beadle some fifteen years ago. This concept, however, applies to part of the information contained in the genome. The study of bacteria indicates that although an important fraction of the information contained in the bacterial chromosome does specify the structure of individual polypeptide chains, another fraction is concerned with the determination of the rate at which this structural information is transferred to the cytoplasm. Regulator genes are not restricted to bacteria, as shown by the recent finding by Horowitz, Fling, MacLeod, and Sueoka (1960) that regulator genes in *Neurospora* govern the synthesis of the enzyme, tyrosinase.

The results of genetic study in bacteria also provide some new insights into the activity of genetic material. The fact that the expression of linked genes may be coordinated by common structures indicates the existence of a supragenic arrangement, frequently postulated in the past. In addition, gene expression appears to involve a continuous flow of information to the cytoplasm, in the form of unstable messengers which bring structural specificity to an unspecialized machinery synthesizing the proteins. Regulation appears to operate at the level of the genes to determine, at any time, which types of messengers are sent to the machinery, and therefore which types of proteins are synthesized.

The mode of action of mutations affecting regulator genes and operators is illustrated in Figs. 49, 50, and 51.

CHAPTER XV

The Prophage as a Bacterial Genetic Element

As stated in the Preface, this monograph has been designed to give an account both of the mechanism of bacterial conjugation and of the genetic determination of lysogeny. Since our knowledge of these two subjects has progressed in a parallel manner, it is hardly possible to describe one of them without also describing the other. Indeed, if bacterial crosses have made it possible to elucidate the genetic determination of lysogeny, the information gained from the study of lysogeny has contributed largely to our understanding of the process of bacterial conjugation.

In the preceding chapters, we have considered certain of the genetic problems which can be profitably studied in the light of the knowledge acquired about the mechanism of bacterial conjugation. In the following two chapters, we shall examine some of the genetic implications of lysogeny.

As shown in Chapter VI, a prophage is the genetic material of a bacteriophage, attached to the bacterial chromosome at a specific locus. The problem arises, therefore, of the nature of the link between the genetic material of the virus and that of the bacterial host cell. The genetic material of a phage behaves differently, both in its ability to multiply and in the expression of its genetic potentialities depending on whether it is in the vegetative or the proviral state. This difference raises the problem of the expression of genetic functions in relation to the state of the determining genetic elements. Finally, lysogeny provides an example of integration of a virus into its host at the cellular level. It may serve, therefore, as a model for analyzing other situations in which a permanent association between a virus and its host appears to exist; this is the problem of latent viral infections. The present chapter will be devoted to the analysis of these several questions.

I. THE RELATIONS BETWEEN PROPHAGE AND THE BACTERIAL CHROMOSOME

When the genetic material of a temperate bacteriophage is introduced into a bacterium, whether by infection or by any other process (conjugation, transduction), there lie before it two alternative fates. It can either multiply autonomously in the vegetative state, or attach itself to the bacterial chromosome, and from then on replicate, in the prophage state, at the same pace as the bacterial genome.

There is every reason to believe that, in either state, the genetic material of the phage consists essentially of DNA. On the one hand, it has been shown (in the case of virulent phage T_2, the DNA of which can be distinguished from that of the bacterium) that it is the DNA of the phage which penetrates into the bacterium upon infection (Hershey and Chase, 1952) and that there is a correlative increase of phage DNA and of phage genomes in the course of vegetative multiplication (Hershey, 1956, 1957a, b). On the other hand, when λ lysogenic Hfr H bacteria which have been labeled with P^{32} of high specific activity are crossed with nonlabeled, nonlysogenic recipient bacteria in a medium devoid of P^{32}, it is found that the prophage λ which has been transferred by conjugation (zygotic induction) is sensitive to P^{32} disintegration and that its sensitivity is identical to that of infectious λ particles (Stent, Fuerst, and Jacob, 1957). This experiment shows not only that the prophage is a structure which contains phosphorus, in all likelihood in DNA, but also that this structure contains approximately the same number of phosphorus atoms as the phage genome in the infectious state.

A. The Prophage, a Genetic Structure Added to the Bacterial Chromosome

In the prophage state, the genetic material of a phage behaves, in many respects, as a normal constituent of the bacterium. Each type of prophage (with the exception of a type which gives rise to transducing particles) occupies its own particular site on the bacterial chromosome. There exists, therefore, a definite relationship between the genetic material of a temperate phage and a particular region of the host's chromosome.

The existence of such a relationship is supported by many indirect lines of evidence (Garen and Zinder, 1955; Stent, 1958). For example, different bacteriophages, be they virulent or temperate, are the more sensitive to X-ray inactivation the greater their DNA content. Their sensitivity to ultraviolet light, however, does not follow such a simple law, since a temperate phage exhibits much lower sensitivity to ultraviolet light than a virulent phage of the same size. In contrast, the bacterial capacity to reproduce a temperate bacteriophage is much more sensitive to ultraviolet light than the capacity of the same bacterium to reproduce a virulent phage of the same size. Such facts would imply that the genome of the host plays a role in the reproduction of a temperate phage.

Another example of an interaction between the genome of the host and that of a temperate phage is provided by Weiglé's finding (1953) that particles of phage λ inactivated with U.V. light are reactivated when introduced into bacteria which have themselves been irradiated with ultraviolet light. Among the phages recovered after such treatment, there is a high proportion of various mutant types. Some increase in the mutation frequency may be observed also when bacteria irradiated with ultraviolet light are infected with nonirradiated phages (Jacob, 1954b).

The existence of such interactions between the genome of the host bacterium and that of a temperate bacteriophage would suggest that some homology exists between these two structures. In fact, no qualitative difference in chemical composition has been observed yet between the DNA of a temperate phage such as λ and that of its bacterial host, *E. coli* K12, and the proportions in which purine and pyrimidine bases are found in both materials appears to be the same (Smith and Siminovitch, 1953). These findings, however, are insufficient to justify the hypothesis that the genetic material of a temperate phage is equivalent to a segment of the bacterial chromosome and the prophage an integral part of this chromosome. Since a given prophage occupies a specific position on the bacterial chromosome, the prophage might be envisaged as homologous to a short segment of the bacterial chromosome. According to such an hypothesis, lysogenization would consist in the substitution of the genetic material of the phage for this supposed "allelic" segment of the bacterial chromosome by a process analogous to crossing over.

All the available information is opposed to such an hypothesis. It must be emphasized first that the difference between lysogenic and non-lysogenic bacteria is not of the same nature as the difference between two bacterial mutant strains. A prophage is a complex genetic structure which carries a large number of elementary genetic units (genes). It is not surprising, therefore, that a mutation $(ly)^- \rightarrow (ly)^+$ has never been observed since, even in the hypothesis of a complete homology between the genome of a temperate phage and a segment of the bacterial chromosome, such an event would be highly improbable. In spite of its complexity, however, the lysogenic character behaves as a single unit, both physiologically and genetically. The acquisition of a prophage, as well as its loss, are all-or-none events. A bacterium is either lysogenic, or non-lysogenic, and there is no indication of the existence of intermediary states in which bacteria contain more or less important segments of the phage genome. When lysogenic bacteria are exposed to ultraviolet light or to the decay of radiophosphorus atoms contained in their DNA, non-lysogenic bacteria may be recovered in significant proportions among the survivors (see Chapter V). These bacteria do not retain any recognizable trace of their previous lysogenic state. It is not possible, for instance, to detect in such bacteria the presence of any genetic marker from the prophage carried by the original bacteria. If these bacteria were of the K12 (λ) strain, their nonlysogenic derivatives may be infected by phage λ, or by a mutant of λ, and give rise to new lysogenic systems. If lysogenization consisted in the substitution of the phage genome for an homologous segment of the bacterial chromosome, the curing of lysogeny ought to be visualized as consisting of the reverse operation—i.e., the reconstitution of the homologous segment of the bacterial chromosome, an event difficult to conceive.

One is led to conclude, therefore, that lysogenization corresponds to the *addition* of a new structure, the prophage, to the bacterial chromosome and that the curing of lysogeny corresponds to the *loss* of this structure. Between the prophage and the normal genetic constituents of the bacterial chromosome, there exists, therefore, a fundamental difference: the chromosome of a nonlysogenic bacterium does not contain a structure allelic to a given prophage. The characters $(ly)^+$ and $(ly)^-$ are not alleles in the usual sense of this term since the symbol $(ly)^+$ corresponds to the *presence* of a genetic element and the symbol $(ly)^-$ to its *absence*.

B. The Link between the Prophage and the Bacterial Chromosome

Lysogenization results from the addition of a phage genome to the bacterial genome. How can the link between these two structures be envisaged? One possibility is that the whole phage genome might be *inserted into the continuity* of the bacterial chromosome. A second possibility is that this genome might be *attached* to the bacterial chromosome in such a way that the major part, if not all, of the phage structure would not be inserted as an integral part of the bacterial chromosome. All the information now available favors the second model.

The hypothesis of complete insertion predicts that if the site of a prophage is found to lie in between two closely linked markers, the actual presence of the prophage in the bacterial chromosome should decrease the apparent linkage between the two bacterial markers. Since the amount of DNA contained in a prophage may be estimated to be between 1/50 and 1/100 that of a bacterial chromosome, detection of decreased linkage requires the use of very closely linked bacterial markers. This requirement is met in the case of the noninducible prophage 18, the site of which has been located between two closely linked methionine markers in a region of the bacterial chromosome where several other closely linked markers are known (see Chapter X, page 174).

When one compares the results of crosses between Hfr and F− bacteria, either both nonlysogenic or both lysogenic for prophage 18, no significant difference is found in the recombination frequency between the M_1 and M_2 markers. This result, if not due to interference in the prophage region, makes it doubtful that prophage 18 could be inserted in the continuity of the bacterial chromosome (Jacob and Wollman, 1959a). Attempts to determine the precise location of the prophage itself on the donor chromosome have been made with prophage 18, since its transfer from a lysogenic donor to a nonlysogenic recipient does not give rise to zygotic induction. The results obtained are slightly different ac-

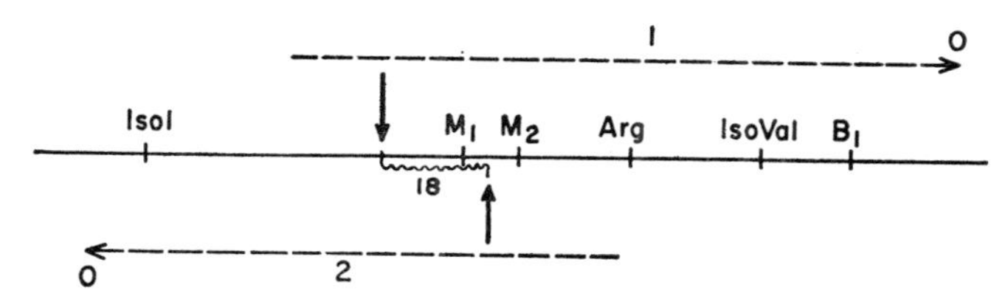

FIG. 52. Diagrammatic representation of the relation of prophage 18 with respect to the bacterial chromosome. Dotted lines represent the order of transfer of bacterial characters by two Hfr strains (1 and 2). Arrows represent the location of the prophage as deduced from crosses between lysogenic Hfr (either 1 or 2) and nonlysogenic F− cells. The two locations do not coincide and the prophage is assumed to synapse with the bacterial chromosome and to overlap the M_1 marker.

cording to the method of analysis used, although the actual location of the prophage appears to be identical in all lysogenic strains so far examined. Transduction experiments, on the one hand, lead to the location of the prophage between two methionine markers, M_1 and M_2. Similarly, in interrupted mating experiments with an Hfr donor which injects the following markers in the order: isoleucine-methionine$_1$-methionine$_2$-arginine, the lysogenic character of the donor is transferred between M_1 and M_2. However, with another Hfr donor which injects the same markers in the reverse order: arginine-methionine$_2$-methionine$_1$-isoleucine, the lysogenic character of the Hfr parent appears to be transferred shortly after the M_1 marker, i.e. between M_1 and isoleucine (Fig. 52). It must be pointed out that what is scored in such experiments is the transmission to recombinants of the lysogenic character, that is, of an entire prophage. This prophage behaves as a genetic segment of a certain length which overlaps the M_1 marker without, however, altering its properties. One possible model would represent the noninducible prophage 18 as actually synapsed over the whole, or the major part, of its length with the bacterial chromosome (Fig. 52). The two locations found for this prophage would then correspond to the most distant sites (perhaps the two extremities of the prophage) of its attachment to the bacterial chromosome.

These experimental results, although not providing conclusive evidence against the complete insertion hypothesis, nevertheless favor the view that a prophage is an added structure, which is linked to the bacterial chromosome but is not an integral part of it.

Previous experiments on the relationships of a prophage to the bacterial chromosome had been done with the inducible prophage λ (Jacob and Wollman, 1957a). Strains of Hfr H and F⁻ K12 bacteria, both lysogenic but carrying different, genetically marked, λ prophages were crossed in order to investigate whether recombination between prophage

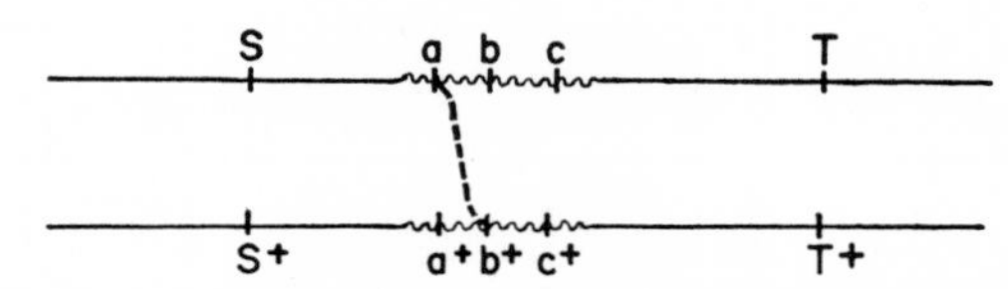

FIG. 53. Diagrammatic representation of prophage recombination, according to the hypothesis of a prophage inserted in the continuity of the bacterial chromosome. Each of the parental strains carries a mutant prophage a b c or a+ b+ c+. The two bacterial strains also differ by a marker S on one side and a second marker T on the other side of the prophage. According to this scheme, a bacterium carrying a recombinant prophage should be recombinant for the outside markers S and T (except when multiple cross-overs occur in the prophage). Experimental results are not in agreement with the complete insertion hypothesis.

markers was correlated with recombination between bacterial markers located on each side of the prophage (see Fig. 53). Although the markers used in such crosses (Gal_b on one side and prophage 21 on the other) were not as adequate as those available in the case of prophage 18, the results obtained indicated an orientation of the prophage with regard to the bacterial chromosome—the order being Gal-(mi co m_5)-(21). Recombination between the prophage markers was too frequent, however, with respect to the recombination observed between the outside bacterial markers to allow a definite conclusion to be drawn. The result could be due either to a high degree of negative interference within the prophage region or to a relative independence of prophage λ with respect to the bacterial chromosome. More recent experiments on a similar material (Calef and Licciardello, 1960) suggest that there is a linear arrangement of the prophage markers with respect to outside bacterial markers, although the order found for the prophage markers is different from that demonstrated in crosses between genetically marked λ bacteriophages. These results, if taken to indicate an orientation of the prophage genome with respect to the bacterial chromosome, do not seem to permit the conclusion that prophage λ is inserted in the continuity of the bacterial chromosome.

The position that a given prophage occupies on the bacterial chromosome is, as already stated, highly specific. Genetic analysis of temperate bacteriophages suggests that this specificity of location is not a property of the entire genome of a phage, but rather of a limited segment

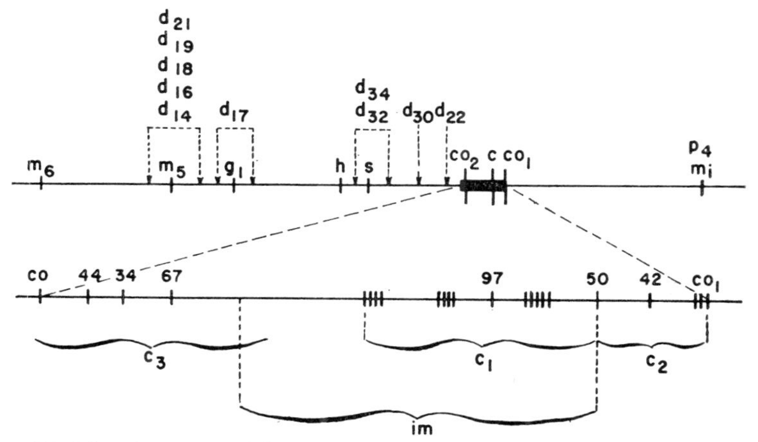

FIG. 54. The C region of bacteriophage λ. The upper diagram represents the whole linkage group of phage λ. Symbols refer to markers of plaque size, plaque types, host range and defective character (d). The C region represented by a thicker line is enlarged in the lower diagram. Figures represent various C mutations. The C region can be subdivided into three functional units, C_1, C_2, and C_3; *im* represents the segment controlling the immunity pattern.

of its linkage group. Studies of bacteriophage λ by Kaiser (1957) and of a temperate phage of *Salmonella* by M. Levine (1957) have established that the capacity of a temperate phage to lysogenize, i.e., to attach itself to the bacterial chromosome, is controlled by a short region of the phage linkage group, the *C region* (C standing for clear, since mutations occurring in this region determine the formation of clear instead of turbid plaques). In the case of λ, the C region, which contains only a small number of functional units, lies approximately in the middle of the phage linkage group, which is thus divided in two arms (Fig. 54). On each of these arms, there appear to be loci which play a role in the stability of the link between the prophage and the bacterial chromosome (Jacob and Wollman, 1954b). The C region controls the reactions that enable the genetic material of a phage to establish itself as a prophage and determine the specific immunity conferred by the prophage upon the lysogenic bacterium (page 301). It appears also to control the specific location that a prophage occupies on the bacterial chromosome (Kaiser and Jacob, 1957).

The various inducible bacteriophages that we have studied (see Chapter VI, page 86) have different locations on the bacterial chromosome. Pairs of such inducible phages can multiply simultaneously within the same bacterium; and recombinant phages can be isolated from the products of such mixed infections. For instance, one can cross a clear mutant of λ, genetically marked on both arms of its linkage group, with a wild type 434 and recover a recombinant hybrid which possesses the C region of 434 and the arms of λ. Such a recombinant (434 hybrid), the genome of which is mainly that of λ, exhibits nevertheless the specificity of 434. It confers upon the bacterium the immunity characteristic of 434 and occupies on the bacterial chromosome the position of 434, not that of λ. It may be concluded, therefore, that the specific location of a prophage is not determined by the whole genome of the phage but is controlled rather by a short region of the linkage group of the phage (Kaiser and Jacob, 1957).

Although located in the same small segment of the phage linkage group, the determinants which control immunity on the one hand and the specific location of the prophage on the other do not need necessarily to be identical. For example, from a cross between phages λ and 21, a recombinant has been obtained which confers the immunity of phage 21 but appears to occupy the position of λ on the bacterial chromosome.

C. The Case of Transducing Bacteriophages λ

The remarkable correspondence which exists between a prophage and a region of the bacterial chromosome is further exemplified by the case of transducing bacteriophages λ which has been summarized in Chapter XI (page 190). On rare occasions, a prophage λ happens to recombine with the adjacent region of the bacterial chromosome and to incorporate into its linkage group the closely linked markers which control the fermentation of galactose. The resulting recombinant prophage is a defective one (λdg) in which a segment of the prophage genome which amounts to about 1/4 to 1/3 of its total length has been replaced by a segment of the bacterial genome. The Gal^- sensitive bacteria that are lysogenized by phages λdg are defective lysogenics which have acquired simultaneously the Gal^+ character. Such transduced Gal^+ bacteria, however, are heterogenotes, i.e., they carry both the Gal^- and the Gal^+

alleles of the same gene, the Gal^- allele being part of the bacterial chromosome (endogenote) whereas the Gal^+ allele usually remains part of the prophage (exogenote). Such Gal^-/ex Gal^+ heterogenotes segregate stable Gal^- haploid progeny at a rather high rate, as a consequence of the loss of the λdg prophage as a whole. This is additional evidence that a prophage such as λdg is not part of the bacterial chromosome, although linked to it.

When λdg phages arising from different, independent Lft lysates are examined for their content of λ genetic markers, they are found to differ (Campbell, 1959). The indications are that both the segment of the phage genome that is eliminated and the segment of bacterial genome which replaces it are variable in length; and further, that a given length of phage genome is not, in general, replaced by an equal length of bacterial genome. Independently isolated λdg defective phages differ also in their density, and hence presumably in the amount of their DNA, some being "heavier" and some being "lighter" than normal, control phages λ. The extreme difference found between a light and a heavy phage λdg amounts to 22 per cent of the DNA of λ (Weiglé, Meselson, and Paigen, 1959).

The original act of recombination that gives rise to a λdg prophage appears, therefore, to be nonreciprocal. It does not obey the precise mechanism which governs recombination between homologous genetic structures but resembles more closely an error of copying which occurred as an accident at the time of prophage replication. Once formed, a λdg genome, whether "heavy" or "light," retains this property throughout prophage replication, induction, vegetative growth, and maturation. It also retains its characteristic density when genetic recombination occurs between the bacterial segment of λdg and the bacterial chromosome (to yield, for instance, a defective prophage λgal^-) or between the phage part of λdg and a normal phage λ. It appears, therefore, that, although the recombinational act between the prophage and the bacterial chromosome is nonreciprocal, recombination between homologous structures, whether viral or bacterial, is reciprocal. These results (Weiglé, Meselson, and Paigen, 1959) suggest that a prophage and the adjacent region of the bacterial chromosome, although able to undergo recombination, are not homologous genetic structures.

The study of λ transducing bacteriophage has brought to light other interesting facts concerning the relationship between the prophage and the bacterial chromosome. The segment of the prophage genome which is replaced by a bacterial segment is on the left arm of λ (see Fig. 54) and always includes the m_5 and h markers. It seems to be rather sharply defined on its right-hand side toward the C region (Arber, 1958), whereas its limits are variable on the left-hand side between m_6 and m_5 (Campbell, 1959). On the assumption that prophage λ is oriented linearly in a rather rigid way in relation to the bacterial chromosome, genetic tests (see page 290) would indicate an order Gal^- (mi c h m_5), thus placing the left arm of λ which contains the h and m_5 markers on the distal part of the phage linkage group with respect to Gal. The fact that it is the left arm of λ which recombines with the Gal region of the chromosome speaks against the existence of such a rigid orientation of the prophage with respect to the bacterial chromosome. If the prophage is attached to the chromosome by its C region, it is likely that occasional pairing must take place between the left arm of λ and the Gal region of the bacterial chromosome. There is additional evidence against a rigid and fixed pairing between the entire prophage and the bacterial chromosome. The site of attachment of prophage 82 is closer to, and that of prophage 434 further from, Gal with respect to the site of attachment of λ. Wild phages 82 and 434 are also able to transduce the Gal region of the bacterial chromosome, but with a much lower frequency than λ (J. L. Reissig, unpublished results). However, the 434 hybrid recombinant, which has the site of attachment of 434 but the left arm of λ, is able to recombine with the Gal region of the bacterial chromosome and to transduce the Gal character with the same efficiency as λ (Campbell and Balbinder, 1959). There is every reason to believe that phage λ, which recombines freely with phage 434, is more homologous with it than with the Gal region of the bacterial chromosome. These results, therefore, indicate that the ability of a prophage to recombine with a segment of the bacterial chromosome is less dependent on structural homology or on the exact location of the prophage than on the ability of a segment of its genome to undergo specific pairing with a region of the chromosome.

As already indicated, Gal^-/ex Gal^+ heterogenotes segregate Gal^- haploid progeny with rather high frequency; more rarely, they also segregate partially diploid (syngenotes) or haploid recombinants. The exogenotic segment which was part of a λdg prophage may therefore become incorporated into the chromosome. However, haploid segregants with the immunity pattern of λ, i.e., in which the C region of λdg is incorporated to the bacterial chromosome, have never been encountered. Paradoxically, therefore, a segment of the bacterial chromosome may become incorporated to a phage genome, whereas the converse situation does not appear to occur. A λdg prophage possesses the C region of the phage genome, which corresponds specifically to a site of the bacterial chromosome, and, adjacent to the C region, a bacterial segment which amounts to about 1/4 of the phage genome. Such a structure, the homology of which to the bacterial chromosome is greater than that of a normal λ prophage, not only appears never to be incorporated into the bacterial chromosome, but its linkage to this chromosome is much weaker than that of a normal prophage. This fact seems to be of fundamental importance for an understanding of the relationships between a prophage and a bacterial chromosome. It may indicate that a prophage and the corresponding region of the bacterial chromosome are structures which are not homologous but in some way complementary.

* * *

Both the study of lysogeny and the study of limited specific transduction lead to the same conclusion. The genetic material of a temperate phage, when in the prophage state, is integrated to the genetic apparatus of the host. It is an added structure, located on the bacterial chromosome at a specific site, but not really part of the chromosome. Although specifically attached to the chromosome, it remains at least in its major part, extrinsic to it. It is gained as a whole unit by lysogenization, and it is also lost as a whole unit. Although a segment of the bacterial chromosome has been found occasionally to replace a segment of the prophage, the converse situation has not been as yet encountered.

II. FUNCTIONS OF A PHAGE GENOME IN RELATION TO ITS STATE

Infection of a sensitive bacterium with a temperate bacteriophage corresponds to the introduction of a new genetic structure, the genetic material of the phage, into the bacterium. As already pointed out, this extraneous genetic structure may follow two very different courses. It may either enter the *vegetative state* where it multiplies actively, bringing about the destruction of the infected cell and the liberation of a new crop of infectious virus particles, or it may enter the *prophage state*, being integrated with the bacterial genome and replicating at the same pace. The identical genetic material can, therefore, exist in the same cell in two widely different states. In these two alternative states, it occupies different locations, replicates at different rates and exerts different functions.

Like any other genetic structure, the genetic material of a phage is endowed with two main properties: the property of self-replication and the property of controlling, through the different genetic determinants of its linkage group, a number of genetic functions. It is noteworthy that, in the case of a temperate phage, these two different properties are expressed differentially according to the state of the phage genome. The pertinent information now available will be summarized briefly in this section.

A. The Functions Exerted in the Vegetative State

Vegetative multiplication of a bacterial virus includes all the events which take place between the penetration of the phage DNA into the infected cell and the liberation of new mature phage particles following cell lysis. This complex series of events has just begun to be unraveled in recent years in the case of virulent phage T_2 and the related T even phages, T_4 and T_6. Such phages are complex, organized structures composed of a protein outer coat and of a DNA inner core. The DNA of these phages differs from that of the *E. coli* host both qualitatively and quantitatively. The phage DNA contains the pyrimidine 5-hydroxy-methyl-cytosine instead of cytosine (Wyatt and Cohen, 1953), with glucose residues coupled to this base (Jesaitis and Goebel, 1953; Sinsheimer, 1954), and the purine-pyrimidine base ratio is different from that of *E. coli.* The protein coat, head and tail, are composed of a variety of molecular species: head protein subunits, tail contractile sheath, tail core, tail plate, tail fibers (Kellenberger and Arber, 1955; Kozloff and Lute, 1959; Brenner *et al.*, 1959). Other minor components have also been found: an internal protein which is injected together with the DNA (Van Vunakis, Baker, and Brown, 1958; L. Levine, Barlow, and Van Vunakis, 1958); polyamines (Ames, Dubin, and Rosenthal, 1958); and a tail enzyme similar to lysozyme (G. Koch and Dreyer, 1958), etc.

The pioneer work of S. S. Cohen and his colleagues has shown that, following infection with a phage such as T_2, the metabolic machinery of the infected bacterium is altered drastically, being directed toward the synthesis of phage instead of bacterial constituents (S. S. Cohen, 1949). Not only do the structural proteins which enter in the composition of the phage particles have to be synthesized, but also a variety of new enzymes which are necessary for the synthesis of the constituents of the phage, including phage DNA itself. For example, if protein synthesis is prevented by addition of chloramphenicol in the first minutes following infection, no phage DNA is synthesized, whereas if the same treatment is applied after the 7th minute following infection, phage DNA is synthesized but phage proteins are not (see Hershey, 1957b). The possibility which exists in T_2-infected bacteria of distinguishing phage DNA from bacterial DNA has permitted division of the latent period schematically into three different phases. During a first phase which follows infection, a variety of new enzymes involved in the synthesis of phage DNA, or preventing the synthesis of bacterial DNA, are formed (Flaks and Cohen, 1959a, b; Kornberg, Zimmerman, Kornberg, and Josse, 1959) together with an RNA fraction which has a rapid turnover (Volkin and Astrachan, 1957). In a second phase, genetically active phage DNA is synthesized at a high rate and directs the synthesis of the different species of phage proteins until a pool of these several constituents is formed. In a third phase of the latent period, DNA and proteins are withdrawn from the pool and assembled into mature phage particles, while new constituents continue to be synthesized. This third phase, and the latent period as a whole, terminate when lysis occurs as a result of the action of the lysozyme-like enzyme on the bacterial cell wall.

After infection by a virulent phage such as T_2, the synthetic mechanisms of the bacterial cell are thus directed toward the synthesis of the virus. It seems that bacterial "messengers" which, in the growing cell, bring to the synthetic machinery the structural information for the production of bacterial proteins are no longer made. They are replaced by viral messengers which bring to the cellular machinery instruction for the synthesis of viral proteins (Brenner, Jacob, and Meselson, 1961). An important characteristic of the vegetative reproduction of the virus seems to be that of unrestricted synthesis. As pointed out in Chapter XIV, whereas the growth of a cell involves an harmonious equilibrium in the synthesis of its different components, the genetic material of the virus is not submitted to the regulating mechanisms of the cell. When the second phase of the latent period is reached, the genetic material of the virus replicates at what appears to be the maximal possible rate. The different functions controlled by the genetic material of the virus appear, however, to be expressed at different times after infection, as evidenced by the sequential appearance of the phage-determined protein constituents.

Studies as extensive as those carried out with virulent phage T_2 have not yet become possible with temperate bacteriophages such as λ, mainly because no differences have so far been detected between the DNA of the phage and that of the host bacterium. It is likely, however, that the vegetative reproduction of a temperate phage follows a similar course and that the genetic material of the phage directs not only the synthesis of the protein constituents of the phage but also that of new specific RNA and new specific enzymes. An indication of this is provided by experiments in which protein synthesis is blocked at the time of infection by the addition of chloramphenicol. In the case of phage λ as in that of other phages, the synthesis of phage genetic material does not take place (Thomas, 1959). Although it is not easy to look for the appearance of protein species of known activity in the course of vegetative multiplication of temperate bacteriophages, a more general route of approach appears to be available. It is furnished by the existence of defective lysogenic strains (page 76).

Such bacterial strains perpetuate hereditarily a defective prophage, i.e., a prophage bearing a mutation which prevents an essential step in the formation of infective particles. If such mutation occurred in a virulent bacteriophage or in the vegetative state of a temperate phage, it could not be detected, since it would be lethal for the phage. This situation does not apply to the mutations which take place in the prophage state, since they do not interfere with the continued reproduction of the defective genome as long as it remains in the prophage state.

Genetic analysis of a large number of defective prophages λ has permitted the location of the corresponding mutations on the linkage group of bacteriophage λ (see Fig. 54). In parallel, the physiological effects of these mutations on the vegetative reproduction of the phage have been investigated by examining such properties as the ability of the defective genome to multiply during the latent period following induction, the formation of the tail antigen capable of reacting with a neutralizing anti-λ serum, of the tail protein responsible for the adsorption to the bacterial surface, of a lysozyme-like enzyme called endolysine, etc. (Jacob, Fuerst, and Wollman, 1957). The results of such tests are summarized in Table XLI. It can be seen that the mutations which are responsible for the defective character of a prophage λ belong to two main groups:

1. Mutations of the *first group* affect a late step in the production of infective particles. The defective phage genome is able to multiply vegetatively and most of the recognizable constituents of the phage are formed, but an essential reaction of maturation or morphogenesis is blocked. In most of the cases, the missing component can be provided by another phage λ: upon ultraviolet induction followed by superinfection with a normal phage λ, defective lysogenic bacteria liberate by lysis a mixture of helper and defective particles. This result indicates that the product of the blocked reaction, like most of the phage constituents, may be supplied by the helper phage, pooled and reassorted randomly at the time of maturation. Most of the mutations belonging to this group are located on the left arm of the λ linkage group close to the m_5 and g_1 markers.

2. Mutations of the *second group* affect, in contrast, an early step of vegetative reproduction. After ultraviolet induction of the defective lysogenic bacteria, the genetic material of the phage is unable to initiate vegetative multiplication. Individual members of the group differ as to

the recognizable protein species they are still able to manufacture. These mutations point to the existence of early reactions which are prerequisites for the vegetative replication of the phage genome. As in the case of the mutations of the first group, the product of the blocked reaction may be supplied by a normal, superinfecting phage λ. What is more interesting is the fact that two different defective genomes, both unable to enter the vegetative phase, are able to cooperate. This finding indicates that sev-

TABLE XLI
PROPERTIES OF DEFECTIVE LYSOGENIC STRAINS[a]

Strains	Vegetative multiplication of the phage genome	Synthesis of lysin	Synthesis of blocking antigen	Synthesis of h protein	Production of defective particles after superinfection with a helper phage	Lysogenization in single infection with defective particles
P16	+	+	+	+	+	+
P17	+	+	+	+	X	X
P18	+	+	+	+	+	+
P19	+	+	+	+	X	X
P21	+	+	+	+	X	X
P22	0	0	0	H	+	0
P30	0	0	+	+	+	0
P32	0	+	0	H	+	0
P34	0	+	+	0	X	X

[a] From Jacob, Fuerst, and Wollman (1957).

KEY: + Accomplishes the reaction after U.V. induction
0 Does not accomplish the reaction after U.V. induction
X Not investigated
H Can accomplish the reaction after U.V. induction only upon superinfection with a helper phage.

eral functions are required for the initiation of vegetative multiplication. The genetic determinants of these functions are all located on the left arm of λ, between the h and c markers.

The existence of these defective lysogenic strains provides evidence for the fact that the genetic material, although unable to multiply vegetatively, is still perfectly capable of reproducing when integrated as a prophage. The functions that appear therefore to be involved are not those concerned with synthesis and replication of the phage DNA, but those essential to its multiplication *in the autonomous state.* It would seem that, when subjected to the control mechanisms of the cell, the genetic material is relieved of performing certain functions which are necessary for its own reproduction.

The availability of defective prophages carrying mutations which affect functions essential for vegetative reproduction makes it possible to investigate the sequence of reactions which lead to the formation of infectious viral particles. Experiments are in progress to distinguish the different protein species synthesized in the course of vegetative multiplication of phage λ and to ascertain those which are not formed after induction of defective lysogenic strains of different types.

Vegetative reproduction of temperate as well as of virulent bacteriophage, therefore involves a series of reactions which appear to take place in a sequential, orderly way. All the functions controlled by the genetic material of the virus are not expressed simultaneously. There seems to be a precise time schedule for the expression of the various structural genes of the phage during the latent period. The internal protein is the first component the synthesis of which can be detected after infection: it is followed by the series of enzymes required for the vegetative replication of the genetic material of the phage. The components of the protein coat appear only in the middle of the latent period, and the lysozyme-like enzyme seems to be produced only a few minutes before lysis. Such an order in the expression of the phage genes might be explained by the assumption that the genetic material of the phage is constituted of a series of operons, the activity of which is sequentially turned on, a product of an earlier reaction acting as an inducer for a later operon, in a way similar to the sequential induction described by Stanier (1951). In any case, if infection by a virus corresponds to the introduction into a cell of a genetic element which does not obey the regulatory mechanisms of the cell, it seems probable that this genetic element nonetheless brings with it its own system of control, or its own "clock" for the expression of its viral functions.

B. The Functions Exerted in the Prophage State

When entering the prophage state, the genetic material of a temperate phage appears to come under the control of the regulating mechanisms of the host. It replicates at the pace of the host genome, and protein constituents of the virus are not synthesized. None of the viral functions of the virus therefore appears to be expressed. The reduction of the phage genome to the prophage state is correlated however, with a new property of the lysogenized bacterium which is under the control of phage determinants: immunity.

Immunity, as stated already (page 22) is the property of lysogenic bacteria which allows them to survive infection by a phage homologous to the prophage they perpetuate. The immune state appears to be responsible for prevention of the expression of viral functions whether this be the viral functions controlled by the genome of the prophage or by the genome of a superinfecting phage.

The functions which are involved in the establishment and maintenance of the prophage state all appear to be located in a rather short segment of the linkage group of a temperate bacteriophage, the C region. As discussed already (page 291), mutations occurring in this region abolish or greatly reduce the ability of a phage to lysogenize. Several functions appear to be involved in the reduction of a phage genome to the prophage state. For instance, lysogenization may be obtained as a result of mixed infection with two different C mutants each of which is unable to lysogenize by itself (Kaiser, 1957; M. Levine, 1957). Both the ability of a prophage to confer specific immunity upon the bacterium and the sensitivity of an infecting phage to the immunity of the lysogenic bacterium are controlled by the C region. The mutations which are responsible for the virulent inducer character in phage λ, i.e., for the ability of certain mutants of λ to overcome the immunity conferred by a λ prophage, have been mapped in this region (Jacob and Wollman, 1954b; Kaiser, 1957). Similarly crosses between temperate bacteriophages such as λ and 434, which differ in their sites of attachment to the bacterial chromosome as well as in their specific immunity, have shown that the determination of both immunity and sensitivity to immunity are controlled by the C region of the phage linkage group (Kaiser and Jacob, 1957).

An understanding of the mechanism of immunity has come from the results of reciprocal crosses between lysogenic and nonlysogenic bacteria described in Chapters VI and VII. In crosses between a lysogenic, immune Hfr strain and a nonimmune F^- strain, vegetative multiplication of the prophage takes place in the zygotes (zygotic induction). In the reciprocal cross between a nonimmune Hfr bacterium and an immune lysogenic recipient, on the contrary, the zygotes are immune against superinfection with homologous phages and no development of the prophage takes place. As the main difference between the two sorts of $(\lambda)^+/(\lambda)^-$ or $(\lambda)^-/(\lambda)^+$ zygotes is in the cytoplasm of the recipient, the most likely interpretation of these results is that immunity is expressed in the cytoplasm (Jacob and Wollman, 1956b). There would appear to exist, therefore, in the cytoplasm of lysogenic bacteria an immunity factor which prevents the vegetative multiplication of the prophage, as well as of homologous superinfecting phages. Similar conclusions can be derived from the properties of certain bacterial heterogenotes obtained by sexduction. Sex factors have been obtained (page 196) which are able to transfer the Gal markers and the chromosomal site of prophage λ. Heterogenotes with the constitutions $Gal^-(\lambda)^+/F\ Gal^+(\lambda)^-$ and $Gal^-(\lambda)^-/F\ Gal^+(\lambda)^+$ can thus be prepared. Both types of heterogenotes are immune to λ, but segregate $(\lambda)^-$ nonimmune progeny. This finding confirms that "immunity" is dominant over "nonimmunity" and is cytoplasmically expressed (Jacob, Schaeffer, and Wollman, 1960). More indirect evidence obtained with coliphages P_1 (Luria, Fraser, Adams, and Burrous, 1958) and P_2 (Bertani, 1958) and with the *Salmonella* phage P_{22} (Zinder, 1958) points in the same direction.

The immunity exhibited by lysogenic bacteria represents, therefore, a situation comparable to that which has been analyzed in Chapter XIV concerning the induced synthesis of enzymes. The most likely interpretation of immunity is that there exists, in the C region of a temperate phage such as λ, a genetic unit responsible for the synthesis of a specific immunity substance, a repressor. This repressor would act on a specific structure of the phage genome, thereby preventing the synthesis of one (or several) protein(s) necessary for the initiation of vegetative reproduction either of the prophage or of homologous superinfecting phages (Jacob, 1960; Jacob and Campbell, 1959).

According to this model, the introduction into the bacterium of the genetic material of a temperate phage, either by infection or by genetic transfer (conjugation, transduction, sexduction) leads to one of two mutually exclusive reactions: the synthesis of the repressor or the synthesis of the early proteins required for vegetative reproduction. On the outcome depends the fate of the infected host: its survival and eventual lysogenization, or its death as a result of phage multiplication. This is the classical "decision" which follows infection with a temperate bacteriophage (see Lwoff, 1953; Bertani, 1958). It is known that external factors such as growth conditions, multiplicity of infection, changes in temperature, or addition of chemicals may influence the nature of the response. In particular, interference with protein synthesis by addition of chloramphenicol, for instance, favors the transition to or the maintenance of the prophage state. This effect is observed in lysogenization following infection (see Bertani, 1958) as well as in the prevention of zygotic induction (Jacob and Campbell, 1959). In terms of this model, the transition from the prophage to the vegetative state would be a consequence of a transient disturbance of the system of regulation. The action of inducing agents, for instance, could be visualized as resulting from an arrest, or a decrease in rate, of the synthesis of a labile repressor. Initiation of vegetative replication would take place when the level of the repressor inside the cell had fallen below a certain threshold.

The different types of mutations which affect the capacity of a temperate phage to lysogenize, its sensitivity to immunity or its inducibility are readily explained by the repressor model. For example, in phage λ, three main types of mutations appear to alter the system of regulation determining immunity.

1. The clear (C_1) mutants are unable to lysogenize by themselves in single infection. In mixed infection with C_1^+ phages, however, they may undergo transition to the prophage state. From the doubly lysogenic (C_1 C_1^+) clones single lysogenic segregants may be recovered, which carry the C_1^+ but never the C_1 type (Kaiser, 1957). The C_1^+ character is, therefore, dominant over the C_1 character. These results suggest that the C_1 locus is responsible for the synthesis of the repressor and that the C_1 mutants have lost the ability to produce a functionally active repressor. They remain sensitive, however, to the repressor produced by C_1^+ prophages.

2. The virulent (V) mutants are not only unable to lysogenize, but they can also grow on bacteria lysogenic for a normal λ prophage. The V character is, therefore, dominant over the V^+ character and may be visualized as resulting from a loss of sensitivity to the repressor. The V character, however, has been shown to be polygenic (Jacob and Wollman, 1954b). It appears to result from a summation of a mutation at a particular region of the C_1 locus and of mutations at other loci. Such mutations might affect *operator* loci which, as in the case of the regulation of enzyme synthesis, would be responsible for the sensitivity of a λ genome to the immunity-repressor.

3. Finally, noninducible (ind^-) mutants of λ have been isolated. Lysogenic (λ ind^-) bacteria are no longer sensitive to inducing agents such as ultraviolet light although an ind^-λ prophage still gives rise to zygotic induction. Double lysogenics or λ ind^+/λ ind^- heterogenotes are not inducible by ultraviolet light, which shows that the λ ind^- character is dominant over ind^+. Superinfection of ultraviolet induced lysogenic (λ ind^+) bacteria with a λ ind^- phage prevents the development of the normal λ prophage. This ability to repress vegetative reproduction is specific and applies only to the prophages which exhibit the immunity of λ (Jacob and Campbell, 1959). The ind^- mutation, which occurs at a particular site of the C_1 locus, may be interpreted, therefore, as modifying the formation of the repressor either in quality (greater stability) or in quantity (larger amount). The immunity-conferring property of

the ind$^-$ mutation appears to be independent of the rest of the genotype of the λ phages bearing this mutation, except in the clear C_1 ind$^-$ double mutants which have lost this property. This finding suggests that both the ind$^-$ and the C_1 mutations affect the synthesis of the repressor, although their effects are opposite.

The presence of a prophage may sometimes be expressed by properties which do not bear an obvious relation to the activities expected of a phage genome (see p. 23). Such cases of lysogenic conversion extend from the ability conferred upon *Corynebacterium diphtheriae* to synthesize diphtheria toxin to modifications in the specificity of surface antigens in *Salmonella.* These properties, which were first recognized as changes brought about by lysogenization, were at first thought to be functions expressed only in the prophage state. It has been found, however, that such functions are also expressed in the vegetative state, both in the case of antigenic conversion in *Salmonella* (Uetake, Luria, and Burrous, 1958) and in the case of toxin production by the diphtheria bacillus (Barksdale, 1959). Bacterial genes incorporated into transducing phage genomes appear also to be expressed both in the prophage and in the vegetative phage. This finding might favor the view that the characters conferred by lysogenic conversion are under the control of bacterial genes which have become permanently incorporated into a viral genome (Luria, Fraser, Adams, and Burrous, 1958).

* * *

The genome of a temperate phage such as λ appears to contain two main classes of genetic determinants. Most of them are concerned with the multiple functions involved in vegetative reproduction. Little is known at present about the sequence and regulation of the events of vegetative reproduction, but they seem to proceed in an orderly way. Other determinants, located mainly in the C region of the phage linkage group, control the establishment and maintenance of the prophage state. The maintenance of the prophage state and the exclusion of homologous superinfecting phages which are functions essential to the survival of lysogenic bacteria, are assured by a system of regulation very similar to that which operates in the regulation of enzyme synthesis. A regulator gene directs the synthesis of a specific repressor which is probably not a protein. This repressor in turn probably acts on a specific structure (operator) of the phage genome, thereby preventing the expression of early function(s) essential for the initiation of vegetative reproduction. The two sets of functions appear to be mutually exclusive, lysogenization being characterized by the prevalence of the repressor mechanism and vegetative replication by that of the productive chain of synthetic reactions.

III. THE PROPHAGE AS A MODEL OF PROVIRUS

The permanent association which exists at the intracellular level between the virus and the bacterium in lysogenic bacteria may eventually explain some of the findings encountered in the study of latent viral infections. It is quite conceivable that viruses other than temperate bacteriophages may exist in a proviral state. Among the many cases of chronic viral infections which have been described in vertebrates as well as in insects or in plants, some might be due to a permanent association between the virus and certain cells of the host. In fact, since their existence has been recognized, lysogenic bacteria have served as an example of a latent viral infection. The definition and characterization of the prophage have raised the problem of the possible existence of *proviruses* endowed with similar properties (see Lwoff, 1953; Jacob, 1954a).

The latent viral infections, which provide one of the most interesting problems of virology, are probably heterogeneous in nature. In most cases, nothing is known about the form in which the virus persists in the infected organism or about its relations with the host at the cellular level. When a sufficient number of cases have been analyzed, it will probably be found that a variety of different situations have been lumped together under the same designation. It is likely that in many cases the association between virus and host is at the extracellular level. One should therefore be cautious in drawing a parallel between latent viral infections and lysogeny. For such a comparison to be valid, it must first be demonstrated in a specific latent infection that the permanent association between virus and host is really at the intracellular level. The term "*moderate viruses*" (by analogy with temperate bacteriophages) has been proposed to designate those viruses which can persist in a cell line, their reproduction being compatible with the survival and multiplication of the host cell (Dulbecco, 1955).

Among latent viral infections, two classes may be distinguished: those in which the persistence of the virus is asymptomatic and those in which infection is manifested by pathological changes. The most remarkable examples of the latter class are the tumors of viral origin. In each, there are only few cases in which indications exist that the association between the virus and the host is likely to be at the intracellular level. We shall restrict ourselves to the examples which appear to be most illustrative: the agent of hereditary CO_2 sensitivity in *Drosophila* and two tumor viruses, the causative agents of the Rous sarcoma in fowl and of polyoma in rodents.

A. Hereditary Sensitivity to Carbon Dioxide in *Drosophila*

The hereditary sensitivity of the fruit fly *Drosophila* to carbon dioxide has been studied extensively by L'Héritier and his collaborators (see L'Héritier, 1954, 1955, 1958). Certain lines of *Drosophila* have the hereditary property of being killed by CO_2. This property is due to the presence of an agent, σ, which can be extracted from the infected flies and injected into normal flies, which are resistant to CO_2. The "virus" thus transferred multiplies in the inoculated flies and, after a noninfectious latent period, can again be extracted and passed serially to uninfected flies. The flies which have acquired CO_2 sensitivity by inoculation transmit this property only occasionally to their progeny, and those descendants which harbor the virus transmit it, in turn, to only part of their progeny.

Two very different situations, therefore, may be distinguished. In one of them, all the females regularly transmit CO_2 sensitivity to all their progeny; they are said to be *stabilized.* In the other, the females transmit CO_2 sensitivity only in an irregular fashion; they are said to be *nonstabilized. Drosophila* from stabilized lines and *Drosophila* from nonstabilized lines produce the same σ "virus" but the former contain slightly less "virus" than the latter. The permanence of the association between virus and host observed in stabilized lines which contrasts with the precariousness of the association found in nonstabilized lines cannot be ascribed, therefore, to a difference either in the nature or in the amount of the virus contained in the flies. The difference between the two lines of flies appears to lie in the nature of the association established between virus and host. In the flies of stabilized lines, virus and host seem to be integrated (L'Héritier, 1955). Stabilized lines can thus be compared to lysogenic bacterial strains, with which they share certain properties (small spontaneous production rate, immunity). Conversely, nonstabilized flies may be compared to cultures of sensitive bacteria infected with a temperate bacteriophage (carrier cultures) in which an equilibrium between virus and cells may be set at the extracellular level.

In addition, a third type of association between "virus" and host has been discovered; it is that which exists in the so-called ϱ lines of flies. These are stabilized lines of a particular type. The ϱ flies contain only a small amount of a virus indistinguishable from σ, and are immune to σ. All the females of such lines transmit the ϱ condition regularly to all their progeny. The ϱ lines may be compared, therefore, to the defective strains of lysogenic bacteria.

The integration which has become established in stabilized lines of *Drosophila,* between host and virus, whether of the normal σ or of the ϱ type is still of an unknown nature. In reciprocal crosses between flies from a stabilized line (CO_2 sensitive) and virus-free flies (CO_2 resistant), the stabilized character of sensitivity is maternally inherited. For this reason, since its discovery, hereditary CO_2 sensitivity in *Drosophila* has been considered as an example of cytoplasmic inheritance, even before the role of a virus in its determination had been suspected. If it is assumed that, both in CO_2 sensitive *Drosophila* and in lysogenic bacteria, the hereditary ability to produce a virus is perpetuated in the form of a provirus, it is remarkable that genetic analysis of these two situations has led to such different conclusions.

B. Tumor Viruses

In animals, there is an increasing number of examples of tumors, especially malignant ones, which appear to be induced by viruses or to be associated with the presence of a virus. Viral infection in such cases results not in the destruction of the infected cells, but in their permanent alteration. In recent years, considerable progress has been made in the study at the cellular level of infection with animal viruses (see Dulbecco, 1955). Such studies, undertaken with tumor viruses, have given support to the hypothesis that permanent cell modifications brought about by viral infection may indeed be the consequence of an intracellular integration of the virus.

One of the best known cases is that of the Rous sarcoma of chickens which is caused by an RNA virus. When chicken fibroblasts are infected *in vitro* with this virus, a certain fraction, the size of which depends on the cultural conditions both at the time of infection and after infection, is transformed permanently into Rous sarcoma cells. These cells can be distinguished easily from normal fibroblasts from which they differ both in their morphology and in their behavior in cultures. Rous sarcoma cells can be maintained in culture for several generations in the presence of an antiviral serum and every cell of the infected clone retains its altered morphology and its capacity to produce virus. These properties have thus been maintained intracellularly in succeeding generations. A permanent association has been established between the cell and the virus, the consequence of which is a modification of the properties of the cell and its transformation to a malignant state (Rubin, 1959). That these properties are indeed under the genetic control of the virus is evidenced by the fact that different mutants of the Rous virus, when infecting the same normal chicken fibroblasts, induce different morphologic changes (Temin, 1960). One is thus led to conclude that in Rous sarcoma cells, just as in lysogenic bacteria, virus and cell are integrated, the genetic material of the virus endowing the cell with new and permanent properties. As to the nature of this integration, it is likely to be different from that which exists in lysogenic bacteria. Each cell of a Rous sarcoma line is able to multiply and to release infectious virus, although in small amount. It is not yet known whether the genetic material of the virus is perpetuated in an autonomous vegetative state or in an integrated state resembling a proviral state. It should be emphasized, however, that the Rous sarcoma virus is an RNA virus, and its mode of association with the constituents of the host cell may well differ from that observed in the case of temperate bacteriophage.

A striking example of virus-cell integration has been analyzed recently in the case of the polyoma virus, a DNA virus that causes a variety of malignant tumors in rodents. When embryonic cells are infected *in vitro* by this virus, two very different types of response may be observed: a cytocidal response with extensive multiplication of the virus and degeneration of the infected cells, and a "moderate" type of response in which the infected cells survive and become permanently modified. These converted cells, which can be distinguished easily from normal cells by their cultural properties, no longer release infectious virus in measurable amount, are resistant to superinfection with the homologous virus, and have acquired a malignant character. The type of response varies with the conditions of infection and with the origin of the infected cells. Infection of embryonic cells of mice results primarily in a cytocidal effect; only a minority of infected cells eventually survive and become malignant. In the case of the hamster, however, it is the "reductive" type of response which prevails, the infected culture being converted to malignancy without appreciable signs of degeneration. In either case, when the converted cells, which no longer produce infectious virus are inoculated into animals, they provoke the formation of malignant tumors at the site of inoculation (Vogt and Dulbecco, 1960).

There is little doubt that both the polyoma and the Rous viruses belong to the moderate type of viruses, since they can propagate intracellularly from cell generation to cell generation. The case of polyoma virus is especially reminiscent of that of temperate bacteriophage, with its two types of response, either cytocidal or reductive, the latter resulting in a permanent association between a converted cell and what appears to be a noninfectious form of the virus. Although the nature of this association is still unknown, the characteristics of this integration are very suggestive of a proviral state.

* * *

The few examples which have just been examined suggest that certain animal viruses may become integrated with the cells they infect. There are many other cases of latent viral infections which might be accounted for similarly by such an intracellular integration. As to the nature of the relations which may become established between the genetic material of a virus and the normal constituents of the host cell, they are likely to differ according to the nature of the genetic material of the virus. In particular, DNA and RNA viruses may behave in a completely different fashion. That prophages become associated with the bacterial chromosome might be due to the fact that, like this chromosome, they are composed of DNA. It is quite possible that RNA viruses, such as plant viruses and many animal viruses, are unable to become associated with chromosomal DNA. Such viruses, however, might eventually become associated with RNA structures of the host, whether nuclear or cytoplasmic, or persist as autonomously replicating particles. These possibilities may explain the difference in behavior of the Rous and polyoma viruses. There are no indications, however, which permit one to select or to reject any one of these hypotheses. The case of temperate bacteriophage is the only one for which chemical, virological, and genetic data exist. It is also the only example in which chromosomal location of a provirus has been demonstrated. In the case of hereditary sensitivity to CO_2 in *Drosophila,* where genetic data were obtained initially, chemical information is still lacking and virological studies are incomplete. It has not been possible yet to purify or to characterize the causative agent. The converse is true for some tumor viruses. Although their viral and chemical properties are rather well known, no genetic methods exist at present which will permit investigation of the nature of their association with host cells. In view of the analogies observed between bacteriophages on the one hand and the viruses of animals and of plants on the other, it may be anticipated that the notion of provirus, which has proved already so fruitful as a model for certain cases of latent viral infection, will be substantiated by additional examples in the near future.

CHAPTER XVI

The Episomes

Lysogeny, as discussed in the preceding chapter, represents the clearest example of integration between the genetic material of a virus and that of the host cell. From the genetic point of view, it also constitutes a remarkable situation since the genetic material of a temperate bacteriophage is an extrinsic genetic structure which, when introduced into a bacterium, may exist there in two different states, an autonomous state and an integrated state. In the autonomous (vegetative) state, the genetic material of the phage reproduces independently, and at a rate which is faster than that of the bacterial genome. In contrast, in the integrated (proviral) state, the genetic material of the phage behaves in many respects as a bacterial genetic element: it is replicated with the bacterial chromosome, on which it occupies a well-defined location, and it confers upon the host bacterium specific phenotypic properties. In the typical case of inducible lysogenic bacteria, it is rather easy to distinguish the prophage from the normal genetic elements of the bacterium. On the contrary, in the extreme case of defective, noninducible, lysogenic bacteria, it may become extremely difficult, and even impossible, to assign to the presence of a prophage the bacterial properties which it actually determines.

The genetic material of a temperate bacteriophage provides therefore the example of a genetic structure which is *added* to the genome of a cell and which, inside this cell, may exist in two distinct, and even mutually exclusive, states: the *autonomous* state and the *integrated* state (see Fig. 55). Studies on bacterial conjugation have shown that there exist in bacteria other genetic elements which exhibit genetic properties very similar to those just mentioned for temperate bacteriophages, but which we have no reason to believe to be bacteriophages. To designate genetic elements endowed with such properties, we have proposed the term *episomic elements* or *episomes* (Jacob and Wollman, 1958b).

It was pointed out to us later, that the term episomes had already been used in 1931 by D. H. Thompson, but with a somewhat different meaning. In order to account for certain mutations in *Drosophila*, Thompson advanced the hypothesis that "a gene is consisting of a main particle ("protosome") firmly anchored in the chromosome, with varying numbers of one or more kinds of other particles attached ("episomes") . . . Gene mutation is due most frequently to the loss of one or more episomes from the protosome and less frequently to the addition of episomes. The genetic chromosome is visualized as the conventional string of beads, except that almost every bead bristles with side chains of episomes." Thompson thus considered the possibility of genetic elements being attached to, or detached from, a chromosome, although he did not assume an alternative cytoplasmic state for such elements. Actual knowledge of the fine structure of the genetic material and of the mechanism

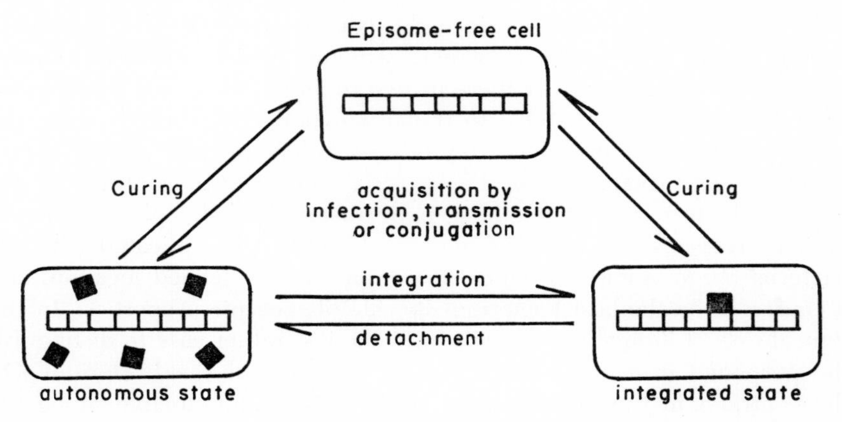

FIG. 55. Diagrammatic representation of the states of an episome.

of mutations has rendered Thompson's conception obsolete. Since there is no need to maintain the term episome in Thompson's sense, it can be unambiguously applied to the kind of genetic elements which will be dealt with in this last chapter.

I. EPISOMIC ELEMENTS IN BACTERIA

The special attributes of the process of sexual conjugation in bacteria, have made it possible to recognize the existence, in these microorganisms of a category of genetic elements, or episomes, which differ both from the normal chromosomal structures and from purely cytoplasmic elements. We shall describe first the properties of those elements that can already be regarded as episomes. We shall then discuss the common properties of those elements, as well as the criteria which must determine the recognition of other categories of bacterial episomes.

A. Examples of Bacterial Episomes

Three types of elements have been hitherto analyzed in bacteria which exhibit the genetic properties characteristic of episomic elements. There are the temperate bacteriophages, the sex factor (or factors) and the genetic determinants that control the production of certain antibiotics called bacteriocins.

1. *The temperate bacteriophages.* They provide the clearest example, and the model of episomic elements. Their case having already been discussed at length, only a few essential points need be recalled here. Temperate bacteriophages are genetic elements which are extrinsic to the bacterial cell and therefore dispensable. When introduced into the cytoplasm of the bacterium they may enter either an autonomous (vegetative) state of replication or an integrated (proviral) state. These two states are mutually exclusive. Passage to the autonomous state generally leads to the death of the bacterium. In the integrated state the genetic material of the phage is located on the bacterial chromosome but does not seem to be an inserted part of this chromosome. To a given temperate bacteriophage corresponds, in general, a specific site on the bacterial chromosome. Genetic recombination between the prophage and the adjacent part of the bacterial chromosome may eventually take place. A segment of bacterial genome may thus become incorporated in the phage genome and share its fate in autonomous as well as in integrated replication. Since it is a rather complex genetic structure, the genetic material of a phage may undergo a variety of mutations. There are, however, numerous different types of temperate bacteriophages and for some of them no definite chromosomal location has been found. When this is the case, it seems likely that they can occupy transient and variable positions on the bacterial chromosome.

Whatever the biological origin of bacteriophages—and of the viruses in general—they constitute, in the present stage of their evolution, a well-defined category, distinct from the organisms that they infect (see Lwoff, 1957). Such elements may therefore be considered unambiguously as being extrinsic to their host cells. It is all the more remarkable that certain viruses, such as the temperate bacteriophages, may establish with their host cells the very special relationships which have just been summarized. It is no less remarkable, however, that other genetic elements of bacteria, which we have no reason to believe to be extrinsic infectious elements, exhibit genetic properties which are very similar to those of temperate bacteriophages.

2. *The sex factor of bacteria.* The properties of the genetic elements

which are responsible for sexual differentiation in bacteria have also been described in detail (see Chapter XI). They will therefore only be summarized here. All evidence suggests that the sex factor of bacteria is a dispensable genetic element, since it seems to be absent from female bacteria while present in males. When absent, it can be acquired only from bacteria that already possess it (donor bacteria), either by conjugation or by transduction (Arber, 1960). When present, the sex factor can exist in bacteria in one of two different states. In the *autonomous* state, as in F^+ bacteria, the sex factor appears to replicate independently of the bacterial chromosome. In the *integrated state,* as in Hfr bacteria, the sex factor is located on the bacterial chromosome, and reproduces with it. Unlike the majority of prophages, a sex factor can occupy a number of different positions on the bacterial chromosome, the location of the sex factor being correlated with the properties of the particular Hfr strain that carries it. The autonomous and the integrated states are both reversible. Transition from the autonomous to the integrated state determines an $F^+ \rightarrow$ Hfr mutation, and transition from the integrated to the autonomous state determines an Hfr $\rightarrow F^+$ mutation. These two states also appear to be mutually exclusive, since the presence of a sex factor in the integrated state seems to prevent the autonomous replication of the same sex factor. When it is in the integrated state, the sex factor may undergo genetic recombination with the adjacent region of the bacterial chromosome and thus incorporate a chromosomal segment of the bacterium. Sex factor and chromosomal segment thereafter behave as a single unit of reproduction, even in the autonomous state. Finally, the sex factor can mutate toward a defective state and there seems to be a variety of genetically different sex factors; it is possible that some of them may have arisen by mutations of a single original sex factor.

3. *The colicinogenic factors.* A third class of genetic elements of bacteria which appear to be episomes are the genetic factors that control the synthesis of certain antibiotics of the bacteriocin type. The term *bacteriocins* has been coined to designate antibiotic substances, very likely of protein nature, that are produced by certain strains of bacteria and active on other strains of the same species (Jacob, Lwoff, Siminovitch, and Wollman, 1953). Among these substances, the best known are the colicins, discovered by Gratia (1932), which owe their name to the fact that they are active on *E. coli,* and which have been studied extensively by Frédéricq (1948, 1957). Bacteria that possess the hereditary property of producing a colicin are called colicinogenic. The production of colicin by colicinogenic bacteria, like that of phage by lysogenic bacteria is

however a potential property, since the actual synthesis of a colicin is lethal for the producing bacteria (Jacob, Siminovitch, and Wollman, 1952, 1953). The genetic determinants of colicin synthesis are called *colicinogenic factors.*

Colicinogeny is an extremely stable property which is very seldom lost. Mutations from noncolicinogeny to colicinogeny have never been observed. A noncolicinogenic bacterium can acquire the colicinogenic character only by contact with colicinogenic bacteria, and such acquisition seems to be a consequence of conjugation (Frédéricq, 1954b). In a cross between colicinogenic (col^+) F^+ bacteria—which produce a certain colicin of type E—and noncolicinogenic (col^-) F^- bacteria, a high proportion of the recipient bacteria acquire the col^+ character. Since transmission of the col^+ character is independent of that of the other genetic characters of F^+ bacteria, the genetic determinant of colicinogeny, like the F factor, is apparently not located on the chromosome of F^+ bacteria. In the reciprocal cross between noncolicinogenic (col^-) F^+ donors and colicinogenic (col^+) F^- recipients, the col^- character is never transmitted to the progeny of the zygotes. This asymmetry in the results of reciprocal crosses, together with the fact that the colicinogenic character is transmitted independently of the other genetic characters of F^+ bacteria, led Frédéricq (1955b) to postulate that the genetic determinant of colicinogeny is cytoplasmic.

The results just described were obtained with a colicin classified by Frédéricq as being of type E_1, originally produced by a strain of *E. coli* called K30. With other colicins, very different results may be observed. The efficiency of transmission of colicinogeny from col^+ F^+ donors to col^- F^- recipients may be rather low. Furthermore, the influence of the colicinogenic character of the donor on the formation of recombinants varies according to the colicin. Thus for colicins B, K, and E_2, no recombinants are formed in F^+ $col^+ \times F^-$ col^- crosses, whereas the number of recombinants formed in similar crosses where the F^+ parent is colicinogenic for colicins E_1 or I is identical to the number of recombinants obtained in control crosses (Frédéricq, 1958).

In order to obtain additional information on the genetic determination of colicinogeny E_1, a variety of Hfr and F^- strains were rendered colicinogenic. Each strain was previously made resistant to the colicin in order to avoid any distortion of the results of the subsequent crosses due to a lethal effect of external colicin. In crosses between Hfr H col^+ and F^- col^- bacteria, transmission of colicinogeny takes place at very high frequency and independently of the genetic characters of the Hfr H bacteria which are transmitted to recombinants at high frequency. Furthermore, when the donor bacteria, whether F^+ or Hfr H, are colicinogenic, the transfer of the colicinogenic factor occurs very early. Interrupted mating experiments indicate that this factor begins entering the zygotes less than 5 minutes after mixing of the parental strains. If individual zygotes are isolated by micromanipulation, it is found that whenever a zygote gives rise to a colicinogenic progeny, all the progeny of such a zygote is colicinogenic. It may be thus concluded that in such zygotes the colicinogenic factors reproduce in an autonomous fashion and at a faster rate than the genome of the recipient bacterium. Very different results are obtained in the reciprocal crosses between Hfr H col^- bacteria and F^- col^+ recipients. In such crosses the col^- character of the donor is never transmitted to the recipient or to its progeny. It is found however that this lack of transmission of the col^- character of the donor is the consequence of a selection effect: many of the zygotes are killed as a result of conjugation. This *lethal zygosis* is very pronounced, since about 80 per cent of the zygotes are killed (see Fig. 56), a fraction comparable to the fraction of zygotes that inherit the col^+ character in the reciprocal Hfr H $col^+ \times F^-$ col^- cross (Alfoldi, Jacob, and Wollman, 1957; Alfoldi, Jacob, Wollman, and Mazé, 1958).

The colicinogenic factor therefore behaves very differently from the other genetic determinants of bacteria. From the results of crosses between colicinogenic donors and noncolicinogenic recipients, it can be concluded that the colicinogenic factor, both in the F^+ donors and in the zygotes after transfer, exists in an autonomous "cytoplasmic" state. The results of the reciprocal crosses between noncolicinogenic donors and colicinogenic recipients are, however, not readily interpreted by assuming a cytoplasmic determination for the noncolicinogenic character. A chromosomal location of this character as well as a chromosomal state of the colicinogenic factor are indicated by the results of a series of crosses involving a variety of Hfr types (Alfoldi *et al.*, 1958). When different Hfr strains, all colicinogenic for colicin E_1, are crossed with the same noncolicinogenic recipient, the frequencies at which the col^+ character is transmitted vary from one cross to the other (Fig. 56 A). Similarly the time at which the col^+ character begins to enter the zygotes depends on the type of Hfr involved in the cross. Conversely, in the reciprocal crosses between various noncolicinogenic recipients, the extent of lethal zygosis varies from cross to cross (Fig. 56 B). For each Hfr type, there is a strict correlation between the frequency of transmission of the col^+ character in an Hfr $col^+ \times F^-$ col^- cross and the extent of lethal zygosis in the reciprocal Hfr $col^- \times F^-$ col^+ cross. These results indicate that the col^- character is determined by a chromosomal locus; in the case of colicin E_1, this locus is situated between the MB_1 region and the TL region. The observations can be interpreted by assuming that in the Hfr strains studied the colicinogenic factor is located at this chromosomal site, but undergoes transition from the integrated to the autonomous state as a consequence of conjugation.

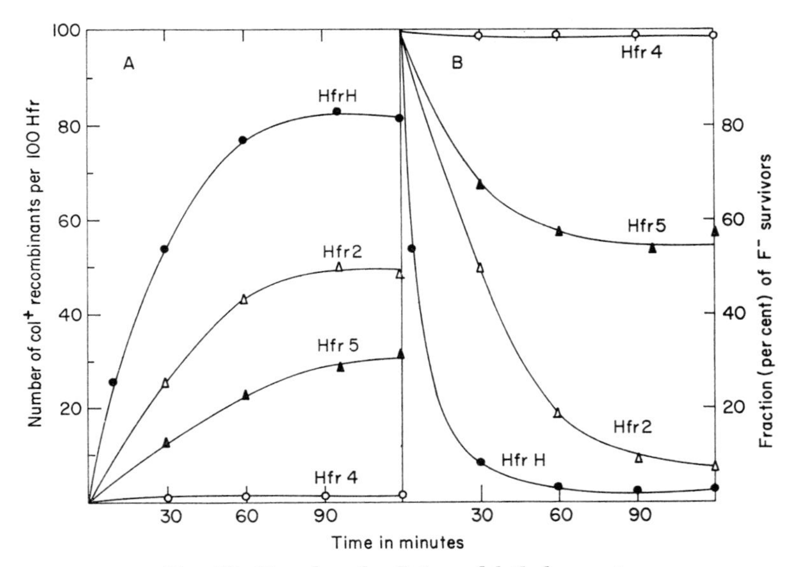

FIG. 56. Transfer of colicin and lethal zygosis.

A. Col+S^s bacteria of Hfr types H, 2, 4 or 5 are mixed at time 0 with an excess of F− col−S^r bacteria and the mixture is aerated at 37°C. At various time intervals, samples are diluted, plated on streptomycin-agar and assayed for the col+ character. The proportion of input Hfr bacteria which have transmitted the col+ character is plotted versus the time of sampling.

B. Col+S^rF− bacteria are mixed at time 0 with an excess of col−S^s bacteria of Hfr types H, 2, 4 or 5 and the mixture is aerated at 37°C. At various time intervals, samples are diluted and plated on streptomycin-agar. The proportion of input F− bacteria which are still able to form colonies is plotted versus the time of sampling.

Detailed genetic analysis has so far been restricted to colicin E_1. The results of such analysis lead to the conclusion that the corresponding colicinogenic factor has the properties of an episome. It is indeed a dispensable structure that is absent from noncolicinogenic bacteria and can be acquired by them only from bacteria which already harbor it, either by conjugation or, as shown more recently, by transduction (Frédéricq, 1959; Ozeki and Stocker, 1958). When present, it can be either autonomous, as in F^+ bacteria and after transfer to F^- recipients, or integrated, as in Hfr donors. We do not yet know whether the conclusions which have thus emerged from the study of colicin E_1 would also apply to other colicinogenic factors, such as E_2, I, or K, the behavior of which appears to be very different from that of E_1 in $F^+ \times F^-$ crosses. Indirect evidence obtained in the case of a colicin of type I already indicates, however, that it may exist in two alternative states, autonomous and integrated (see Stocker, 1960).

Since the discovery of colicins, bacteriocins have often been compared with bacteriophages (see Frédéricq, 1953b). It should be stressed that there is a fundamental difference between these two classes of antibacterial agents: whereas the bacteriophages reproduce in the bacteria that they infect, the bacteriocins, being proteins, kill sensitive bacteria without being reproduced. They can be best compared, therefore, with the protein coat of virulent bacteriophages, and more especially with the tail-end proteins of such phages, which, like the bacteriocins, are adsorbed by specific receptors of the bacterial cell wall and kill sensitive bacteria. It has been shown that several receptors are common for certain bacteriophages and for certain colicins: however, the bacteriophages and colicins which share a common receptor site do not exhibit any serological cross reactions.

The parallel between colicins and bacteriophages may be extended to the genetic determinants of colicinogeny on the one hand and of lysogeny on the other. Both types of genetic elements appear indeed to possess the properties of episomes. Just as lysogenic bacteria are immune against the bacteriophage they are able to produce, so colicinogenic bacteria are immune against the homologous colicin, although this immunity is less absolute than that of lysogenic bacteria (Frédéricq, 1956). In both cases, the survival of the bacteria appears to depend on a repression of the synthesis of either phage or colicin, since colicin production like phage production is lethal for the producing bacterium. In certain colicinogenic strains, colicin production can be induced by the same agents that induce phage production in certain lysogenic strains (Jacob, Siminovitch, and Wollman, 1952). In lysogenic bacteria, however, phage production and lethality are a consequence of the transition of the prophage to the autonomous state. In colicinogenic bacteria, transition of the colicinogenic factor from the integrated to the autonomous state, as it seems to occur in a cross between Hfr col^+ and F^- bacteria, does not seem to be followed by synthesis of colicin and is not lethal for the recipient bacterium. It is in the reciprocal cross between Hfr col^- and F^- col^+ bacteria that a phenomenon of lethal zygosis, analogous but inverse to zygotic induction, appears to take place. The mechanism of this phenomenon of lethal zygosis is not yet understood. It would seem that the introduction into a colicinogenic bacterium of a defined chromosomal segment results in a release of the system of regulation prevailing in the recipient, which then becomes sensitive to the action of its own colicin.

There are, accordingly, both similarities between the colicins and the tail proteins of virulent bacteriophage, and similarities between the colicinogenic factors and the genetic material of temperate bacteriophages. In the case of temperate bacteriophages, the genetic material in the vegetative state (an episome in the autonomous state) is capable of being enclosed within a coat composed of proteins that are synthesized under its own control. The colicinogenic factors, like defective phage genomes, do not possess this property. Although there is no experimental basis for such an hypothesis, one could imagine that there is an evolutionary relationship between colicinogenic factors and bacteriophages. According to such a view, colicinogenic factors might be regarded either as degraded viral genomes which have lost their morphogenetic capacities, or as an intermediary stage in the phylogenetic evolution of viruses, i.e., episomes that have not yet acquired the power of forming complexes with the products synthesized under their own control.

The three classes of genetic elements just reviewed control widely different bacterial characters, but behave similarly in bacterial crosses. It was from the comparison of the properties manifested in crosses that the concept of episomes was evolved.

B. The Properties of Bacterial Episomes

The genetic elements which have been just reviewed have common properties which may be considered as being characteristic of episomes. It seems useful at this point to summarize these properties and also to stress the differences which are a necessary consequence of the diversity and heterogeneity of the elements which behave as episomes.

1. *Episomes are genetic elements which may be either present or absent.* They control, therefore, genetic properties which are dispensable.

2. *When absent from a bacterium, an episome can be acquired only from an external source.* Such acquisition may take place by infection, as in the case of temperate bacteriophages, which possess their own infective apparatus. In the case of episomes which are not viruses, their acquisition depends on the existence of an adequate mechanism of transfer from a bacterium which harbors an episome to a bacterium that is devoid of it. Such transfer, for the episomes which have been considered, may be accomplished either by conjugation or by transduction. A case

of acquisition of an episome by transformation has been recently described (Kaiser and Hogness, 1950).

3. *When present in a bacterium, episomic elements may be either in an autonomous or in an integrated state.* For the temperate bacteriophages and the sex factor of *E. coli* this alternation of states appears to be clearly established. The demonstration is not as definite for the colicinogenic factor. There is some evidence that this is the case for the colicinogenic factor E_1, but evidence is lacking for other colicins.

4. *The behavior of an episome in the autonomous state and the phenotypic expression of this state are specific attributes of the particular type of episomes concerned.* In the temperate bacteriophages, the genetic material of the phage in the autonomous state escapes the regulatory mechanisms of the host cells and undergoes unrestricted multiplication which leads to the destruction of the bacterium. Even in the case of defective prophages, transition from the integrated to the nonintegrated state, whether or not it is followed by autonomous multiplication, always appears to be lethal for the bacterium. Rather different is the behavior of the two other classes of episomes when in the autonomous state. Autonomous replication of both the sex factor and the colicinogenic factor appears to be subjected to a mechanism of regulation. Although the precise number of such elements per bacterium is not yet known, this number does not seem to be very large. A system of regulation, perhaps analogous to immunity, is therefore likely to exist, the replication of the particles being prevented when their number exceeds a certain level. A further difference from the temperate bacteriophages is that the existence of these elements in the autonomous state has no pathological effect on the host bacterium.

5. *When in the integrated state, episomic elements are located on the bacterial chromosome, but do not appear to form part of its linear structure.* There is good evidence that this is true in the case of the prophages. The evidence is only indirect for the other classes of episomes, particularly for the colicinogenic factors, where information concerning the integrated state is still very scanty. The chromosomal location is very specific in the case of most of the prophages, and possibly also in the case of the colicinogenic factor E_1. On the contrary, the sex factor may occupy any one of a large number of chromosomal locations, defined in terms of linkage relationships. In a certain sense, however, the location of the integrated sex factor may be considered unique, since it is always terminal on the chromosome of any type of Hfr. It should also be remembered that no definite chromosomal site has been found for the strain of bacteriophage able to perform generalized transduction. One

of the possible interpretations of this fact is that such prophages might occupy variable and transient positions on the chromosome. Another interpretation might be that the genetic material of the phage is perpetuated as a nonchromosomal element, like the sex factor or the colicinogenic factors in the autonomous state.

6. *Episomic elements can alternate between the integrated and the autonomous state.* Transition from one state to the other is a relatively rare event for temperate phages and for the sex factor. It can be affected by changes in the environmental conditions. Thus ultraviolet irradiation raises considerably the rate of transition of an inducible prophage from the integrated to the autonomous state, whereas the same treatment appears to increase the transition of the sex factor from the autonomous to the integrated state. The alternation of states becomes much more frequent following incorporation of a chromosomal segment of the bacterium into the episome as evidenced by the case of transducing bacteriophages λ and of the intermediate donor types.

7. *The autonomous and the integrated state appear in general to be mutually exclusive.* Transition to the prophage state brings as a corollary a repression of the autonomous replication of the homologous phage genome which is consequently lost in the course of bacterial divisions. Similarly, transition of the sex factor to the integrated state is correlated with a loss of the sex factor in the autonomous state. In the cases where a more rapid alternation takes place between the two states, the reciprocal interactions between the elements in one or in the other state have not been yet analyzed in detail.

8. *Episomic elements in the integrated state may undergo genetic recombination with the neighboring region of the bacterial chromosome.* A chromosomal segment incorporated in an episome thereafter shares the fate of the episome both in the integrated and in the autonomous states. In this fashion, typical bacterial genes may become endowed with the properties of episomic elements. The first example of genetic recombination between an episome and the bacterial chromosome was furnished by the discovery of specific, limited transduction by phage λ (see p. 190). When temperate bacteriophages and the sex factor were taken as the first examples of bacterial episomes it could have been anticipated that a situation similar to that observed in the case of phage λ would also be encountered in the case of the sex factor of bacteria. This was indeed established experimentally shortly after. If it were confirmed that colicinogenic factors may also occupy a chromosomal location, it could also be predicted that bacterial genes might become incorporated in such factors.

Chromosomal segments introduced in a bacterium whether by conjugation or by transduction, are not capable of undergoing autonomous replication. They either undergo genetic recombination with the chromosome of the recipient or are diluted out in the course of bacterial divisions (unilinear inheritance). When they become structurally connected with the bacterial chromosome, as seems to be the case for the nondisjunctional exceptions described by J. Lederberg (1949b) or for the heterogenotes obtained after transduction, they are replicated at the same pace as the bacterial chromosome. They are then subjected to the system of regulation of the genetic apparatus of the cell. Only when they are incorporated in an episome may chromosomal segments escape the normal regulatory mechanisms and multiply in an autonomous fashion, independently and faster than the chromosome.

The analysis of transduction by phage λ, and the extension of this analysis to other bacteriophages which perform nonspecific transductions (see Luria *et al.*, 1958; Starlinger, 1958) seemed to provide a general model for the mechanism of transduction. According to this model, transduction does not, as first thought, represent a passive inclusion of chromosomal fragments into phage coats, but rather a genetic recombination between the genome of the phage and the bacterial chromosome. It might be expected therefore that only chromosomal elements would be transducible, whereas nonchromosomal, autonomous elements would not. Such a conclusion may not be justified, however, in view of recent findings that the sex factor of F^+ bacteria (Arber, 1960) and a variety of colicinogenic factors, apparently also in the autonomous state (Ozeki and Stocker, 1959; Frédéricq, 1959) may also be transduced by phage.

9. *As to the nature and size of episomic elements,* the available information is still rather meager. It may be suspected that in all cases they contain nucleic acid. For the temperate bacteriophages, it is DNA, which appears to be present in similar amounts whether the genetic material of the phage is included in an infective particle or whether it is in the vegetative or in the prophage state. In these different states the genetic material of phage λ, for instance, exhibits the same sensitivity to P^{32} decay (Stent, Fuerst, and Jacob, 1957) and to ultraviolet inactivation (Arber, 1960). Similar experiments have been made in the case of the sex factor of bacteria. Although the exact chemical nature of this factor has not yet been established, it is known that it exhibits a sensitivity to P^{32} decay (Lavallé and Jacob, 1961) and to ultraviolet inactivation (Arber, 1960) which is similar to that of phage λ. These results would indicate that both types of episomes are probably composed of DNA and are of comparable dimensions. Little is known as yet about the colicino-

genic factors. The colicinogenic factor E_1, which appears to have been the only one examined so far in this respect, has been found to be very resistant to P^{32} decay (Lavallé and Jacob, 1961). As it seems unlikely that this hereditary factor would not be composed of nucleic acid, this finding is interpreted as meaning that colicinogenic factor E_1 is much smaller than phage λ or than the sex factor.

Another line of information which bears both on the nature and on the state of episomic elements comes from the results of treatments with acridine dyes. It is known that acridine dyes interact specifically with nucleoproteins (McIlwain, 1941). They interfere with the self-reproduction of intracellular structures containing nucleic acids such as certain organelles of protozoa (see Lwoff, 1949) or the mitochondria of yeasts (see Ephrussi, 1953). They arrest the development of bacteriophages (Foster, 1948; De Mars, Luria, Fisher, and Levinthal, 1953) and even induce mutations in these viruses (De Mars, 1953). It seems that in bacteria, and in other microorganisms as well, treatment with acridine dyes allows a distinction between nuclear and extranuclear genetic structures. Thus in the case of the sex factor of bacteria, acridines are effective in eliminating the sex factor from F^+ bacteria, while they are without action on Hfr bacteria (Hirota, 1960). Similarly, although interacting with the vegetative reproduction of bacteriophages, acridines are without effect on the prophage of lysogenic bacteria. It is seen, therefore, that acridines interfere with the autonomous reproduction of episomes but are not effective in eliminating these elements while in the integrated state. Similar effects are achieved by salts of heavy metals such as cobalt or nickel (Hirota, 1956). Elimination of a colicinogenic factor has been obtained by this procedure, and the elimination of the colicinogenic factor has been found to be independent of that of the F factor in the autonomous state (Furness and Rowley, 1957).

C. Criteria for the Recognition of New Classes of Bacterial Episomes

Our discussion has been restricted so far to those characters of bacteria that appear most likely to be controlled by episomic elements. The properties of these elements, which have just been summarized, provide the criteria which eventually permit the recognition of other characters determined by genetic structures having the properties of episomes (see Fig. 55).

1. Such characters must obviously be dispensable ones, since episomes are not necessary constituents of the cell.

2. Such characters may be lost irreversibly since episomes can themselves be lost irreversibly.

3. Finally attention must be focused on characters that may exhibit an alternation of phenotype, since episomic elements may alternate from one state to the other and since each state may be characterized by a different phenotypic expression.

Needless to say, these criteria are not sufficient by themselves to assess the episomic control of any given genetic character. In all cases, a precise genetic analysis would be necessary, since deletions, purely cytoplasmic structures, phenomena of epistasis, environmentally controlled regulation mechanisms, etc., may determine one or several of these characteristics. The only usefulness of these criteria is to select those cases which, if they were amenable to genetic analysis, might lead to the recognition of episomic elements. The genetic determination of toxin production by *Corynebacterium diphtheriae* may serve as an example *a posteriori* to illustrate the validity of the criteria mentioned. Production of toxin is not a universal property of all the strains of corynebacteria which have the general characteristics of *C. diphtheriae*. When lost, the toxinogenic character is never regained spontaneously. The expression of toxinogenesis is strongly dependent on the environmental conditions. Although genetic analysis of corynebacteria cannot be carried out yet, the episomic nature of the factor which controls toxin production could be established in this case, because this property can be acquired by lysogenic conversion, i.e., is strictly correlated with lysogenization by certain bacteriophages.

There exists a variety of bacterial characters which apparently satisfy the previous criteria. Example may be found in the ability to form a capsule in *Pneumococcus* or in *B. anthracis,* certain pigments in *Pseudomonas* or in *Serratia,* spores in numerous species of *Bacillus,* in the phenomenon of phase-variation in *Salmonella* and so on. In some of these cases, genetic information is still completely lacking; in other cases some genetic information exists, but the available data do not allow any definite conclusion as to the nature of the genetic factors involved.

A very interesting case of alternation of phenotype is that of phase variation in *Salmonella* which has been admirably analyzed by J. Lederberg and Iino (1956). Flagellated bacteria of most *Salmonella* serotypes may exist in one of two mutually exclusive antigenic states, the so-called 1 and 2 antigenic phases. These phases are relatively stable, but transition from one phase to the other occurs with a low probability per bacterial generation. Genetic analysis by transduction has shown that each phase is controlled by a specific locus, H_1 for phase one and H_2 for phase two, but that alternation of phases depends on peculiar interrelations between these two loci. The allele present at the H_2 locus may alternate between two states, one epistatic to H_1 in which the H_2 phenotype is expressed, the other hypostatic to H_1 which results in the H_1 phenotype being expressed. This alternation of states at the H_2 locus could be interpreted by a variety of mechanisms (see J. Lederberg and Iino, 1956) one of them being possibly the alternation of an episomic element from the integrated (epistatic) state to the autonomous (hypostatic state). Such an hypothesis, for which, needless to say, there does not exist any direct evidence, could not have been tested experimentally until recently. The demonstration of phenomena of conjugation in *Salmonella* (Baron, Carey, and Spilman, 1959b) has now made such an investigation possible.

Another dispensable character of bacteria which is of special interest is the ability of many species of bacilli to form spores when the cultural conditions become unfavorable for vegetative growth. The process of sporulation involves an orderly sequence of events, the end product of which, the spore, differs markedly from the original vegetative cell. Conversely, when placed under favorable conditions, the spores undergo an orderly process of germination, the result of which is a return to the normal vegetative state. Such an alternation of states expresses very probably the existence of mechanisms of regulation, which repress reactions involved in the formation of spores during vegetative growth. Mutations governing the ability to form spores are known, and asporogenous mutants are often unable to revert to the original sporogenous condition. The existence of an alternation of states as well as the irreversible loss of the ability to sporulate made it tempting to speculate that sporulation in bacilli might involve the existence of genetic elements having the properties of episomes (see Jacob, Schaeffer, and Wollman, 1960).

It is only since the discovery of transformation in *B. subtilis* (Spizizen, 1958) that the problem of sporulation in bacteria has been posed in genetic terms (Schaeffer and Ionesco, 1959; Schaeffer, Ionesco and Jacob, 1959). A large number of asporogenous mutants of *B. subtilis*, either spontaneous or induced by mutagens, have been isolated. Some of these mutants are completely asporogenous; others are "defective" in the sense that the process of sporulation can be initiated but goes to completion only in a very small proportion of the bacteria. In both classes, there exist mutants which are revertible and others which never revert to the sporogenous condition. A large fraction of the mutants of this last category can be transformed for the spore-forming ability, not only by DNA extracted from the wild type but also by DNA extracted from other asporogenous mutants (Schaeffer and Ionesco, 1960). There is little doubt therefore that sporulation is a complex process from the genetic point of view and one which involves a variety of genetic determinants which control a variety of functions. There is no possibility of deciding so far whether some of the determinants of sporulation might be of an episomic nature. It is not known whether characters controlled by episomes can be transferred by the techniques presently used in transformation experiments. As long as transformation remains the only known mechanism of genetic transfer in bacilli, the relationships between the different genetic determinants of sporulation and the existence of interactions between nuclear and cytoplasmic factors in this phenomenon will remain difficult to establish.

A genetic element which has been found recently to have the properties of an episome is that which is responsible for the transfer of multiple drug resistance among the Enterobacteriaceae (Watanabe and Fukasawa, 1960). Simultaneous resistance to a variety of drugs can be transferred from resistant to sensitive strains in mixed cultures, and such transfer is apparently a consequence of conjugation. The acquisition of multiple drug resistance is independent of the other genetic characters of the donor bacteria. The genetic element involved does not have the properties of a temperate bacteriophage but behaves in a manner rather similar to the sex factor of bacteria. Multiple drug resistance may also be transferred by transduction, but, in this case, segregation of the individual determinants of resistance is observed to take place. Integration of individual resistance markers is also found to occur after transduction. The interpretation of these results would be that the different determinants of drug resistance may be carried by an episome in a way very similar to what is observed in sexduction. It is not possible to draw conclusions from these early observations regarding the identity of the presumed episome.

The different situations which have just been mentioned represent only examples of bacterial characters in the genetic analysis of which the concept of episome might prove useful. It should be stressed that in these cases the intervention of episomes is completely conjectural. In view of the references which have already been made or which will be made in the future to the possible role of episomes in the determination of complex genetic characters, it should be repeated that the criteria considered at the beginning of this section do not constitute by any means a proof of the existence of an episomic element. It is only after elaborate genetic tests that such an hypothesis can be preferred to any of the other hypotheses which might account for the same observed facts.

II. THE EPISOMES AS HEREDITARY FACTORS

Since they can be either present or absent, chromosomal or cytoplasmic, endogenous or exogenous, pathogenic or harmless, the episomes represent a category of genetic elements which have properties in common with the normal structures of a cell and with intracellular parasites, with chromosomal components and with cytoplasmic elements. Although they were discovered in bacteria, genetic elements having similar properties may also perhaps exist in organisms other than bacteria. For instance, the genetic elements described in maize under the name of controlling elements (McClintock, 1956) also appear to be either present or absent, and, when present have been shown to be able to occupy different positions on the chromosomes, which would seem to indicate the possibility of an intermediary, extrachromosomal state. The existing knowledge about the nature of such elements is however insufficient to determine whether they can be homologized with the episomes of bacteria. They have been mentioned only to indicate that the concept of episome may prove useful for an understanding of certain cases of nucleo-cytoplasmic interactions in organisms other than bacteria.

A. Episomes, Genes, Plasmids, and Viruses

Since the beginning of genetics, the role of the cytoplasm in heredity has been the subject of many investigations and of even more discussions (see Caspari, 1948; Ephrussi, 1953). In many cases the existence of cytoplasmic self-reproducing units has been postulated. At the present time it is generally admitted that nonchromosomal structures such as plastids, centrosomes, various organelles described in protists, and perhaps also mitochondria can reproduce only from preexisting identical structures, and that these structures bear hereditary properties. Extrinsic genetic structures, such as viruses, are also able to reproduce intracellularly and, in certain cases, can be transmitted from one cell generation to the other. The general term *plasmid* has been proposed to designate all extranuclear structures which are able to reproduce in an autonomous fashion (J. Lederberg, 1952).

Episomic elements differ both from the normal genetic structures of the cell—the genes—which cannot exist in an extranuclear state of autonomous reproduction, and from the plasmids, which do not possess an integrated chromosomal state. Since they are able to assume in turn one or the other of two alternative states, episomes constitute a link between these two classes of genetic elements. Moreover, the episomes permit the passage from one category to the other, since a single step mutation transforms an episome into a plasmid, while a recombinational event may confer the properties of episomes on chromosomal determinants. Between the exogenous infectious structures such as viruses and the chromosomal determinants of a cell, there exists therefore a continuous gradation in behavior and properties, and interconversions from one category to the other may be observed as a result of simple genetic processes.

These considerations, which represent perhaps one of the main contributions of bacterial genetics, are illustrated by Fig. 57. They are particularly well exemplified by the behavior of temperate bacteriophages, as discussed in the preceding chapter. The ability of a temperate bac-

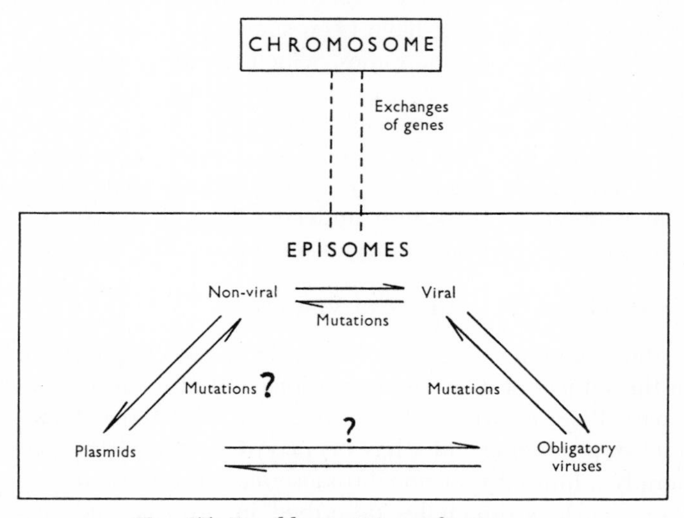

FIG. 57. Possible variations of episomes.

teriophage to become integrated is determined by a small number of genes which control both the specific attachment of the phage genome to the bacterial chromosome and the establishment of a specific system of repression which prevents the expression of those functions which are properly viral. As a result of a single mutation, the power to lysogenize may be lost and the mutant phage consequently loses its episomic character. It behaves henceforth as an obligatory virus which, when introduced into a cell, can only reproduce autonomously bringing about the death of the infected cell. Conversely, the ability of the phage genome to reproduce in an autonomous fashion is controlled by a set of genetic determinants. A mutation affecting any one of these genes suppresses a function essential for vegetative multiplication of the phage. Henceforth such a defective phage genome can only be perpetuated in the integrated prophage state. It has become hardly distinguishable from a purely chromosomal element. Finally, when in the integrated state, an episome can undergo genetic recombination with the neighboring region of the bacterial chromosome. As a consequence of this event, the bacterial genes, which have become incorporated in the episomic element, now participate in the properties of this element and can reproduce both in the integrated and in the autonomous state.

A similar gradation of properties is observed when the pathogenic character of episomes is considered. The sex factor does not exhibit any pathogenic property. Colicinogenic factors are potentially lethal for the host but are not infectious. The genetic material of a temperate phage is not only potentially lethal, it is also potentially infectious since it is able to direct the synthesis of an infectious apparatus and become enclosed into it. It is very probable that mutations or recombinational events may affect any of these characters. A defective phage genome, whether arising from mutation or from recombination with the bacterial chromosome loses its properly viral attributes. It cannot any longer give rise to infectious particles. In certain cases, however, it can still direct, when in the autonomous state, the synthesis of specific viral proteins, but it has lost the ability to enclose itself into these proteins. It is still potentially pathogenic, but it can no longer become infectious. It resembles therefore the colicinogenic factor. One may similarly speculate that genetic events, whether mutational or recombinational, might alter the pathogenic character of an episome such as the colicinogenic factor which would then be brought into the same class of innocuous episomes as the sex factor.

The conclusion is thus reached that, by appropriate genetic events, all intermediary categories may be formed between the viruses (extrinsic, infectious, plasmids) and the normal genetic determinants of a cell (intrinsic, noninfectious, and integrated). Between heredity and infection, between cellular pathology and cellular physiology, between nuclear and cytoplasmic heredity, the episomes, as studied in bacteria, provide therefore the link which, although frequently postulated on theoretical grounds (see Haddow, 1944; Altenburg, 1946; Darlington, 1949), had not hitherto received experimental support.

B. Episomes and Extranuclear Inheritance

Most examples of so-called cytoplasmic inheritance are based on differences observed in the results of reciprocal crosses. Certain hereditary characters are indeed transmitted to the progeny of crosses only when carried by the maternal parent. The cytoplasm of the zygotes being almost totally that of the female gametes it appears likely that, in most of the cases, the cause of the observed asymmetry in the results of reciprocal crosses lies in the cytoplasm.

Phenotypic characters which are controlled by episomic elements, even in the integrated state, may also exhibit peculiarities in their inheritance, when the results of reciprocal crosses are compared. The case of bacteriophage λ will again be taken as an example. In crosses between lysogenic bacteria $(\lambda)^+$ and nonlysogenic bacteria $(\lambda)^-$, the lysogenic character is transmitted to the progeny only when carried by the recipient female bacteria (see Chapters VII and VIII). When carried by the donor male bacteria, not only is lysogeny never transmitted to the products of the cross, but if one considers only those zygotes that have received prophage λ, these zygotes are killed. When the character $(\lambda)^+$ is carried by the male, it behaves therefore as a lethal: the cross is sterile. The inheritance of the lysogenic character $(\lambda)^+$ has the characters of maternal inheritance. It is known however that the genetic determinant of lysogeny is not cytoplasmic but located on the chromosome and that the asymmetry of the results observed in reciprocal crosses is a consequence of zygotic induction of prophage λ. In crosses between noncolicinogenic bacteria and bacteria colicinogenic for colicin E_1 the opposite result has been observed. The colicinogenic character $(\text{col})^+$ is inherited when borne by the male, while the reciprocal cross between $(\text{col})^-$ males and $(\text{col})^+$ females is practically sterile.

In the two examples just mentioned, conjugation between male bacteria carrying an episome in the integrated state and female bacteria which do not carry the episome, brings as a consequence the passage of the episome from the integrated to the autonomous state. It may be asked whether a similar mechanism might not operate in organisms other than bacteria, where anomalies have been observed in the results of reciprocal crosses. Once again the case of hereditary sensitivity to CO_2 in *Drosophila*, offers a striking analogy with that of lysogenic bacteria (L'Héritier, 1955, 1958). In crosses between females of stabilized lines, in which the "virus" is in the integrated state, and males free of "virus," the character "stabilized" is inherited by the whole progeny of the cross. The results are quite different in the reciprocal crosses between males of stabilized lines and "virus-free" females. In this latter case only a fraction of the progeny inherits CO_2 sensitivity, but these sensitive flies are of the "nonstabilized" type, i.e., they are individuals which carry the virus in the nonintegrated, autonomous state. Let us, for language convenience, call provirus the virus in the integrated state. The above results could then be interpreted as meaning that transfer of the provirus from the male to the zygote would result in a transition from the integrated to the autonomous state. Such a phenomenon would be analogous in every respect to zygotic induction of a prophage. The only difference would be that while zygotic induction in phage is lethal for the zygotes, transition of virus σ to the autonomous state is not pathogenic for the flies as long as they are not exposed to CO_2. Such an analogy between the case of CO_2 sensitivity in *Drosophila* and that of lysogenic bacteria is all the more remarkable in that the former case has long been a classical example of maternal inheritance cytoplasmically determined.

It is conceivable that phenomena similar to zygotic induction of a prophage might be responsible for other cases of asymmetrical results in reciprocal crosses. If the presence of an episomic element (a virus for instance) in the integrated state is represented as E_i^+ and the episome free organism as E^- one may conceive that, in a cross ♀ $E^- \times$ ♂ E_i^+ fecundation might result in the transition of the episome from the integrated state E_i^+ to the autonomous state E_a^+. The manifestations of such a "zygotic induction" would of course depend on the phenotypic expression particular to each of the states E_i^+, E_a^+, and E^-. If, for instance, the E_i^+ state were the only one to have a distinct phenotypic expression, in a cross ♀ $E^- \times$ ♂ E_i^+ the character E_i^+ of the male would never (excepting the rare cases of integration) be transmitted to the progeny. The E_i^+ character would therefore be maternally inherited. If the autonomous state E_a^+ had its own phenotypic expression, zygotic induction, in the same cross, would manifest itself by the appearance of new characters which would depend both on the nature of the episomic element and on other factors. Such new characters might therefore be very diverse, ranging from sterility of the cross as in the case of an inducible prophage, to various pathological symptoms or to simple changes in phenotype.

It is not yet possible to assess whether a model of this type might eventually apply to known cases of maternal inheritance or of cytoplasmic influence. The close, although formal, parallelism which may be drawn between the case of CO_2 sensitivity in *Drosophila* and that of lysogenic bacteria seems however to indicate that the findings made with microorganisms might prove useful in the analysis of situations encountered in other material. Cases which exhibit some analogy with that of CO_2 sensitivity have been recently uncovered in *Drosophila.* One of them is the so-called "sex ratio" character which has been found in a number of species of *Drosophila.* Females of such lines lay only female progeny, independently of the origin of the males. The zygotes which would give rise to males are lethal. In certain lines the agent of the sex ratio character is sensitive to temperature, as is the agent σ of CO_2 sensitivity (Magni, 1954). In other lines, it has been possible to introduce the agent of the sex ratio character by inoculation of normal females with the ooplasm of lethal XY zygotes (Malogolowkin and Poulson, 1957). The causative agent of the sex ratio character, like that of CO_2 sensitivity, is therefore transmissible and has been assimilated to a "virus."* In neither case, however, is there any direct evidence of a possible chromosomal location of the causative agent. Another example taken from *Drosophila* is that of the melanotic pseudotumors which are determined by chromosomal determinants but in which cytoplasmic influences have been demonstrated (Barigozzi, 1958). Recent findings would indicate that the genetic element involved might well have some of the properties of episomic elements. It should be also pointed out that many of the known examples of cytoplasmic inheritance, the causative agents of which are still of an unknown nature, resemble viral diseases in their manifestations. It suffices to mention here the classical examples of pollen sterility, the multiple anomalies observed in crosses of *Epilobium* or in mosquitoes (see reviews by Caspari, 1948; Michaelis, 1954; Kitzmiller, 1953; L'Héritier, 1955). Although the presence of a virus, when investigated, has not been demonstrated, it is well known that such a demonstration is often difficult particularly for plant viruses. Defective prophages and other bacterial episomes, moreover, which do not go through an infectious phase, may nevertheless undergo transitions from the integrated to the autonomous phase as a consequence of conjugation. In cells other than bacteria, such genetic elements in their autonomous state would also undoubtedly be transmissible by inoculation. The old distinction between infectious and transmissible factors appears to have a useful descriptive value. In fact, as shown from the study of episomes, it may become extremely difficult, in any particular case, to decide whether an intracellular element must be considered as a normal constituent of the cell or must be likened to a virus.

C. Episomes and Cellular Regulation

Episomes are genetic elements which can be added to the genome of a cell and thus bring to this cell new potentialities. The acquisition of an episome thus results in an heritable alteration of the properties of a cell line when compared with the properties of a cell line lacking the episome. It corresponds therefore to a cellular differentiation. Moreover, episomes may exist in a cell in alternative states, nuclear or cytoplasmic, and such

* Recent microscopic observations have shown that this agent is not a virus but a spirochete! (Poulson and Sakaguchi, 1961.)

alternation of states may also result in an heritable difference between cell lines carrying the episomes in one or the other state. It is thus seen that if a cellular property may be affected by an episomic element, the corresponding cell may exhibit three different phenotypes depending on whether the cell is free from the episome (E^-), or carries it in the integrated state (E_i^+) or in the autonomous state (E_a^+). The properties of episomes could thus provide a model of cellular differentiation and nucleo-cytoplasmic interactions controlled by particulate elements.

The example of lysogenic bacteria may once more serve as an example. As discussed in Chapter XV the introduction into a bacterium of the genetic material of a temperate bacteriophage brings into this cell new genetic potentialities. Lysogenic conversions are particularly clear cases of cellular differentiation, and it has been seen that the functions expressed by the phage genome differ according to whether this genome is in the integrated or in the autonomous state. Oxidizing agents favor the transition from the integrated to the autonomous state whereas the inhibition of protein synthesis after infection favors the transition to the integrated state. Therefore changes in the metabolism or in the environmental conditions of the cell may induce one or the other of the two alternative states of an episome. The alternation of states of an episome affects also the internal regulatory mechanisms of the cell. Whereas the replication of the episome in the integrated state is subjected to the regulatory mechanism of the cell genome, the episome in the autonomous state sets its own system of regulation. This extends to other genetic structures, even to normal genetic determinants of the cell when incorporated into an episome as exemplified by the case of transducing phages λdg, in which the determinants of galactose fermentation replicate at the same pace as the phage determinants both in the integrated and in the autonomous state. Recent findings have shown that such bacterial determinants are not only affected in their so-called autocatalytic functions, but also in their heterocatalytic functions. For instance the enzyme galactokinase is, in *E. coli*, an inducible enzyme, i.e., an enzyme the synthesis of which occurs only in the presence of an external inducer. Mutant Gal^- bacteria which have been made lysogenic with a phage λdg, i.e., Gal^-/ ex λ Gal^+ heterogenotes are also inducible as far as the synthesis of galactokinase is concerned. But when in such heterogenotes transition of the λdg exogenote takes place from the integrated to the autonomous state, then the synthesis of galactokinase is no longer inducible but constitutive, i.e., it occurs in the absence of an external inducer (Buttin, Jacob, and Monod, 1960). It seems therefore that in this case the expression of the bacterial determinants incorporated into an episome, and not only their replication, is subjected to the system of regulation established by the episome.

It is tempting to extrapolate the notions gained from bacterial episomes to other cases of cellular differentiation. The induction processes which are known to occur during embryonic development can hardly be explained without assigning a major role to cytoplasmic effects and eventually to cytoplasmic factors (see Ephrussi, 1953). Until recently it was generally assumed that the nuclei of the different cells of a metazoon are qualitatively identical. The findings of Briggs and King (1955), in experiments of nuclear transplantation, suggest that cellular differentiation is accompanied by irreversible changes of the nuclei. The problem is thus raised of the mechanisms which determine such nuclear modifications in differentiating cells. It is well beyond the scope of this monograph to discuss this major problem of biology. Whatever the hypotheses which could be considered, and the episome model could be one of them, any insight into this problem still depends on a knowledge of the genetics and physiology of somatic cells, for which the recent progress accomplished in the *in vitro* culture of animal cells has opened hopeful prospects (see J. Lederberg, 1956b). Even so, the main mystery of differentiation is likely to remain for a long time the orderly and precise timing of its evolution.

Another problem which is not unrelated to cellular differentiation and to which the concept of episomes might be applied more fruitfully is that of the genesis of neoplastic transformations. The transformation of a normal cell into a neoplastic cell, far from being a constant and ordered process like cellular differentiation, is on the contrary a rare and fortuitous event that resembles a mutation in many respects. As mentioned in the previous chapter, an ever-increasing importance is given to viruses or to transmissible elements which may be likened to viruses, among the factors involved in the genesis of malignant transformation (Oberling, 1954). The two classical theories of cancer, the mutation theory and the viral theory, which seemed mutually exclusive for many decades, no longer appear to be so. In the light of the progress made in bacterial genetics, the formerly opposed notions of heredity and of infection can now be reconciled. A permanent change in hereditary properties, similar in many respects to a mutation, may, as is the case in lysogenization, correspond to the acquisition of a new genetic structure. It may likewise correspond to an alternation in state of an episome, as in the case of an $F^+ \rightarrow$ Hfr "mutation." The finding that a far from negligible number of malignant tumors are caused by viruses or may be transmitted by cell-free extracts provides a valuable item of evidence. The fact that this is not the case for a still greater number of cancers, and particularly for most human cancers, however important, is not in itself sufficient proof to conclude that such tumors must be due to other unknown mechanisms. In particular, the properties of episomic elements in bacteria illustrate to what extent the criteria of infection and even of transmissibility may be circumstantial and difficult to establish (Wollman and Jacob, 1959).

One of the main characteristics of neoplastic cells is their ability to escape the normal regulatory mechanisms of the organism to which the original cells are subjected. As added genetic elements which confer on the cells new phenotypic characters, episomes and temperate viruses may already serve as model for such behavior. *Salmonella* converted from the antigenic type X to the antigenic type XV as a consequence of infection with a temperate bacteriophage become able to escape the action of antibodies against somatic antigen of type X. Similarly, chicken cells infected with the Rous Sarcoma virus or hamster cells infected with the polyoma virus are modified in shape with respect to the original noninfected cells and are concurrently not subjected, in cell cultures, to the contact interactions characteristic of the normal cells. Moreover, as discussed above, an episomic element may superimpose an additional system of regulation on the cellular systems of control. One might even imagine that, in certain cases, the presence of an episomic element might eventually withdraw the host cell from the control system of the organism and confer upon it its own system of regulation (Jacob, 1960).

* * *

The preceding discussion did not aim at formulating any hypothesis as to the mechanism of the different biological processes which have been briefly considered. It was intended even less to suggest that elements having the properties of episomes might actually play a role in such processes. More modestly, its object was only to illustrate the concept of episome and to draw attention to the properties of these elements and to their possible role in nucleo-cytoplasmic interactions. But if the model offered by episomic elements might prove useful in certain of these studies, it is worth emphasizing the possible dangers of extrapolating from the model to the actual existence of elements having these properties in any particular system. In bacteria the episomic nature of certain genetic elements has been demonstrated because of the existence of diverse mechanisms of genetic transfer, and more particularly because of the peculiarities of the process of sexual conjugation. However tempting it might seem to extend these findings to organisms other than bacteria, and especially to multicellular organisms, it seems likely that this will not be possible until methods permitting a genetic analysis of somatic cells have been developed.

Conclusions

> "L'homme est né menteur: la vérité est simple et ingénue, et il veut du spécieux et de l'ornement; elle n'est pas à lui, elle vient du ciel toute faite, pour ainsi dire, et dans toute sa perfection; et l'homme n'aime que son propre ouvrage, la fiction et la fable."
>
> La Bruyère (*Caractères*)

Conclusions

The ultimate goal of genetics consists in establishing the nature of the genetic material as well as its mode of replication and of functioning. The objects used in classical genetics provided the means of analyzing mainly the behavior of complex and often nonessential characters. In contrast, bacterial genetics essentially allows an analysis at the cellular level. Accordingly genetic investigation of bacteria, by means of the conjugation process described in this monograph or of the other processes of meromixis, is likely to increase our knowledge concerning the basic cellular mechanisms. To conclude this monograph, we will summarize the main findings and concepts drawn from bacterial conjugation and incorporate them into a more general picture of the bacterial cell.

Our conceptions of the role and the activity of the genetic material in the organism and in the cell have been modified progressively in the last two decades by the combined work of geneticists and of biochemists as well as by the impact of new ideas principally derived from considerations relating molecular structure to information theory. For this latter change in approach to biological problems, physicists and physical chemists are mainly responsible. In the words of Schrödinger (1944), the genetic material is considered as "an aperiodic structure . . . containing in some kind of a code-script the entire pattern of the individual's future development and of its functioning." In recent years the most spectacular advances in genetics and biochemistry have been those which cast some light on the nature of the hereditary message. The analysis of fine genetic structure provides a picture of genetic material as a continuous and linear sequence of interchangeable letters. The demonstration that the hereditary message is contained in nucleic acids and the almost infinite coding possibilities contained in the structure of DNA proposed by Watson and Crick, satisfy the requirements for a suitable code-script and provide some clues as to what the letters of the code may be. The most likely function of DNA is ultimately to specify the molecular organization of proteins, a process which implies a transcription from the polynucleotidic code into the polypeptidic code.

In the bacterial cell, the hereditary message appears to be written in a single, linear structure, the bacterial chromosome, which determines the basic macromolecular pattern of the bacterium. The intercellular transfer of fragments of the hereditary message is brought about by a variety of processes of meromixis. The fragments thus introduced into a bacterium may eventually be substituted by recombination for homologous fragments of the original message. Depending on the process of meromixis, the size of the transferred fragment may vary from a few words to the entire message.

An important part of the hereditary message of the bacterial cell appears to determine the structure of individual proteins. Although not yet completed, the available data support the idea that the word (gene) is a characteristic sequence of letters (nucleotides) which functions as a single unit for the production of a particular protein, for instance a particular enzyme. Mutational alterations of the sequence of letters in the hereditary message result in small changes in the protein, which, for instance, may become enzymatically inactive although it still retains the antigenic properties of the original protein. There is no evidence that words overlap in the message but nothing is known as yet about the intervals betweeen words. In contrast to what is observed in higher organisms, there is a tendency for the genes which specify functionally related proteins to remain structurally associated in the chromosome. This structural association might well reflect a selective advantage for those bacteria in which a common step regulates simultaneously the transcription of such linked genes into proteins.

The transcription of the structural message appears to involve a continuous reading and a continuous flow of information from the genetic material to a nonspecialized protein-synthesizing machinery. The transfer of information is mediated by unstable *messenger* molecules (probably RNA) which are synthesized continuously as mediators of the genetic message. They do not accumulate in the cytoplasm, but bring structural information to the synthetic machinery, being rapidly destroyed in the process of protein synthesis. Whether or not the genetic code is universal and whether different translating machines do operate in bacteria containing different base ratios in their DNA remains to be determined. The fact that transcription of the hereditary message involves unstable messengers as information carriers has an important consequence. It means that the only place in the cell where the genetic message is written in a persistent form is in the bacterial chromosome and that there are no other *stable* cellular constituents which keep a durable copy of the hereditary message. The only errors of copy which have a lasting effect are therefore those which occur in the hereditary material itself.

Another part of the hereditary message has the task, not of determining the structure of proteins but rather of determining the rate at which the individual parts of the message specifying protein structures are read and expressed. Regulation in bacteria implies that the mechanisms which ensure transfer of structural specificity from genes to proteins may be influenced by specific metabolites. The regulatory part of the genetic message determines a system of transmitters and receivers of cytoplasmic signals under the form of repressor molecules which have the double capacity of recognizing a particular metabolite and a particular operator. By combining with the operator, the repressor blocks the expression of the fragment of the genetic message which specifies the structure of the proteins concerned with the production or utilization of the metabolite. Most probably what is blocked by the repressor is not the synthesis of protein by the machinery, but the production of structural messengers by the genetic material. In the bacterial cell, the expression of a whole chromosomal segment determining the structure of several proteins involved in the same biochemical sequence can be switched on or off by a single operator which may be visualized tentatively as the site in the genetic sequence where structural messengers for the whole series of enzymes begin to be copied. The transfer of structural information from gene to protein and the regulation of protein synthesis in bacteria are diagrammatically represented in Fig. 58.

This process appears to be most economical for the bacterial cell. The reading and expression of the protein-specifying part of the genetic message involves a *continuous flow of selected information* from the genetic material to the nonspecialized machinery which translates it into proteins. At any time, the cell appears to recognize what part of the structural message has to be expressed, depending on its actual state and requirements. Consequently, it selects the proper information and sends to the machinery only those messengers which are required at that particular time. Messengers mediating syntheses unnecessary at that time are not produced. Although not yet known, similar devices probably regulate other cellular systems, for example the processes which allow the cell to produce one copy of the genetic message per generation. In Schrödinger's words, the bacterial cell contains not only a series of independent molecular blue prints for the building of individual cellular constituents but also a coordinated program of protein synthesis and the means of controlling its execution.

The macromolecular pattern of the bacterial cell is determined by the hereditary message contained in the chromosome which controls the indispensable processes of metabolism, growth and division. To the nondispensable message contained in the chromosome, extra pieces of genetic information may be added in the form of episomic elements. Episomes provide the cell with supplementary instructions, and therefore determine nonessential reactions, which may either be simply added to the basic operations of the cell or result in an alteration of some normal processes. Whether or not the episomic messages are read and expressed depends on the state of the episomes, a state which may itself be in-

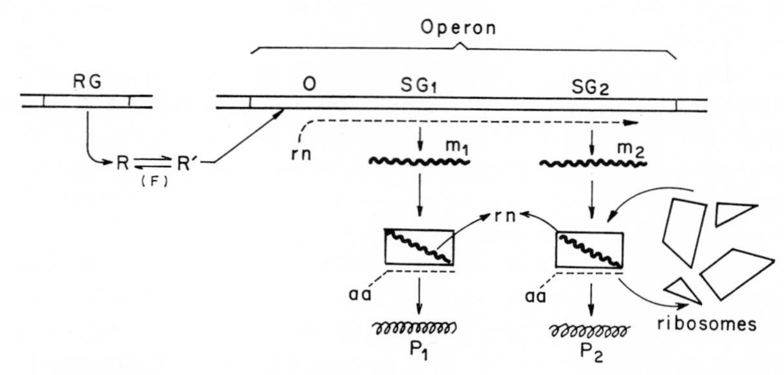

FIG. 58. Diagrammatic representation of the activity of structural genes and of the regulation of protein synthesis in bacteria.

The two structural genes (SG_1 and SG_2) are under the control of a single operator (o) and form therefore an operon. The transfer of information from structural genes (SG_1 and SG_2) to proteins involves the production of two messengers (m_1 and m_2, probably polyribonucleotides, rn). The messengers associate with ribosomal particles, and they direct the assembly of amino acids (aa) into polypeptide chains. The messengers are destroyed in the process. Once completed, the polypeptides fold, forming proteins P_1 and P_2 which are detached from ribosomal particles. These particles are set free for a new cycle, involving the same or any other specific messenger. The synthesis of the two messengers m_1 and m_2 is a polarized process along the operon and is initiated in the operator region. A regulator gene (RG) produces a specific repressor (R) which interacts with specific small molecules (F = inducing or repressing metabolite, depending on the system) thus producing an altered repressor (R'). The active form of the repressor (R in inducible systems, R' in repressible systems) interacts specifically with the operator (o) and thus blocks the production of the two messengers m_1 and m_2. (After Jacob and Monod, 1961.)

fluenced by environmental and cytoplasmic factors. This variability in the state and in the expression of episomic elements is the source of a clonally inherited differentiation among bacterial populations carrying identical hereditary messages in their chromosome.

Likewise, the infection of a bacterium by a bacteriophage results in the introduction of extra pieces of genetic message into the bacterial cell. The genetic material of a virus may be considered as a genetic element of a particular type, transmitted from cell to cell with the help of an infectious apparatus. The presence of the viral genome in the bacterial cell brings about the formation of new structural messengers, which can be substituted for, or added to, the cellular ones and carry to the cellular machinery instructions for the synthesis of new macromolecular patterns required for the production of viral particles. In contrast to what occurs in the synthesis of cellular components, no regulating restraint appears to be brought to the synthesis of the viral components. Such unrestricted syntheses result in the destruction of the cellular harmony. In some cases, however, the viral genome can establish a specific system of inhibition which prevents the formation of the viral structural messengers and therefore the synthesis of the viral components. As long as the viral message is not read and transcribed, the genetic material of the virus may persist inside the bacterial cell as an integrated element.

* * *

Since the formulation of the Cell Theory, a cell has appeared as an integrated system, much more elaborate than the simple sum of its individual constituents. The methods of experimental biology as well as those of biochemistry and of genetics, however, are essentially analytical. They tend mostly to a dissection of the cellular systems and to the recognition of its components. An amazing amount of information has thus been gathered on the structure of the macromolecules, on the biosynthetic pathways and on the energy metabolism of the cell. In every cell one (or two) copies of a particular nucleotide sequence determine a function qualitatively different from that determined by other nucleotide sequences and this is so for thousands of different functions. At the present time, it does not seem too chimerical to expect, for a reasonable future, a rather complete understanding of the mechanism by which the thousands of specific macromolecules are manufactured. At the same time, it becomes increasingly clear that within the cell, the individual components of the cellular system work in more subtle conditions than they do when isolated *in vitro*. We begin to detect the mechanisms which allow the cell not only to manufacture a specific component when necessary but also not to produce it when unnecessary. To the old bag of genes and enzymes is progressively substituted a new picture of the bacterial cell as a society of macromolecules just as a multicellular organism is a society of cells. A society implies that every component of the intracellular community is subject to the restraints implicit in an integrated system. It requires therefore a complex system of communications and signals which appears to be determined by a part of the hereditary message of the bacterial cell.

The fundamental unity of biology is nowadays universally admitted. Each biological system has its own genius and requires a particular methodology and a particular way of thinking. It is clear, however, that the main natural laws constitute a common fund which applies to all branches of biological science. It is for the future to evaluate the contribution of bacteria and their genetics to this common fund. But even now it may be pointed out that many of the concepts and of the methods derived from bacteriology have proved to be fruitful in the study of other biological systems. The study of animal cells in culture, for instance, is already a branch of microbiology. If genetics of somatic cells is to be developed, it will probably be a direct consequence of progress in the genetics of microorganisms and viruses.

References

Adams, M. (1950). Methods of study of bacterial viruses. *In* "Methods in Medical Research" (J. H. Comroe, Jr., ed.), Vol. 2, pp. 1-73. Year Book Publishers, Chicago.

Adams, M. (1959). "Bacteriophages." Interscience Publishers, New York.

Adelberg, E. A., and Burns, S. N. (1959). A variant sex factor in *Escherichia coli. Genetics* **44**, 497.

Adelberg, E. A., and Burns, S. N. (1960). Genetic variation in the sex factor of *Escherichia coli. J. Bacteriol.* **79**, 321-330.

Adelberg, E. A., and Myers, J. W. (1953). Modification of the penicillin technique for the selection of auxotrophic bacteria. *J. Bacteriol.* **65**, 348-353.

Alfoldi, L., Jacob, F., and Wollman, E. L. (1957). Zygose létale dans les croisements entre souches colicinogènes et non colicinogènes. *Compt. rend. acad. sci.* **244**, 2974-2976.

Alfoldi, L., Jacob, F., Wollman, E. L., and Mazé, R. (1958). Sur le déterminisme génétique de la colicinogénie. *Compt. rend. acad. sci.* **246**, 3531-3533.

Alloway, J. L. (1932). The transformation in vitro of R pneumococci into S forms of different specific types by the use of filtered pneumococcus extracts. *J. Exptl. Med.* **55**, 91-99.

Altenburg, E. (1946). The "viroid" theory in relation to plasmagenes, viruses, cancer and plastids. *Am. Naturalist* **80**, 559.

Ames, B. N., Dubin, D. T., and Rosenthal, S. M. (1958). Presence of polyamines in certain bacterial viruses. *Science* **127**, 814-815.

Ames, B. N., and Garry, B. (1959). Coordinate repression of the synthesis of four histidine biosynthetic enzymes by histidine. *Proc. Natl. Acad. Sci. U.S.* **45**, 1453-1461.

Anderson, T. F. (1949). The reactions of bacterial viruses with their host cells. *Botan. Rev.* **15**, 477.

Anderson, T. F. (1952). A method for eliminating gross artifacts in drying specimens. *In* "Congrès de microscopie électronique," pp. 567-576. Revue d'optique, Paris.

Anderson, T. F. (1958). Recombination and segregation in *Escherichia coli. Cold Spring Harbor Symposia Quant. Biol.* **23**, 47-58.

Anderson, T. F., and Mazé, R. (1957). Analyse de la descendance de zygotes formés par conjugaison chez *E. coli* K12. *Ann. inst. Pasteur* **93**, 194-198.

Anderson, T. F., Wollman, E. L., and Jacob, F. (1957). Sur les processus de conjugaison et de recombinaison chez *E. coli.* III. Aspects morphologiques en microscopie électronique. *Ann. inst. Pasteur* **93**, 450-455.

Appleyard, R. K. (1954a). Segregation of λ lysogenicity during bacterial recombination in *E. coli* K12. *Genetics* **39**, 429-439.

Appleyard, R. K. (1954b). Segregation of new lysogenic types during growth of a doubly lysogenic strain derived from *E. coli* K12. *Genetics* **39**, 440-452.

Appleyard, R. K., McGregor, J. F., and Baird, K. M. (1956). Mutation to extended host range and the occurrence of phenotypic mixing in the temperate coliphage λ. *Virology* **2**, 565-574.

Arber, W. (1958). Transduction des caractères Gal par le bactériophage λ. *Arch. sci. (Geneva)* **11**, 259-338.

Arber, W. (1960). Transduction of chromosomal genes and episomes in *E. coli. Virology* **11**, 273-288.

Arber, W., Kellenberger, J., and Weiglé, J. J. (1957). La défectuosité du phage λ transducteur. *Schweiz. Z. allgem. Pathol. u. Bakteriol.* **20**, 659-665.

Arkwright, J. A. (1930). Variation. *In* "A System of Bacteriology in Relation to Medicine" (Medical Research Council), Vol. 1, pp. 311-374. H. M. Stationery Office, London.

Austrian, R. (1952). Bacterial transformation reactions. *Bacteriol. Revs.* **16**, 31-50.

Avery, O. T., MacLeod, C. M., and McCarty, M. (1944). Studies on the chemical nature of the substance inducing transformation of pneumococcal types. Induction of transformation by a desoxyribonucleic acid fraction isolated from Pneumococcus type III. *J. Expt. Med.* **79**, 137-158.

Badian, J. (1933). Eine cytologische Untersuchung über das Chromatin und den Entwicklungszyklus der Bakterien. *Arch. Mikrobiol.* **4**, 409-418.

Bail, O. (1925). Der Kolistamm 88 von Gildemeister und Herzberg. *Med. Klin. (Munich)* **21**, 1277-1279.

Barigozzi, C. (1958). Melanotic tumors in Drosophila. *J. Cellular Comp. Physiol.* **52**, Suppl., 371-381.

Barksdale, L. (1959). Lysogenic conversions in bacteria. *Bacteriol. Revs.* **23**, 202-212.

Baron, L. S., Carey, W. F., and Spilman, W. M. (1959a). Genetic recombination between *Escherichia coli* and *Salmonella typhimurium. Proc. Natl. Acad. Sci. U.S.* **45**, 976-983.

Baron, L. S., Carey, W. F., and Spilman, W. M. (1959b). Characteristics of a high frequency of recombination (Hfr) strain of *Salmonella typhosa* compatible with *Salmonella, Shigella* and *Escherichia* species. *Proc. Natl. Acad. Sci. U.S.* **45**, 1752-1756.

Beadle, G. W. (1945). Biochemical genetics. *Chem. Revs.* **37**, 15-96.

Beadle, G. W. (1957). The role of the nucleus in heredity. *In* "The Chemical Basis of Heredity" (W. D. McElroy and B. Glass, eds.), pp. 3-22. Johns Hopkins Press, Baltimore.

Beadle, G. W. (1960). Physiological aspects of genetics. *Ann. Rev. Physiol.* **22**, 45-74.

Beadle, G. W., and Tatum, E. L. (1941). Genetic control of biochemical reactions in *Neurospora. Proc. Natl. Acad. Sci. U.S.* **27**, 499-506.

Beijerinck, M. W. (1900). Mutation bei Mikroben. *Proc. Koninkl. Akad. Wetenschap. Amsterdam* **3**, 352.

Beijerinck, M. W. (1912). Mutation bei Mikroben. *Folia Microbiol. (Delft)* **1**, 4-100.

Belling, J. (1931). Chromomeres in liliaceous plants. *Univ. Calif. (Berkeley) Publs. Botany* **16**, 153-170.

Belozersky, A. N., and Spirin, A. S. (1960). Chemistry of the nucleic acids of microorganisms. *In* "The Nucleic Acids" (E. Chargaff and J. N. Davidson, eds.), Vol. III, p. 147. Academic Press, New York.

Belser, W. L., and Bunting, M. I. (1956). Studies on a mechanism providing for genetic transfer in *Serratia marcescens*. *J. Bacteriol.* **72**, 582-592.

Benzer, S. (1955). Fine structure of a genetic region in bacteriophage. *Proc. Natl. Acad. Sci. U.S.* **41**, 344-354.

Benzer, S. (1957). The elementary units of heredity. *In* "The Chemical Basis of Heredity" (W. D. McElroy and B. Glass, eds.), pp. 70-93. Johns Hopkins Press, Baltimore.

Bernstein, H. L. (1958). Fertility factors in *Escherichia*. Biological replication of macromolecules. *Symposia Soc. Exptl. Biol.* **12**, 93-103.

Bertani, G. (1951). Studies on lysogenesis. I. The mode of phage liberation by lysogenic *E. coli*. *J. Bacteriol.* **62**, 293-300.

Bertani, G. (1958). Lysogeny. *Advances in Virus Research* **5**, 151-194.

Bisset, K. A. (1950). "The Cytology and Life History of Bacteria." Williams & Wilkins, Baltimore.

Boivin, A., Tulasne, R., Vendrely, R., and Minck, R. (1947). Le noyau des bactéries. *Arch. sci. physiol.* **1**, 307-323.

Bordet, J. (1925). Le problème de l'autolyse microbienne transmissible ou du bactériophage. *Ann. inst. Pasteur* **39**, 717-763.

Brachet, J. (1955). The biological role of the pentose nucleic acids. *In* "The Nucleic Acids" (E. Chargaff and J. N. Davidson, eds.), Vol. II, pp. 475-519. Academic Press, New York.

Braun, W. (1947). Bacterial dissociation. *Bacteriol. Revs.* **11**, 75-114.

Braun, W. (1953). "Bacterial Genetics." Saunders, Philadelphia.

Brenner, S., Jacob, F., and Meselson, M. (1961). An unstable intermediate carrying information from genes to ribosomes for protein synthesis. *Nature* **190**, 576-581.

Brenner, S., Streisinger, G., Horne, R. W., Champe, S. P., Barnett, L., Benzer, S., and Rees, M. W. (1959). Structural components of bacteriophage. *J. Mol. Biol.* **1**, 281-292.

Brierley, W. B. (1929). Variation in fungi and bacteria. *Proc. Intern. Congr. Plant Sci. Ithaca, 1926* **2**, 1629-1654.

Briggs, R. W., and King, T. J. (1955). Specificity of nuclear functions in embryonic development. *In* "Biological Specificity and Growth" (E. G. Butler, ed.), pp. 207-228. Princeton University Press, Princeton, New Jersey.

Büchner, H. (1882). *In* Naegeli, C. von, "Untersuchungen über niedere Pilze," pp. 140-177, 231-285. Munich and Leipzig.

Bulloch, W. (1938). "The History of Bacteriology." Oxford University Press, London and New York.

Burnet, E. (1925). Actions d'entraînement entre races et espèces microbiennes. *Arch. inst. Pasteur Tunis* **14**, 384-403.

Burnet, F. M. (1929). "Smooth-rough" variation in bacteria and its relation to bacteriophage. *J. Pathol. Bacteriol.* **32**, 15-42.

Burnet, F. M., and McKie, M. (1929). Observations on a permanent lysogenic strain of *B. enteritidis gaertner*. *Australian J. Exptl. Biol. Med.* **6**, 277-284.

Buttin, G., Jacob, F., and Monod, F. (1960). Synthèse constitutive de galactokinase consécutive au développement des bactériophages λ chez *Escherichia coli* K12. *Compt. rend. acad. sci.* **250**, 2471-2473.

Calef, E., and Cavalli-Sforza, L. L. (1955). Peculiarità degli ibridi fra *coli* B e K12. *Ricerca sci.* **25**, Suppl., 123-127.

Calef, E., and Licciardello, G. (1960). Recombination experiments on prophage host relationships. *Virology* **12**, 81-103.

Campbell, A. (1957). Transduction and segregation in *E. coli* K12. *Virology* **4**, 366-384.

Campbell, A. (1959). Ordering of genetic sites in bacteriophage λ by the use of galactose transducing defective phages. *Virology* **9**, 293-305.

Campbell, A., and Balbinder, E. (1959). Transduction of the galactose region of *E. coli* K12 by the phages λ and λ-434 hybrid. *Genetics* **44**, 309-319.

Cantacuzène, J., and Bonciu, O. (1926). Modifications subies par les streptocoques d'origine non scarlatineuse au contact de produits scarlatineux filtrés. *Compt. rend. acad. sci.* **182**, 1185-1187.

Case, M. E., and Giles, N. H. (1958). Recombination mechanisms at the *pan*-2 locus in *Neurospora crassa. Cold Spring Harbor Symposia Quant. Biol.* **23**, 119-135.

Caspari, E. (1948). Cytoplasmic inheritance. *Advances in Genet.* **2**, 1-66.

Catcheside, D. G. (1951). "The Genetics of Microorganisms." Pittman & Sons, London.

Cavalli-Sforza, L. L. (1950). La sessualità nei batteri. *Boll. ist. sieroterap. milan.* **29**, 281-289.

Cavalli-Sforza, L. L. (1957). Bacterial genetics. *Ann. Rev. Microbiol.* **11**, 391-418.

Cavalli-Sforza, L. L. (1959). Recombination in bacteria. *In* "Recent Progress in Microbiology," 7th Intern. Congr. Microbiol., pp. 40-50. Almquist & Wiksells, Stockholm.

Cavalli-Sforza, L. L., and Calef, E. (1955). Linearità cromosomica in *E. coli* K12. *Ricerca sci.* **25**, Suppl., 129-135.

Cavalli-Sforza, L. L., and Heslot, H. (1949). Recombination in bacteria: outcrossing *E. coli* K12. *Nature* **164**, 1057.

Cavalli-Sforza, L. L., and Jinks, J. L. (1953). Observations on the genetic and mating system of *E. coli* K12. *Proc. 9th Intern. Congr. Genetics, Bellagio,* pp. 967-969.

Cavalli-Sforza, L. L., and Jinks, J. L. (1956). Studies on the genetic system of *E. coli* K12. *J. Genet.* **54**, 87-112.

Cavalli-Sforza, L. L., and Lederberg, J. (1953). Genetics of resistance to bacterial inhibitors. Symposium on growth inhibition and chemotherapy, *Proc. 6th Intern. Congr. Microbiol., Rome,* pp. 108-142.

Cavalli-Sforza, L. L., Lederberg, J., and Lederberg, E. M. (1953). An infective factor controlling sex compatibility in *Bacterium coli. J. Gen. Microbiol.* **8**, 89-103.

Cavalli-Sforza, L. L., and Maccacaro, G. A. (1950). Chloromycetin resistance in *E. coli.* A case of quantitative inheritance in bacteria. *Nature* **166**, 991-992.

Cavalli-Sforza, L. L., and Maccacaro, G. A. (1952). Polygenic inheritance of drug-resistance in the bacterium *E. coli. Heredity* **6**, 311-331.

Chargaff, E. (1950). Chemical specificity of nucleic acids and mechanism of their enzymatic degradation. *Experientia* **6**, 201-209.

Chase, M., and Doermann, A. H. (1958). High negative interference over short segments of the genetic structure of bacteriophage T4. *Genetics* **43**, 332-353.

Clark, J. B., Haas, F., Stone, W. S., and Wyss, O. (1950). The stimulation of gene recombination in *E. coli. J. Bacteriol.* **59**, 375-379.

Clowes, R. C., and Rowley, D. (1954a). Genetic investigation of the inhibition by DL-norleucine of the K12 strain of *E. coli. J. Gen. Microbiol.* **11**, 27-33.

Clowes, R. C., and Rowley, D. (1954b). Some observations on linkage effects in genetic recombination in *E. coli* K12. *J. Gen. Microbiol.* **11**, 250-260.

Cohen, G. N., and Jacob, F. (1959). Sur la répression de la synthèse des enzymes intervenant dans la formation du tryptophane chez *E. coli. Compt. rend. acad. sci.* **248**, 3490-3492.

Cohen, G. N., and Monod, J. (1957). Bacterial permease. *Bacteriol. Revs.* **21**, 169-194.

Cohen, S. S. (1947). The synthesis of bacterial viruses in infected cells. *Cold Spring Harbor Symposia Quant. Biol.* **12**, 35-49.

Cohen, S. S. (1949). Growth requirements of bacterial viruses. *Bacteriol. Revs.* **13**, 1-24.

Cohen, S. S., and Anderson, T. F. (1946). Chemical studies on host virus interactions. I. The effect of bacteriophage adsorption on the multiplication of its host *E. coli* B. *J. Exptl. Med.* **84**, 511-523.

Cohen-Bazire, G., and Jolit, M. (1953). Isolement par sélection de mutants d'*E. coli* synthétisant spontanément l'amylomaltase et la β-galactosidase. *Ann. inst. Pasteur* **84**, 1-9.

Cohn, F. (1872). Untersuchungen über Bacterien. I. *Beitr. Biol. Pflanzen* **1**, No. 2, 126-224.

Cohn, F. (1879). Über die morphologische Einheit der Spaltpilze und über Naegeli's Auffassungstheorie. *Deut. med. Wochschr.* **5**, 73-76.

Cohn, M. (1957). Contributions of studies on the β-galactosidase of *E. coli* to our understanding of enzyme synthesis. *Bacteriol. Rev.* **21**, 140-168.

Cohn, M., and Monod, J. (1953). Specific inhibition and induction of enzyme biosynthesis. *In* "Adaptation in Microorganisms," 3rd Symposium Soc. Gen. Microbiol. (E. R. Gale and F. Davies, eds.), pp. 132-149. Cambridge University Press, London and New York.

Crick, F. H. C. (1958). On protein synthesis. *Symposia Soc. Exptl. Biol.* **12**, 138-163.

Croland, R. (1943). Action des rayons X sur la fréquence d'une mutation bactérienne. *Compt. rend. acad. sci.* **216**, 616-618.

Cuénot, L. (1936). "L'espèce." Doin & Co., Paris.

Darlington, C. D. (1939). "The Evolution of Genetic Systems." Cambridge University Press, London and New York.

Darlington, C. D. (1949). Les plasmagènes. *In* "Unités biologiques douées de continuité génétique," pp. 123-130. C.N.R.S., Paris.

Davern, C. I., and Meselson, M. (1960). The molecular conservation of ribonucleic acid during bacterial growth. *J. Mol. Biol.* **2**, 153-160.

Davis, B. D. (1950a). Studies on nutritionally deficient bacterial mutants isolated by means of penicillin. *Experientia* **6**, 41-50.

Davis, B. D. (1950b). Non-filtrability of the agents of genetic recombination in *E. coli. J. Bacteriol.* **60**, 507-508.

Davis, B. D. (1952). Intermediates in the biosynthesis of proline, ornithine, histidine, lysine and the aromatic amino acids. Symposium sur le métabolisme microbien, *Compt. rend. 2ème congr. intern. biochim., Paris* pp. 32-40.

Dawson, M. H., and Sia, R. H. P. (1931). In vitro transformation of pneumococcal types. *J. Exptl. Med.* **54**, 681-699.

Dean, A. C. R., and Hinshelwood, C. N. (1953). Observations on bacterial adaptation. *In* "Adaptation in Microorganisms," 3rd Symposium Soc. Gen. Microbiol. (E. R. Gale and F. Davies, eds.), pp. 21-39.

Delaporte, B. (1939). Recherches cytologiques sur les bactéries et les cyanophycées. *Rev. gén. botan.* **51**, 615, 689, 748.

Delbrück, M. (1946). Bacterial viruses or bacteriophages. *Biol. Revs. Cambridge Phil. Soc.* **21**, 30-40.

Delbrück, M., and Bailey, W. T., Jr. (1946). Induced mutations in bacterial viruses. *Cold Spring Harbor Symposia Quant. Biol.* **11**, 33-37.

Delbrück, M., and Stent, G. S. (1957). On the mechanism of D.N.A. replication. *In* "The Chemical Basis of Heredity" (W. D. McElroy and B. Glass, eds.), pp. 699-736. Johns Hopkins Press, Baltimore.

De Mars, R. I. (1953). Chemical mutagenesis in bacteriophage T2. *Nature* **172**, 964.

De Mars, R. I., Luria, S. E., Fisher, H., and Levinthal, C. (1953). The production of incomplete bacteriophage particles by the action of proflavine and the properties of the incomplete particles. *Ann. inst. Pasteur* **84**, 113-128.

Demerec, M. (1945). Production of staphylococcus strains resistant to various concentrations of penicillin. *Proc. Natl. Acad. Sci. U.S.* **31**, 16-24.

Demerec, M. (1948). Origin of bacterial resistance to antibiotics. *J. Bacteriol.* **56**, 63-74.

Demerec, M. (1956). A comparative study of certain gene loci in *Salmonella. Cold Spring Harbor Symposia Quant. Biol.* **21**, 113-121.

Demerec, M. (1958). Genetic structure of the *Salmonella chromosome. Proc. 10th Intern. Congr. Genetics, Montreal* **1**, 55.

Demerec, M., and Demerec, Z. E. (1956). Analysis of linkage relationships in *Salmonella* by transduction techniques. *Brookhaven Symposia in Biol.* **8**, 75-84.

Demerec, M., and Fano, U. (1945). Bacteriophage-resistant mutants in *E. coli. Genetics* **30**, 119-136.

Demerec, M., and Hartman, P. E. (1959). Complex loci in microorganisms. *Ann. Rev. Microbiol.* **13**, 377-406.

Dobell, C. C. (1912). Some recent work on mutation in microorganisms. II. Mutations in bacteria. *J. Genet.* **2**, 325-350.

Dobzhansky, T. (1941). "Genetics and the Origin of Species." Columbia University Press, New York.

Dodge, B. O. (1935). The mechanisms of sexual reproduction in *Neurospora. Mycologia* **27**, 418-438.

Doermann, A. H. (1948). Intracellular growth of bacteriophage. *Carnegie Inst. Wash. Yearbook* **47**, 176-186.

Dooren de Jong, L. E. den (1931). Studien über Bakteriophagie. I. Über *Bac. megatherium* und den darin anwesenden Bakteriophagen. *Zentr. Bakteriol. Parasitenk., Abt. I, Orig.* **120**, 1-15.

Dubos, R. J. (1945). "The Bacterial Cell." Harvard University Press, Cambridge, Massachusetts.

Duclaux, E. (1899). "Traité de microbiologie." Masson & Co., Paris.

Dulbecco, R. (1955). Interaction of viruses and animal cells. *Phys. Rev.* **35**, 301-335.

Echols, H., Garen, A., Garen, S., and Torriani, A. (1961). Genetic control of repression of alkaline phosphatase in *E. coli. J. Mol. Biol.* In press.

Ephrussi, B. (1953). "Nucleo-cytoplasmic Relations in Microorganisms. Oxford University Press (Clarendon), London and New York.

Ephrussi, B., and Beadle, G. W. (1937). Développement des couleurs des yeux chez la Drosophile. *Bull. biol. France et Belg.* **71**, 54-90.

Ephrussi-Taylor, H. (1955). Current status of bacterial transformations. *Advances in Virus Research* **3**, 275-307.

Fildes, P., Gladstone, G. P., and Knight, B. C. J. G. (1933). The nitrogen and vitamin requirements of *B. typhosus. Brit. J. Exptl. Pathol.* **14**, 189-196.

Fisher, K. W. (1957a). The role of the Krebs cycle in conjugation in *E. coli* K12. *J. Gen. Microbiol.* **16**, 120-135.

Fisher, K. W. (1957b). The nature of the endergonic processes in conjugation in *E. coli* K12. *J. Gen. Microbiol.* **16**, 136-145.

Flaks, J. G., and Cohen, S. S. (1959a). Virus-induced acquisition of metabolic function. I. Enzymatic formation of 5-hydroxymethyldeoxycytidylate. *J. Biol. Chem.* **234**, 1501-1506.

Flaks, J. G., and Cohen, S. S. (1959b). Virus-induced acquisition of metabolic function. III. Formation and some properties of thymidilate synthetase of bacteriophage infected *Escherichia coli. J. Biol. Chem.* **234**, 2981-2986.

Foster, R. A. C. (1948). An analysis of the action of proflavine on bacteriophage growth. *J. Bacteriol.* **56**, 795-809.

Franklin, R. E., and Gosling, R. (1953). Molecular configuration in sodium thymonucleate. *Nature* **171**, 740-741.

Frédéricq, P. (1948). Actions antibiotiques réciproques chez les Entérobactériacées. *Rev. belge pathol. et med. exptl.* Suppl. 4.

Frédéricq, P. (1953a). Transfert génétique des propriétés lysogènes chez *E. coli. Compt. rend. soc. biol.* **147**, 2046-2048.

Frédéricq, P. (1953b). Colicines et bactériophages. *Ann. inst. Pasteur* **84**, 294-312.

Frédéricq, P. (1954a). Localisation du prophage sur le chromosome. Son intervention dans le taux de ségrégation apparent des recombinants d'*E. coli* K12. *Compt. rend. soc. biol.* **148**, 1501-1504.

Frédéricq, P. (1954b). Transduction génétique des propriétés colicinogènes chez *E. coli* et *Shigella sonnei. Compt. rend. soc. biol.* **148**, 399-402.

Frédéricq, P. (1955a). Recherches génétiques sur la localisation du prophage λ sur le chromosome d'*E. coli* et sur son intervention dans la ségrégation de divers marqueurs. *Compt. rend. soc. biol.* **149**, 840-843.

Frédéricq, P. (1955b). Colicines et bactériophages dans la génétique bactérienne. *Ann. soc. roy. sci. med. et nat. Bruxelles* **8**, 15-27.

Frédéricq, P. (1956). Résistance et immunité aux colicines. *Compt. rend. soc. biol.* **150**, 1514-1517.

Frédéricq, P. (1957). Colicins. *Ann. Rev. Microbiol.* **11**, 7-22.

Frédéricq, P. (1958). Transfert génétique des facteurs colicinogènes par croisement des souches d'*E. coli. Abstr. Communs., 7th Intern. Congr. Microbiol., Stockholm* p. 56.

Frédéricq, P. (1959). *In* "Recent Progress in Microbiology," *7th Intern. Congr. Microbiol.* pp. 74-75. Almquist & Wiksells, Stockholm.

Frédéricq, P., and Betz-Bareau, M. (1952). Recombinants génétiques de souches marquées par résistance aux colicines et aux bactériophages. *Ann. inst. Pasteur* **83**, 283-295.

Freeman, V. J. (1951). Studies on the virulence of bacteriophage-infected strains of *Corynebacterium diphteriae. J. Bacteriol.* **61**, 675-688.

Freese, E. (1958). The arrangement of DNA in the chromosome. *Cold Spring Harbor Symposia Quant. Biol.* **23**, 13-18.

Fried, P. J., and Lederberg, J. (1952). Linkage in *E. coli* K12. *Genetics* **37**, 582.

Fuerst, C. R., Jacob, F., and Wollman, E. L. (1956). Détermination de liaisons génétiques chez *E. coli* K12, à l'aide du radiophosphore. *Compt. rend. acad. sci.* **243**, 2162-2164.

Fuerst, C. R., Jacob, F., and Wollman, E. L. (1961). Sur les processus de conjugaison et de recombinaison génétique chez *E. coli.* VI. Etude du transfert et de la recombinaison à l'aide du radiophosphore. In preparation.

Fuerst, C. R., and Stent, G. S. (1956). Inactivation of bacteria by decay of incorporated radioactive phosphorus. *J. Gen. Physiol.* **40**, 73-90.

Furness, G., and Rowley, D. (1957). The presence of the transmissible agent F in non-recombining strains of *E. coli. J. Gen. Microbiol.* **17**, 550-561.

Garen, A., and Skaar, P. D. (1958). Transfer of phosphorus-containing material associated with mating in *Escherichia coli. Biochim. et Biophys. Acta* **27**, 457-463.

Garen, A., and Zinder, N. D. (1955). Radiological evidence for partial genetic homology between bacteriophage and host bacteria. *Virology* **1**, 347-376.

Giles, N. H. (1958). Mutations at specific loci in *Neurospora crassa. Proc. 10th Intern. Congr. Genetics, Montreal* **1**, 261-279.

Goldschmidt, R. B. (1955). "Theoretical Genetics." University of California Press, Berkeley.

Gorini, L., and Maas, W. (1958). Feed-back control of the formation of biosynthetic enzymes. *In* "The Chemical Basis of Development" (W. D. McElroy and B. Glass, eds.), pp. 469-478. Johns Hopkins Press, Baltimore.

Gowen, J. W., and Lincoln, R. E. (1942). A test for sexual fusion in bacteria. *J. Bacteriol.* **44**, 551-554.

Gratia, A. (1932). Antagonisme microbien et "bactériophage." *Ann. inst. Pasteur* **48**, 413.

Gray, C. H., and Tatum, E. L. (1944). X-ray induced growth factor requirements in bacteria. *Proc. Natl. Acad. Sci. U.S.* **30**, 404-410.

Griffith, F. (1928). The significance of pneumococcal types. *J. Hyg.* **27**, 113-159.

Gros, F., Gilbert, W., Hiatt, H., Kurland, C. G., Risebrough, R. W., and Watson, J. D. (1961). Unstable ribonucleic acid revealed by pulse labelling of *Escherichia coli. Nature* **190**, 581-585.

Guyénot, E. (1930). "L'évolution." Doin & Co., Paris.

Haan, P. G. de (1954a). Genetic recombination in *E. coli* B. I. The transfer of the F agent to *E. coli* B. *Genetica* **27**, 293-300.

Haan, P. G. de (1954b). Genetic recombination in *E. coli* B. II. The cross resistance of *E. coli* B to the phages T3, T4 and T7. *Genetica* **27**, 300-308.

Haan, P. G. de (1955). Genetic recombination in *E. coli* B. III. The influence of experimental conditions on the transfer of unselected markers. *Genetica* **27**, 364-376.

Haas, F., Wyss, O., and Stone, W. S. (1948). The effect of irradiation on recombination in *E. coli. Proc. Natl. Acad. Sci. U.S.* **34**, 229-232.

Haddow, A. M. (1944). Transformation of cells and viruses. *Nature* **154**, 194.

Hadley, P. (1927). Microbic dissociation. *J. Infectious Diseases* **40**, 1-312.

Haldane, J. B. S. (1955). Alternatives to sex. *New Biol.* **19**, 7-26.

Hartman, P. E. (1957). Transduction: a comparative review. *In* "The Chemical Basis of Heredity" (W. D. McElroy and B. Glass, eds.), pp. 408-462. Johns Hopkins Press, Baltimore.

Hartman, P. E., and Goodgal, S. H. (1959). Bacterial genetics (with particular reference to genetic transfer). *Ann. Rev. Microbiol.* **13**, 465-504.

Hartman, P. E., Loper, J. C., and Serman, D. (1960). Fine structure mapping by complete transduction between histidine-requiring *Salmonella* mutants. *J. Gen. Microbiol.* **22**, 323-353.

Hartmann, M. (1929). Verteilung, Bestimmung und Vererbung des Geschlechts bei den Protisten und Thallophyten. *In* "Handbuch der Vererbungswissenschaft," Vol. II. Borntraeger, Berlin.

Hayes, W. (1952a). Recombination in *Bact. coli* K12: unidirectional transfer of genetic material. *Nature* **169**, 118-119.

Hayes, W. (1952b). Genetic recombination in *Bact. coli* K12: analysis of the stimulating effect of ultraviolet light. *Nature* **169**, 1017-1018.

Hayes, W. (1953a). Observations on a transmissible agent determining sexual differentiation in *Bact. coli. J. Gen. Microbiol.* **8**, 72-88.

Hayes, W. (1953b). The mechanism of genetic recombination in *E. coli. Cold Spring Harbor Symposia Quant. Biol.* **18**, 75-93.

Hayes, W. (1955). A new approach to the study of kinetics of recombination in *E. coli* K12. Proceedings of the Society for General Microbiology, *J. Gen. Microbiol.* **13**, ii.

Hayes, W. (1957). The kinetics of the mating process in *E. coli. J. Gen. Microbiol.* **16**, 97-119.

Henrici, A. T. (1928). "Morphologic Variation and the Rate of Growth of Bacteria." Baillière, Tindall & Cox, London.

Hershey, A. D. (1946). Spontaneous mutations in bacterial viruses. *Cold Spring Harbor Symposia Quant. Biol.* **11**, 67-76.

Hershey, A. D. (1956). The organization of genetic material in bacteriophage T2. *Brookhaven Symposia in Biol.* **8**, 6-16.

Hershey, A. D. (1957a). Bacteriophages as genetic and biochemical systems. *Advances in Virus Research* **4**, 25-61.

Hershey, A. D. (1957b). Bacteriophage T2: parasite or organelle? *Harvey Lectures, 1955-1956* **51**, 229-239.

Hershey, A. D., and Chase, M. (1952). Independent functions of viral protein and nucleic acid in growth of bacteriophage. *J. Gen. Physiol.* **36**, 39-56.

Hershey, A. D., Kamen, M. D., Kennedy, J. W., and Gest, H. (1951). Mortality of bacteriophage containing assimilated radioactive phosphorus. *J. Gen. Physiol.* **34**, 305-319.

Hershey, A. D., and Rotman, R. (1948). Linkage among genes controlling inhibition of lysis in a bacterial virus. *Proc. Natl. Acad. Sci. U.S.* **34**, 89-96.

Hinshelwood, C. N. (1946). "The Chemical Kinetics of the Bacterial Cell." Oxford University Press (Clarendon), London and New York.

Hirota, Y. (1956). Artificial elimination of the F factor in *Bact. coli* K12. *Nature* **178**, 92.

Hirota, Y. (1959). Mutants of the sex factor in *E. coli* K12. *Genetics* **44**, 515.

Hirota, Y. (1960). The effect of acridine dyes on mating type factors in *E. coli. Proc. Natl. Acad. Sci. U.S.* **46**, 57-64.

Hirota, Y., and Iijima, T. (1957). Acriflavine as an effective agent for eliminating F factor in *E. coli* K12. *Nature* **180**, 655-656.

Holloway, B. W. (1955). Genetic recombination in *Pseudomonas aeruginosa. J. Gen. Microbiol.* **13**, 572-581.

Holloway, B. W. (1956). Self-fertility in *Pseudomonas aeruginosa. J. Gen. Microbiol.* **15**, 221-224.

Holloway, B. W., and Fargie, B. (1960). Fertility factors and genetic linkage in *Pseudomonas aeruginosa. J. Bacteriol.* **80**, 362-368.

Horowitz, N. H., and Fling, M. (1956). The role of the genes in the synthesis of enzymes. *In* "Enzymes: Units of Biological Structure and Function" (O. H. Gaebler, ed.), pp. 139-145. Academic Press, New York.

Horowitz, N. H., Fling, M., MacLeod, H. L., and Sueoka, N. (1960). Genetic determination and enzymatic induction of tyrosinase in *Neurospora. J. Mol. Biol.* **2**, 96-104.

Hotchkiss, R. D. (1955). Bacterial transformation. *J. Cellular Comp. Physiol.* **45**, Suppl. 2, 1-22.

Hotchkiss, R. D. (1956). The genetic organization of the deoxyribonucleate units functioning in bacterial transformations. *In* "Enzymes: Units of Biological Structure and Function" (O. H. Gaebler, ed.), pp. 119-130. Academic Press, New York.

Hotchkiss, R. D., and Marmur, J. (1954). Double marker transformations as evidence of linked factors in desoxyribonucleate transforming agents. *Proc. Natl. Acad. Sci. U.S.* **40**, 55-60.

Hutchinson, W. G., and Stempen, H. (1954). Sex in bacteria: Evidence from morphology. *In* "Sex in Microorganisms," pp. 29-41. *Am. Assoc. for the Advancement of Science,* Washington, D.C.

Huxley, J. S. (1942). "Evolution: the Modern Synthesis." Harper, New York.

Ingram, V. M. (1957). Gene mutations in human haemoglobin: the chemical difference between normal and sickle-cell haemoglobin. *Nature* **180**, 326-328.

Ionesco, H. (1953). Sur une propriété du *Bacillus megatherium* liée à la présence d'un prophage. *Compt. rend. acad. sci.* **237**, 1794-1795.

Iseki, S., and Sakai, T. (1953). Artificial transformation of O antigens in Salmonella E group. II. Antigen-transforming factor in bacilli of subgroup E_2. *Proc. Japan Acad.* **29**, 127-131.

Jacob, F. (1954a). "Les bactéries lysogènes et la notion de provirus," Monographies de l'Inst. Pasteur. Masson & Co., Paris.

Jacob, F. (1954b). Mutation d'un bactériophage induite par l'irradiation des seules bactéries-hôtes avant l'infection. *Compt. rend. acad. sci.* **238**, 732-734.

Jacob, F. (1955). Transduction of lysogeny in *Escherichia coli. Virology* **1**, 207-220.

Jacob, F. (1958). Transfer and expression of genetic information in *Escherichia coli* K12. *Exptl. Cell Research,* Suppl. 6, 51-68.

Jacob, F. (1960). Genetic control of viral functions. *Harvey Lectures, 1958-1959* **54**, 1-39.

Jacob, F., and Adelberg, E. A. (1959). Transfert de caractères génétiques par incorporation au facteur sexuel d'*Escherichia coli. Compt. rend. acad. sci.* **249**, 189-191.

Jacob, F., and Campbell, A. (1959). Sur le système de répression assurant l'immunité chez les bactéries lysogènes. *Compt. rend. acad. sci.* **248**, 3219-3221.

Jacob, F., Fuerst, C. R., and Wollman, E. L. (1957). Recherches sur les bactéries lysogènes défectives. II. Les types physiologiques liés aux mutations du prophage. *Ann. inst. Pasteur* **93**, 724-753.

Jacob, F., Ionesco, H., and Wollman, E. L. (1961). In preparation.

Jacob, F., Lwoff, A., Siminovitch, L., and Wollman, E. L. (1953). Définition de quelques termes relatifs à la lysogénie. *Ann. inst. Pasteur* **84**, 222-224.

Jacob, F., and Monod, J. (1959). Gènes de structure et gènes de régulation dans la biosynthèse des protéines. *Compt. rend. acad. sci.* **249**, 1282-1284.

Jacob, F., and Monod, J. (1961). Genetic regulatory mechanisms in the synthesis of proteins. *J. Mol. Biol.* **3**, 318-356.

Jacob, F., Perrin, D., Sanchez, C., and Monod, J. (1960). L'opéron: groupe de gènes à expression coordonnée par un opérateur. *Compt. rend. acad. sci.* **250**, 1727-1729.

Jacob, F., Schaeffer, P., and Wollman, E. L. (1960). Episomic elements in bacteria. *In* "Microbial Genetics," 10th Symposium Soc. Gen. Microbiol. (W. Hayes and R. C. Clowes, eds.), pp. 67-91. Cambridge University Press, London and New York.

Jacob, F., Siminovitch, L., and Wollman, E. L. (1952). Sur la biosynthèse d'une colicine et sur son mode d'action. *Ann. inst. Pasteur* **83**, 295-316.

Jacob, F., Siminovitch, L., and Wollman, E. L. (1953). Comparaison entre la biosynthèse induite de la colicine et des bactériophages et entre leur mode d'action. *Ann. inst. Pasteur* **84**, 313-318.

Jacob, F., and Wollman, E. L. (1954a). Induction spontanée du développement du bactériophage λ au cours de la recombinaison génétique chez *E. coli* K12. *Compt. rend. acad. sci.* **239**, 455-456.

Jacob, F., and Wollman, E. L. (1954b). Etude génétique d'un bactériophage tempéré d'*Escherichia coli*. I. Le système génétique du bactériophage λ. *Ann. inst. Pasteur* **87**, 653-673.

Jacob, F., and Wollman, E. L. (1955a). Etapes de la recombinaison génétique chez *E. coli* K12. *Compt. rend. acad. sci.* **240**, 2566-2568.

Jacob, F., and Wollman, E. L. (1955b). Etude génétique d'un bactériophage tempéré d'*Escherichia coli*. III. Effet du rayonnement ultraviolet sur la recombinaison génétique. *Ann. inst. Pasteur* **88**, 724-749.

Jacob, F., and Wollman, E. L. (1956a). Recherches sur les bactéries lysogènes défectives. I. Déterminisme génétique de la morphogenèse chez un bactériophage tempéré. *Ann. inst. Pasteur* **90**, 282-302.

Jacob, F., and Wollman, E. L. (1956b). Sur les processus de conjugaison et de recombinaison génétique chez *E. coli*. I. L'induction par conjugaison ou induction zygotique. *Ann. inst. Pasteur* **91**, 486-510.

Jacob, F., and Wollman, E. L. (1956c). Recombinaison génétique et mutants de fertilité chez *E. coli* K12. *Compt. rend. acad. sci.* **242**, 303-306.

Jacob, F., and Wollman, E. L. (1957a). Genetic aspects of lysogeny. *In* "The Chemical Basis of Heredity" (W. D. McElroy and B. Glass, eds.), pp. 468-498. Johns Hopkins Press, Baltimore.

Jacob, F., and Wollman, E. L. (1957b). Analyse des groupes de liaison génétique de différentes souches donatrices. *Compt. rend. acad. sci.* **245**, 1840-1843.

Jacob, F., and Wollman, E. L. (1958a). Genetic and physical determinations of chromosomal segments in *E. coli*. Biological replication of macromolecules. *Symposia Soc. Exptl. Biol.* **12**, 75-92.

Jacob, F., and Wollman, E. L. (1958b). Les épisomes, éléments génétiques ajoutés. *Compt. rend. acad. sci.* **247**, 154-156.

Jacob, F., and Wollman, E. L. (1958c). Sur les processus de conjugaison et de recombinaison chez *E. coli*. IV. Prophages inductibles et mesures des segments génétiques transférés au cours de la conjugaison. *Ann. inst. Pasteur* **95**, 497-519.

Jacob, F., and Wollman, E. L. (1959a). The relationship between the prophage and the bacterial chromosome in lysogenic bacteria. *In* "Recent Progress in Microbiology," 7th Intern. Congr. Microbiol., pp. 15-30. Almquist & Wiksells, Stockholm.

Jacob, F., and Wollman, E. L. (1959b). Lysogeny. *In* "The Viruses: Plant and Bacterial Viruses" (F. M. Burnet and W. M. Stanley, eds.), pp. 319-351. Academic Press, New York.

Jacob, F., and Wollman, E. L. (1961). Mutations défectives du facteur sexuel d'*E. coli*. *Compt. rend. acad. sci.* In preparation.

Jesaitis, M. A., and Goebel, W. F. (1953). Mechanism of phage action. *Nature* **172**, 622-623.

Kaiser, A. D. (1955). A genetic study of the temperate coliphage λ. *Virology* **1**, 424-443.

Kaiser, A. D. (1957). Mutations in a temperate bacteriophage affecting its ability to lysogenize *E. coli*. *Virology* **3**, 42-61.

Kaiser, A. D., and Hogness, D. (1960). The transformation of *Escherichia coli* with deoxyribonucleic acid isolated from bacteriophage λdg. *J. Mol. Biol.* **2**, 392-415.

Kaiser, A. D., and Jacob, F. (1957). Recombination between related temperate bacteriophages and the genetic control of immunity and prophage localization. *Virology* **4**, 509-521.

Kalckar, H. M., Kurahashi, K., and Jordan, E. (1959). Hereditary defects in galactose metabolism in *Escherichia coli* mutants. I. Determination of enzyme activities. *Proc. Natl. Acad. Sci. U.S.* **45**, 1776-1786.

Kaplan, R. (1952). Genetics of microorganisms. *Ann. Rev. Microbiol.* **6**, 49-76.

Karström, H. (1938). Enzymatische adaptation bei mikroorganismus. *Ergeb. Enzymforsch.* **7**, 350-376.

Kellenberger, E. (1960). The physical state of the bacterial nucleus. *In* "Microbial Genetics," 10th Symposium Soc. Gen. Microbiol. (W. Hayes and R. C. Clowes, eds.), pp. 39-66. Cambridge University Press, London and New York.

Kellenberger, E., and Arber, W. (1955). Die Struktur des Schwanzes der Phagen T2 und T4 und der Mechanismus der irreversiblen Adsorption. *Z. Naturforsch.* **10b**, 698-704.

Kitzmiller, J. B. (1953). Mosquito genetics and cytogenetics. *Rev. brasil. malariol. e doenças trop.* **5**, 285-359.

Knight, B. C. J. G. (1936). Bacterial nutrition. *Med. Research Council (Brit.) Spec. Rept.* **210**.

Koch, G., and Dreyer, W. J. (1958). Characterization of an enzyme of phage T2 as a lysozyme. *Virology* **6**, 291-293.

Koch, R. (1881). Zur untersuchung von pathogenen organismen. *Mitt. Kaiserl. Gesundheitsamte* **i**, 1-48.

Kogut, M., Pollock, M., and Tridgell, E. J. (1956). Purification of penicillin-induced penicillinase of *Bacillus cereus* NRRL 569. A comparison of its properties with those of a similarly purified penicillinase produced spontaneously by a constitutive mutant strain. *Biochem. J.* **62**, 391-401.

Kornberg, A., Zimmerman, S. B., Kornberg, S. R., and Josse, J. (1959). Enzymatic synthesis of deoxyribonucleic acid. VI. Influence of bacteriophage T2 on the synthetic pathway in host cells. *Proc. Natl. Acad. Sci. U.S.* **45**, 772-785.

Kozloff, L. M., and Lute, M. (1959). A contractile protein in the tail of bacteriophage T2. *J. Biol. Chem.* **234**, 539-546.

Kuhn, P., and Ebeling, E. (1916). Untersuchung über die Paraglutination. *Z. Immunitätsforsch.* **25**, 1-43.

Lavallé, R., and Jacob, F. (1961). Sur la sensibilité des épisomes sexuel et colicinogène d'*E. coli* K12 à la désintégration du radiophosphore. *Compt. rend. acad. sci.* **252**, 1678-1680.

Lederberg, E. M. (1951). Lysogenicity in *E. coli* K12. *Genetics* **36**, 560.

Lederberg, E. M. (1952). Allelic relationships and reverse mutation in *E. coli. Genetics* **37**, 469-483.

Lederberg, E. M. (1954). The inheritance of lysogenicity in interstrain crosses of *E. coli. Genetics* **39**, 978.

Lederberg, E. M. (1960). Genetic and functional aspects of galactose metabolism in *Escherichia coli* K12. *In* "Microbial Genetics," 10th Symposium Soc. Gen. Microbiol. (W. Hayes and R. C. Clowes, eds.), pp. 115-131. Cambridge University Press, London and New York.

Lederberg, E. M., and Lederberg, J. (1953). Genetic studies of lysogenicity in *E. coli. Genetics* **38**, 51-64.

Lederberg, J. (1947). Gene recombination and linked segregations in *E. coli. Genetics* **32**, 505-525.

Lederberg, J. (1948). Problems in microbial genetics. *Heredity* **2**, 145-198.

Lederberg, J. (1949a). Bacterial variation. *Ann. Rev. Microbiol.* **3**, 1-22.

Lederberg, J. (1949b). Aberrant heterozygotes in *Escherichia coli. Proc. Natl. Acad. Sci. U.S.* **35**, 178-184.

Lederberg, J. (1950a). Isolation and characterization of biochemical mutants of bacteria. *In* "Methods in Medical Research" (J. H. Comroe, Jr., ed.), Vol. 3, pp. 5-22. Year Book Publishers, Chicago.

Lederberg, J. (1950b). The selection of genetic recombinations with bacterial growth inhibitors. *J. Bacteriol.* **59**, 211-215.

Lederberg, J. (1951a). Streptomycin resistance: a genetically recessive mutation. *J. Bacteriol.* **61**, 549-550.

Lederberg, J. (1951b). Prevalence of *E. coli* strains exhibiting genetic recombination. *Science* **114**, 68-69.

Lederberg, J. (1951c). Genetic studies with bacteria. *In* "Genetics in the 20th Century," pp. 263-289. Macmillan, New York.

Lederberg, J. (1952). Cell genetics and hereditary symbiosis. *Physiol. Revs.* **32**, 403-430.

Lederberg, J. (1955a). Recombination mechanisms in bacteria. *J. Cellular Comp. Physiol.* **45**, Suppl. 2, 75-108.

Lederberg, J. (1955b). Genetic recombination in bacteria. *Science* **122**, 920.

Lederberg, J. (1956a). Conjugal pairing in *E. coli. J. Bacteriol.* **71**, 497-498.

Lederberg, J. (1956b). Prospects for the genetics of somatic and tumor cells. *Ann. N.Y. Acad. Sci.* **63**, 662-665.

Lederberg, J. (1957). Sibling recombinants in zygote pedigrees of *Escherichia coli. Proc. Natl. Acad. Sci. U.S.* **43**, 1060-1065.

Lederberg, J. (1958). Extranuclear transmission of the F compatibility factor in *E. coli. Abstr. Communs., 7th Intern. Congr. Microbiol., Stockholm,* pp. 59-60.

Lederberg, J. (1959). Bacterial reproduction. *Harvey Lectures, 1957-1958* **53**, 69-82.

Lederberg, J., Cavalli, L. L., and Lederberg, E. M. (1952). Sex compatibility in *E. coli. Genetics* **37**, 720-730.

Lederberg, J., and Edwards, P. R. (1953). Serotypic recombination in *Salmonella. J. Immunol.* **71**, 232-240.

Lederberg, J., and Iino, T. (1956). Phase variation in *Salmonella. Genetics* **41**, 743-757.

Lederberg, J., and Lederberg, E. M. (1952). Replica plating and indirect selection of bacterial mutants. *J. Bacteriol.* **63**, 399-406.

Lederberg, J., Lederberg, E. M., Zinder, N. D., and Lively, E. R. (1951). Recombination analysis of bacterial heredity. *Cold Spring Harbor Symposia Quant. Biol.* **16**, 413-441.

Lederberg, J., and Tatum, E. L. (1946a). Novel genotypes in mixed cultures of biochemical mutants of bacteria. *Cold Spring Harbor Symposia Quant. Biol.* **11**, 113-114.

Lederberg, J., and Tatum, E. L. (1946b). Gene recombination in *E. coli. Nature* **158**, 558.

Lederberg, J., and Tatum, E. L. (1953). Sex in bacteria: genetic studies, 1945-1952. *Science* **118**, 169-175.

Legroux, R., and Genevray, J. (1933). Etude comparative entre le bacille de Whitmore et le bacille pyocyanique. *Ann. inst. Pasteur* **51**, 249-264.

Le Minor, L., and Le Minor, S. (1956). *In* Wollman, E. L., Jacob, F., and Hayes, W. Conjugation and genetic recombination in *Escherichia coli. Cold Spring Harbor Symposia Quant. Biol.* **21**, 150.

Lennox, E. S. (1955). Transduction of linked genetic characters of the host by bacteriophage Pl. *Virology* **1**, 190-206.

Levine, M. (1957). Mutations in the temperate phage P22 and lysogeny in Salmonella. *Virology* **3**, 22-41.

Levine, L., Barlow, J. L., and Van Vunakis, H. (1958). An internal protein in T2 and T4 bacteriophages. *Virology* **6**, 702-717.

Levinthal, C. (1954). Recombination in phage T2; its relationship to heterozygosis and growth. *Genetics* **39**, 169-184.

Levinthal, C. (1956). The mechanism of DNA replication and genetic recombination in phage. *Proc. Natl. Acad. Sci. U.S.* **42**, 394-404.

Levinthal, C. (1959). Genetic and chemical studies with alkaline phosphatase of *E. coli.* Structure and function of genetic elements. *Brookhaven Symposia in Biol.* **12**, 76-85.

Lewis, E. B. (1951). Pseudo allelism and gene evolution. *Cold Spring Harbor Symposia Quant. Biol.* **16**, 159-172.

Lewis, I. M. (1934). Bacterial variation with special reference to behavior of some mutable strains of colon bacteria in synthetic media. *J. Bacteriol.* **28**, 619-639.

L'Héritier, Ph. (1954). Le virus héréditaire de la drosophile. *In* "Problèmes actuels de virologie," pp. 88-106. Masson & Co., Paris.

L'Héritier, Ph. (1955). Les virus intégrés et l'unité cellulaire. *Ann. Biol.* **31**, 481-496.

L'Héritier, Ph. (1958). The hereditary virus of Drosophila. *Advances in Virus Res.* **5**, 195-245.

Lieb, M., Weiglé, J. J., and Kellenberger, E. (1955). A study of hybrids between two strains of *E. coli. J. Bacteriol.* **69**, 468-471.

Lindegren, C. C. (1953). Gene conversion in *Saccharomyces. J. Genet.* **51**, 625-637.

Loeb, T. (1960). The isolation of a bacteriophage specific for the F+ and Hfr mating types of *E. coli* K12. *Science* **131**, 932-933.

Löhnis, F. (1921). Studies upon the life cycles of bacteria. *Mem. Natl. Acad. Sci. U.S.* **16**, 1-252.
Luria, S. E. (1945). Mutations of bacterial viruses affecting their host range. *Genetics* **30**, 84-99.
Luria, S. E. (1947). Recent advances in bacterial genetics. *Bacteriol. Revs.* **11**, 1-40.
Luria, S. E. (1953). "General Virology." John Wiley & Sons, New York.
Luria, S. E., and Burrous, J. W. (1957). Hybridization between *Escherichia coli* and *Shigella*. *J. Bacteriol.* **74**, 461-476.
Luria, S. E., and Delbrück, M. (1943). Mutations of bacteria from virus sensitivity to virus resistance. *Genetics* **28**, 491-511.
Luria, S. E., Fraser, D. K., Adams, J. N., and Burrous, J. W. (1958). Lysogenization, transduction, and genetic recombination in bacteria. *Cold Spring Harbor Symposia Quant. Biol.* **23**, 71-82.
Lwoff, A. (1932). "Recherches biochimiques sur la nutrition des protozoaires." Masson & Co., Paris.
Lwoff, A. (1938). Les facteurs de croissance pour les microorganismes. *Compt. rend. 1er congr. Microbiologistes de Langue franç., Paris.*
Lwoff, A. (1943). "L'évolution physiologique." Hermann, Paris.
Lwoff, A. (1949). Les organites doués de continuité génétique chez les protistes. *In* "Unités biologiques douées de continuité génétique," pp. 7-23. C.N.R.S., Paris.
Lwoff, A. (1953). Lysogeny. *Bacteriol. Revs.* **17**, 269-337.
Lwoff, A. (1957). The concept of virus. *J. Gen. Microbiol.* **17**, 239-253.
Lwoff, A., and Gutmann, A. (1950). Recherches sur un *Bacillus megatherium* lysogène. *Ann. inst. Pasteur* **78**, 711-739.
Lwoff, A., Siminovitch, L., and Kjeldgaard, N. (1950). Induction de la production de bactériophages chez une bactérie lysogène. *Ann. inst. Pasteur* **79**, 815-858.
Maccacaro, G. A. (1955). Cell surface and fertility in *E. coli*. *Nature* **176**, 125-126.
Maccacaro, G. A., and Comolli, R. (1956). Surface properties correlated with sex compatibility in *E. coli*. *J. Gen. Microbiol.* **15**, 121-132.
Magasanik, B. (1957). Nutrition of bacteria and fungi. *Ann. Rev. Microbiol.* **11**, 221-252.
Magni, G. E. (1954). Thermic cure of cytoplasmic sex ratio in *Drosophila bifasciata*. *Caryologia* **6**, Suppl., 1213-1216.
Malogolowkin, C., and Poulson, D. F. (1957). Infective transfer of maternally inherited abnormal sex-ratio in *Drosophila willistoni*. *Science* **126**, 32.
Manten, A., and Rowley, D. (1953). Genetic analysis of valine inhibition in the K12 strain of *Bact. coli*. *J. Gen. Microbiol.* **9**, 226-233.
Marchal, J. G. (1932). "Variation et mutation en bactériologie." Le François, Paris.
Mason, D. J., and Powelson, D. M. (1955). Nuclear division as observed in live bacteria by a new technique. *J. Bacteriol.* **71**, 474-479.
Massini, R. (1907). Über einen in biologischer Beziehung interessanten Kolistamm (*Bacterium coli mutabile*). *Arch. Hyg.* **61**, 250-292.
McClintock, B. (1956). Controlling elements and the gene. *Cold Spring Harbor Symposia Quant. Biol.* **21**, 197-216.
McElroy, W. D., and Friedman, S. (1951). Gene recombination in luminous bacteria. *J. Bacteriol.* **62**, 129-130.
McIlwain, H. (1941). A nutritional investigation of the antibacterial action of acriflavine. *Biochem. J.* **35**, 1311-1319.

Meselson, M., and Stahl, F. W. (1958a). The replication of DNA in *Escherichia coli*. *Proc. Natl. Acad. Sci. U.S.* **44**, 671-682.

Meselson, M., and Stahl, F. W. (1958b). The replication of DNA. *Cold Spring Harbor Symposia Quant. Biol.* **23**, 9-12.

Michaelis, P. (1954). Cytoplasmic inheritance in *Epilobium* and its theoretical significance. *Advances in Genet.* **6**, 287-401.

Mitchell, M. B. (1955). Aberrant recombination of pyridoxine mutants in *Neurospora*. *Proc. Natl. Acad. Sci. U.S.* **41**, 215-220.

Miyake, T., and Demerec, M. (1959). *Salmonella-Escherichia* hybrids. *Nature* **183**, 1586.

Monod, J. (1942). "Recherches sur la croissance des cultures bactériennes." Hermann, Paris.

Monod, J. (1958). An outline of enzyme induction. *Rec. trav. chim. pays-bas* **77**, 569-585.

Monod, J., and Audureau, A. (1946). Mutation et adaptation enzymatique chez *E. coli* mutabile. *Ann. inst. Pasteur* **72**, 868-878.

Monod, J., and Cohn, M. (1952). La biosynthèse induite des enzymes (adaptation enzymatique). *Advances in Enzymol.* **13**, 67-119.

Monod, J., and Wollman, E. L. (1947). L'inhibition de la croissance et de l'adaptation enzymatique chez les bactéries infectées par le bactériophage. *Ann. inst. Pasteur* **73**, 937-957.

Morse, M. L. (1954). Transduction of certain loci in *Escherichia coli* K12. *Genetics* **39**, 984-985.

Morse, M. L., Lederberg, E. M., and Lederberg, J. (1956a). Transduction in *E. coli* K12. *Genetics* **41**, 142-156.

Morse, M. L., Lederberg, E. M., and Lederberg, J. (1956b). Transductional heterogenotes in *Escherichia coli*. *Genetics* **41**, 758-779.

Muller, H. J. (1947). The gene. *Proc. Roy. Soc.* **B134**, 1-37.

Naegeli, C. von (1877). "Die niederen Pilze in ihren Beziehungen zu den Infectionskrankheiten und der Gesundheitspflege." Munich.

Nelson, T. C. (1951). Kinetics of genetic recombination in *E. coli*. *Genetics* **36**, 162-175.

Nelson, T. C., and Lederberg, J. (1954). Postzygotic elimination of genetic factors in *E. coli*. *Proc. Natl. Acad. Sci. U.S.* **40**, 415-419.

Newcombe, H. B. (1949). Origin of bacterial variants. *Nature* **164**, 150.

Newcombe, H. B., and Hawirko, R. (1949). Spontaneous mutation to streptomycin resistance and dependence in *E. coli*. *J. Bacteriol.* **57**, 565-572.

Newcombe, H. B., and Nyholm, M. H. (1950a). The inheritance of streptomycin-resistance and dependence in crosses of *E. coli*. *Genetics* **35**, 603-611.

Newcombe, H. B., and Nyholm, M. H. (1950b). Anomalous segregations in crosses of *E. coli*. *Am. Naturalist* **84**, 457-465.

Novick, A., and Szilard, L. (1955). *In* Novick, A. Growth of bacteria. *Ann. Rev. Microbiol.* **9**, 97-110.

Oakberg, E. F., and Luria, S. E. (1947). Mutations to sulfonamide resistance in *Staphylococcus aureus*. *Genetics* **32**, 249-261.

Oberling, C. (1954). "Le cancer." Gallimard, Paris.

Ørskov, I., and Ørskov, F. (1960). An antigen termed F+ occurring in F+ *E. coli* strains. *Acta Pathol. Microbiol. Scand.* **48**, 37-46.

Ozeki, H. (1959). Chromosome fragments participating in transduction in *Salmonella typhimurium. Genetics* **44**, 457-470.

Ozeki, H., and Stocker, B. A. D. (1959). *In* Stocker, B. A. D. Phage-mediated transduction. *In* "Recent Progress in Microbiology," 7th Intern. Congr. Microbiol., pp. 31-39. Almquist & Wiksells, Stockholm.

Pardee, A. B., Jacob, F., and Monod, J. (1958). Sur l'expression et le rôle des allèles "inductible" et "constitutif" dans la synthèse de la β-galactosidase chez des zygotes d'*E. coli. Compt. rend. acad. sci.* **246**, 3125-3128.

Pardee, A. B., Jacob, F., and Monod, J. (1959). The genetic control and cytoplasmic expression of "inducibility" in the synthesis of β-galactosidase by *E. coli. J. Mol. Biol.* **1**, 165-178.

Pardee, A. B., and Prestidge, L. S. (1959). On the nature of the repressor of β-galactosidase synthesis in *E. coli. Biochim. et Biophys. Acta* **36**, 545-547.

Penrose, L. S., and Penrose, R. (1957). A self-reproducing analogue. *Nature* **179**, 1183.

Perrin, D., Bussard, A., and Monod, J. (1959). Sur la présence de protéines apparentées à la β-galactosidase chez certains mutants d'*E. coli. Compt. rend. acad. sci.* **249**, 778-780.

Perrin, D., Jacob, F., and Monod, J. (1960). Biosynthèse induite d'une protéine génétiquement modifiée, ne présentant pas d'affinité pour l'inducteur. *Compt. rend. acad. sci.* **251**, 155-157.

Piekarski, G. (1937). Cytologische untersuchungen an paratyphus und colibakterien. *Arch. Mikrobiol.* **8**, 428-439.

Pontecorvo, G. (1950). New fields in the biochemical genetics of microorganisms. *Biochem. Soc. Symposia (Cambridge, Engl.)* **4**, 40-50.

Pontecorvo, G. (1954). Mitotic recombination in the genetic system of filamentous fungi. *Caryologia* Suppl. 6, 192-200.

Pontecorvo, G. (1956). Allelism. *Cold Spring Harbor Symposia Quant. Biol.* **21**, 171-174.

Pontecorvo, G. (1958). "Trends in Genetic Analysis." Columbia University Press, New York.

Poulson, D. F., and Sakaguchi, B. (1961). Nature of "sex-ratio" agent in Drosophila. *Science* **133**, 1489-1490.

Pritchard, R. H. (1955). The linear arrangement of a series of alleles in *Aspergillus nidulans. Heredity* **9**, 343-371.

Ravin, A. W. (1958). Bacterial genetics. *Ann. Rev. Microbiol.* **12**, 309-364.

Reed, G. B. (1937). Independent variation of several characteristics in S. *marcescens. J. Bacteriol.* **34**, 255-266.

Richter, A. (1957). Complementary determinants of an Hfr phenotype in *E. coli* K12. *Genetics* **42**, 391.

Richter, A. (1958). Recombination analysis of mating type in *E. coli* K12. *Proc. 10th Intern. Congr. Genetics, Montreal* **2**, 232.

Rickenberg, H. V., Cohen, G. N., Buttin, G., and Monod, J. (1956). La galactoside-perméase chez *E. coli. Ann. inst. Pasteur* **91**, 829-837.

Riley, M., Pardee, A. B., Jacob, F., and Monod, J. (1960). On the expression of a structural gene. *J. Mol. Biol.* **2**, 216-225.

Rippel, A. (1929). Variabilität bei Bakterien. *Med. klin. Wochschr. prakt. Ärzte* **25**, 767-769.

Ris, H. (1957). Chromosome structure. *In* "The Chemical Basis of Heredity" (W. D. McElroy and B. Glass, eds.), pp. 23-61. Johns Hopkins Press, Baltimore.

Roberts, R. B. (1958). "Microsomal Particles and Protein Synthesis." Pergamon Press, New York.

Robinow, C. F. (1942). A study of the nuclear apparatus of bacteria. *Proc. Roy. Soc.* **B130**, 299-324.

Robinow, C. F. (1956). The chromatin bodies of bacteria. *Bacteriol. Revs.* **20**, 207-242.

Roepke, R. R., Libby, R. L., and Small, M. H. (1944). Mutation or variation of *E. coli* with respect to growth requirements. *J. Bacteriol.* **48**, 401-419.

Roman, H. (1956). Studies of gene mutation in *Saccharomyces*. *Cold Spring Harbor Symposia Quant. Biol.* **21**, 175-185.

Roman, H., and Jacob, F. (1957). Effet de la lumière ultraviolette sur la recombinaison génétique entre allèles chez la levure. *Compt. rend. acad. sci.* **245**, 1032-1034.

Roman, H., and Jacob, F. (1958). A comparison of spontaneous and ultraviolet-induced allelic recombination with reference to the recombination of outside markers. *Cold Spring Harbor Symposia Quant. Biol.* **23**, 155-160.

Rothfels, K. H. (1952). Gene linearity and negative interference in crosses of *E. coli*. *Genetics* **37**, 297-311.

Rubin, H. (1959). Special interaction between virus and cell in the Rous sarcoma. *In* "Virus Growth and Variation," 9th Symposium Soc. Gen. Microbiol. (A. Isaacs and B. W. Lacey, eds.), pp. 171-184. Cambridge University Press, London and New York.

Ryan, F. J., and Lederberg, J. (1946). Reverse mutation and adaptation in leucineless *Neurospora*. *Proc. Natl. Acad. Sci. U.S.* **32**, 163-173.

Schaeffer, P., and Ionesco, H. (1959). Sur la transformation de *Bacillus subtilis*. *Compt. rend. acad. sci.* **249**, 481-482.

Schaeffer, P., and Ionesco, H. (1960). Contribution à l'étude génétique de la sporogenèse bactérienne. *Compt. rend. acad. sci.* **251**, 3125-3127.

Schaeffer, P., Ionesco, H., and Jacob, F. (1959). Sur le déterminisme génétique de la sporulation bactérienne. *Compt. rend. acad. sci.* **249**, 577-578.

Schrödinger, E. (1944). "What is Life?" Cambridge University Press, London and New York.

Sermonti, G., and Spada-Sermonti, I. (1956). Gene recombination in *Streptomyces coelicolor*. *J. Gen. Microbiol.* **15**, 609-616.

Sevag, M. G. (1946). Enzyme problems in relation to chemotherapy, "adaptations," mutations, resistance and immunity. *Advances in Enzymol.* **6**, 33-127.

Sherman, J. M., and Wing, H. U. (1937). Attempts to reveal sex in bacteria; with some light on fermentative variability in the coli-aerogenes group. *J. Bacteriol.* **33**, 315-321.

Sinsheimer, R. L. (1954). Nucleotides from T2r+ bacteriophage. *Science* **120**, 551-553.

Skaar, P. D., and Garen, A. (1956). The orientation and extent of gene transfer in *E. coli*. *Proc. Natl. Acad. Sci. U.S.* **42**, 619-624.

Skaar, P. D., Richter, A., and Lederberg, J. (1957). Correlated selection for motility and sex incompatibility in *E. coli* K12. *Proc. Natl. Acad. Sci. U.S.* **43**, 329-333.

Smith, J. D., and Siminovitch, L. (1953). *In* Lwoff, A., Lysogeny. *Bacteriol. Revs.* **17**, 320.

Spiegelman, S., and Landman, O. E. (1954). Genetics of microorganisms. *Ann. Rev. Microbiol.* **8**, 181-236.
Spizizen, J. (1958). Transformation of biochemically deficient strains of *Bacillus subtilis* by deoxyribonucleate. *Proc. Natl. Acad. Sci. U.S.* **44**, 1072-1078.
Stanier, R. Y. (1951). Enzymatic adaptation in bacteria. *Ann. Rev. Microbiol.* **5**, 35-56.
Starlinger, P. (1958). Über einen Defekt des transduzierenden *Salmonella*-Phagen P22. *Z. Naturforsch.* **13b**, 489-493.
Stent, G. S. (1953). Mortality due to radioactive phosphorus as an index to bacteriophage development. *Cold Spring Harbor Symposia Quant. Biol.* **18**, 255-259.
Stent, G. S. (1958). Mating in the reproduction of bacterial viruses. *Advances in Virus Research* **5**, 95-149.
Stent, G. S., and Fuerst, C. R. (1955). Inactivation of bacteriophages by decay of incorporated radioactive phosphorus. *J. Gen. Physiol.* **38**, 441-458.
Stent, G. S., and Fuerst, C. R. (1960). Genetic and physiological effects of the decay of incorporated radioactive phosphorus in bacterial viruses and bacteria. *Advances in Biol. Med. Phys.* **7**, 1-75.
Stent, G. S., Fuerst, C. R., and Jacob, F. (1957). Inactivation d'un prophage par la désintégration du radiophosphore. *Compt. rend. acad. sci.* **244**, 1840-1842.
Stocker, B. A. D. (1960). Introduction: micro-organisms in genetics. *In* "Microbial Genetics," 10th Symposium Soc. Gen. Microbiol. (W. Hayes and R. C. Clowes, eds.), pp. 1-11. Cambridge University Press, London and New York.
Stocker, B. A. D., Zinder, N. D., and Lederberg, J. (1953). Transduction of flagellar characters in *Salmonella*. *J. Gen. Microbiol.* **9**, 410-433.
Sturtevant, H. (1949). *In* Hershey, A. D., and Rotman, R. Genetic recombination between host-range and plaque-type mutants of bacteriophage in single bacterial cells. *Genetics* **34**, 44-71.
Tatum, E. L. (1945). X-ray induced mutant strains of *E. coli*. *Proc. Natl. Acad. Sci. U.S.* **31**, 215-219.
Tatum, E. L. (1946). Induced biochemical mutations in bacteria. *Cold Spring Harbor Symposia Quant. Biol.* **11**, 278-284.
Tatum, E. L., and Lederberg, J. (1947). Gene recombination in the bacterium *Escherichia coli*. *J. Bacteriol.* **53**, 673-684.
Tatum, E. L., and Perkins, D. D. (1950). Genetics of microorganisms. *Ann. Rev. Microbiol.* **4**, 129-150.
Taylor, A. L., and Adelberg, E. A. (1960). Linkage analysis with very high frequency males of *Escherichia coli*. *Genetics* **45**, 1233-1243.
Taylor, J. H. (1958a). The organization and duplication of genetic material. *Proc. 10th Intern. Congr. Genetics, Montreal* **1**, 63.
Taylor, J. H. (1958b). The duplication of chromosomes. *Sci. American* **198**, 37.
Taylor, J. H., Woods, P. S., and Hughes, W. L. (1957). The organization and duplication of chromosomes as revealed by autoradiograph studies using tritium-labeled thymidine. *Proc. Natl. Acad. Sci. U.S.* **43**, 122-128.
Temin, H. M. (1960). The control of cellular morphology in embryonic cells infected with Rous sarcoma virus *in vitro*. *Virology* **10**, 182-197.
Thomas, R. (1959). Effects of chloramphenicol on genetic replication in bacteriophage λ. *Virology* **9**, 275-289.
Thompson, D. H. (1931). The side-chain theory of the structure of the gene. *Genetics* **16**, 267.

Timakov, V. D. (1959). "Microbial Variation." Pergamon Press, New York.

Tomizawa, J. (1960). Genetic structure of recombinant chromosomes formed after mating in *Escherichia coli* K12. *Proc. Natl. Acad. Sci. U.S.* **46**, 91-101.

Torriani, A. M. (1960). Influence of inorganic phosphate in the formation of phosphatases by *E. coli. Biochim. et Biophys. Acta* **38**, 460-469.

Tulasne, R. (1949). Mise en évidence du noyau chez les bactéries vivantes grâce au dispositif à contraste de phase. *Compt. rend. acad. sci.* **229**, 5610.

Uetake, H., Luria, S. E., and Burrous, J. W. (1958). Conversion of somatic antigens in *Salmonella* by phage infection leading to lysis or lysogeny. *Virology* **5**, 68-91.

Umbarger, H. E. (1956). Evidence for a negative-feedback mechanism in the biosynthesis of isoleucine. *Science* **123**, 848.

Van Loghem, J. J. (1929). Die Individualitätstheorie der bakteriellen Veränderlichkeit. *Z. Hyg.* **110**, 382-390.

Van Niel, C. B. (1946). The classification and natural relationships of bacteria. *Cold Spring Harbor Symposia Quant. Biol.* **11**, 285-300.

Van Vunakis, H., Baker, W. H., and Brown, R. K. (1958). Structural studies on the proteins of bacteriophages. I. Alcaline dissociation of the protein coat "ghost" of bacteriophage T2r+. *Virology* **5**, 327-336.

Visconti, N., and Delbrück, M. (1953). The mechanism of genetic recombination in phage. *Genetics* **38**, 5-33.

Vogel, H. J. (1957). Repression and induction as control mechanisms of enzyme biogenesis: the "adaptive" formation of acetylornithinase. *In* "The Chemical Basis of Heredity" (W. D. McElroy and B. Glass, eds.), pp. 276-289. Johns Hopkins Press, Baltimore.

Vogt, M., and Dulbecco, R. (1960). Virus-cell interaction with a tumor-producing virus. *Proc. Natl. Acad. Sci. U.S.* **46**, 365-370.

Volkin, E., and Astrachan, L. (1957). RNA metabolism in T2-infected *Escherichia coli. In* "The Chemical Basis of Heredity" (W. D. McElroy and B. Glass, eds.), pp. 686-694. Johns Hopkins Press, Baltimore.

Watanabe, T., and Fukasawa, T. (1960). "Resistance transfer factor," an episome in Enterobacteriaceae. *Biochem. Biophys. Research Communs.* **3**, 660-665.

Watson, J. D., and Crick, F. H. C. (1953a). A structure for desoxyribose nucleic acids. *Nature* **171**, 737-738.

Watson, J. D., and Crick, F. H. C. (1953b). The structure of DNA. *Cold Spring Harbor Symposia Quant. Biol.* **18**, 123-131.

Watson, J. D., and Hayes, W. (1953). Genetic exchange in *E. coli* K12: evidence for three linkage groups. *Proc. Natl. Acad. Sci. U.S.* **39**, 416-426.

Weiglé, J. J. (1953). Induction of mutations in a bacterial virus. *Proc. Natl. Acad. Sci. U.S.* **39**, 628-636.

Weiglé, J. J. (1957). Transduction by coliphage λ of the galactose marker. *Virology* **4**, 14-25.

Weiglé, J. J., and Bertani, G. (1953). Variations des bactériophages conditionnées par les bactéries hôtes. *Ann. inst. Pasteur* **84**, 175-179.

Weiglé, J. J., and Delbrück, M. (1951). Mutual exclusion between an infecting phage and a carried phage. *J. Bacteriol.* **62**, 301-318.

Weiglé, J. J., Meselson, M., and Paigen, K. (1959). Density alterations associated with transducing ability in the bacteriophage λ. *J. Mol. Biol.* **1**, 379-386.

Wilkins, M. H. F., Stockes, A. R., and Wilson, H. R. (1953). Molecular structure of desoxypentose nucleic acids. *Nature* **171**, 738-740.

Winge, Ø. (1935). On haplophase and diplophase in some saccharomycetes. *Compt. rend. trav. lab. Carlsberg, Sér. physiol.* **21**, 77-112.

Winge, Ø. (1955). On interallelic crossing over. *Heredity* **9**, 373-384.

Winkler, H. (1930). "Die Konversion der Gene." Verlag Gustav Fischer, Jena.

Witkin, E. M. (1947). Genetics of resistance to radiation in *Escherichia coli. Genetics* **32**, 221-248.

Witkin, E. M. (1951). Nuclear segregation and the delayed appearance of induced mutants *E. coli. Cold Spring Harbor Symposia Quant. Biol.* **16**, 357-371.

Wollman, E. (1925). Recherches sur la bactériophagie I. *Ann. inst. Pasteur* **39**, 789-833.

Wollman, E. (1927). Recherches sur la bactériophagie II. *Ann. inst. Pasteur* **41**, 883-919.

Wollman, E. (1928). Bactériophagie et processus similaires. Hérédité ou infection? *Bull. inst. Pasteur* **26**, 1-22.

Wollman, E., and Wollman, Mme E. (1925). Sur la transmission parahéréditaire de caractères chez les bactéries. *Compt. rend. soc. biol.* **93**, 1568-1569.

Wollman, E., and Wollman, Mme E. (1936). Régénération des bactériophages chez le *B. megatherium* lysogène. *Compt. rend. soc. biol.* **122**, 190-192.

Wollman, E., and Wollman, Mme E. (1937). Les phases des bactériophages (facteurs lysogènes). *Compt. rend. soc. biol.* **124**, 931-934.

Wollman, E., and Wollman, Mme E. (1938). Recherches sur le phénomène de Twort d'Hérelle (bactériophagie ou autolyse hérédo-contagieuse). *Ann. inst. Pasteur* **60**, 13-58.

Wollman, E. L. (1953). Sur le déterminisme génétique de la lysogénie. *Ann. inst. Pasteur* **84**, 281-294.

Wollman, E. L., and Jacob, F. (1954a). Lysogénie et recombinaison génétique chez *E. coli* K12. *Compt. rend. acad. sci.* **239**, 455-456.

Wollman, E. L., and Jacob, F. (1954b). Etude génétique d'un bactériophage tempéré d'*E. coli.* II. Mécanisme de la recombinaison génétique. *Ann. inst. Pasteur* **87**, 674-690.

Wollman, E. L., and Jacob, F. (1955). Sur le mécanisme du transfert de matériel génétique au cours de la recombinaison chez *E. coli* K12. *Compt. rend. acad. sci.* **240**, 2449-2451.

Wollman, E. L., and Jacob, F. (1957). Sur les processus de conjugaison et de recombinaison chez *E. coli.* II. La localisation chromosomique du prophage λ et les conséquences génétiques de l'induction zygotique. *Ann. inst. Pasteur* **93**, 323-339.

Wollman, E. L., and Jacob, F. (1958a). Sur le déterminisme génétique des types sexuels chez *E. coli* K12. *Compt. rend. acad. sci.* **247**, 536-539.

Wollman, E. L., and Jacob, F. (1958b). Sur les processus de conjugaison et de recombinaison chez *E. coli.* V. Le mécanisme du transfert de matériel génétique. *Ann. inst. Pasteur* **95**, 641-666.

Wollman, E. L., and Jacob, F. (1959). Lysogeny, transduction and cancer genesis. *In* "Genetics and Cancer," pp. 43-59. University of Texas Press, Austin.

Wollman, E. L., Jacob, F., and Hayes, W. (1956). Conjugation and genetic recombination in *Escherichia coli. Cold Spring Harbor Symposia Quant. Biol.* **21**, 141-162.

Wollman, E. L., and Stent, G. S. (1961). In preparation.

Wyatt, G. R., and Cohen, S. S. (1953). The bases of the nucleic acids of some bacterial and animal viruses: the occurrence of 5-hydroxymethylcytosine. *Biochem. J.* **55**, 774-782.

Wyss, O., and Haas, F. L. (1953). Genetics of micro-organisms. *Ann. Rev. Microbiol.* **7**, 47-82.

Yanofsky, C. (1960). The tryptophan synthetase system. *Bacteriol. Revs.* **24**, 221-245.

Yanofsky, C., and Crawford, I. P. (1959). The effects of deletions, point mutations, reversions and suppressor mutations on the two components of the tryptophan synthetase of *E. coli. Proc. Natl. Acad. Sci. U.S.* **45**, 1016-1026.

Yanofsky, C., and Lennox, E. S. (1959). Transduction and recombination study of linkage relationships among the genes controlling tryptophan synthesis in *E. coli. Virology* **8**, 425-447.

Yates, R. A., and Pardee, A. D. (1957). Control by uracil of formation of enzyme required for orotate synthesis. *J. Biol. Chem.* **227**, 677-692.

Yčas, M., and Vincent, W. S. (1960). A ribonucleic acid fraction from yeast related in composition to desoxyribonucleic acid. *Proc. Natl. Acad. Sci. U.S.* **46**, 804-810.

Zabin, I., Kepes, A., and Monod, J. (1959). On the enzyme acetylation of isopropyl β-D-thiogalactoside and its association with galactoside permease. *Biochem. Biophys. Research Communs.* **1**, 289-292.

Zelle, M. R. (1955). Genetics of microorganisms. *Ann. Rev. Microbiol.* **9**, 45-98.

Zelle, M. R., and Lederberg, J. (1951). Single cell isolations of diploid heterozygous *E. coli. J. Bacteriol.* **61**, 351-355.

Zinder, N. D. (1953). Infective heredity in bacteria. *Cold Spring Harbor Symposia Quant. Biol.* **18**, 261-269.

Zinder, N. D. (1958). Lysogenization and superinfection immunity in *Salmonella. Virology* **5**, 291-326.

Zinder, N. D., and Lederberg, J. (1952). Genetic exchange in *Salmonella. J. Bacteriol.* **64**, 679-699.

Zopf, W. (1885). "Die Speltpilze, nach dem neuesten Standhankte bearbeitet." Breslau.

Additional References

Borek, E., and Ryan, A. (1960). The transfer of a biologically active irradiation product from cell to cell. *Biochim. Biophys. Acta* **41**, 67-73.

Fisher, K. W. (1961). Conjugal transfer of immunity to phage multiplication in *E. coli* K12. *J. Gen. Microb.*, in press.

Kellenberger, G., Zichichi, M. L., and Weiglé, J. J. (1961). Exchange of DNA in the recombination of bacteriophage λ. *Proc. Nat. Acad. Sci.* **47**, 869-878.

Levinthal, C., and Davison, P. F. (1961). In press.

Meselson, M., and Weiglé, J. J. (1961). Chromosome breakage accompanying genetic recombination in bacteriophage. *Proc. Nat. Acad. Sci.* **47**, 857-868.

Subject Index